HUMAN SEXUALITY 98/99

Twenty-Third Edition

Editor

Susan J. Bunting
Lincoln College

Susan Bunting is the coordinator of curriculum and instruction at Chestnut Health Systems in Illinois, and she is an instructor of sociology and psychology at Lincoln College. Dr. Bunting received her B.S. and M.S. in sociology and her Ed.D. in curriculum and instruction from Illinois State University. She has taught, counseled, trained, and developed curriculum in human sexuality, sexual abuse, substance abuse, self-esteem, child and human development, learning disabilities, marriage, family, and intimate relationships. Dr. Bunting publishes pamphlets, instructional materials, articles, and books in these areas.

Annual Editions
A Library of Information from the Public Press
Dushkin/McGraw·Hill
Sluice Dock, Guilford, Connecticut 06437

Visit us on the Internet—http://www.dushkin.com/annualeditions

The Annual Editions Series

ANNUAL EDITIONS, including GLOBAL STUDIES, consist of over 70 volumes designed to provide the reader with convenient, low-cost access to a wide range of current, carefully selected articles from some of the most important magazines, newspapers, and journals published today. ANNUAL EDITIONS are updated on an annual basis through a continuous monitoring of over 300 periodical sources. All ANNUAL EDITIONS have a number of features that are designed to make them particularly useful, including topic guides, annotated tables of contents, unit overviews, and indexes. For the teacher using ANNUAL EDITIONS in the classroom, an Instructor's Resource Guide with test questions is available for each volume. GLOBAL STUDIES titles provide comprehensive background information and selected world press articles on the regions and countries of the world.

VOLUMES AVAILABLE

ANNUAL EDITIONS

Abnormal Psychology
Accounting
Adolescent Psychology
Aging
American Foreign Policy
American Government
American History, Pre-Civil War
American History, Post-Civil War
American Public Policy
Anthropology
Archaeology
Astronomy
Biopsychology
Business Ethics
Canadian Politics
Child Growth and Development
Comparative Politics
Computers in Education
Computers in Society
Criminal Justice
Criminology
Developing World
Deviant Behavior
Drugs, Society, and Behavior
Dying, Death, and Bereavement

Early Childhood Education
Economics
Educating Exceptional Children
Education
Educational Psychology
Environment
Geography
Geology
Global Issues
Health
Human Development
Human Resources
Human Sexuality
International Business
Macroeconomics
Management
Marketing
Marriage and Family
Mass Media
Microeconomics
Multicultural Education
Nutrition
Personal Growth and Behavior
Physical Anthropology
Psychology
Public Administration
Race and Ethnic Relations

Social Problems
Social Psychology
Sociology
State and Local Government
Teaching English as a Second
    Language
Urban Society
Violence and Terrorism
Western Civilization, Pre-Reformation
Western Civilization, Post-Reformation
Women's Health
World History, Pre-Modern
World History, Modern
World Politics

GLOBAL STUDIES

Africa
China
India and South Asia
Japan and the Pacific Rim
Latin America
Middle East
Russia, the Eurasian Republics, and
    Central/Eastern Europe
Western Europe

Cataloging in Publication Data
Main entry under title: Annual Editions: Human sexuality. 1998/99.
        1. Sexual behavior—Periodicals. 2. Sexual Hygiene—Periodicals. 3. Sex education—Periodicals.
4. Human relations—Periodicals. I. Bunting, Susan J., comp.
II. Title: Human sexuality.
ISBN 0–697–39183–3   155.3'05   75–20756   ISSN 1091-9961

Twenty-Third Edition

Cover: "Invisible Tension" © Bharati Chaudhuri/SuperStock Inc.

Printed in the United States of America

Printed on Recycled Paper

Editors/Advisory Board

Members of the Advisory Board are instrumental in the final selection of articles for each edition of ANNUAL EDITIONS. Their review of articles for content, level, currentness, and appropriateness provides critical direction to the editor and staff. We think that you will find their careful consideration well reflected in this volume.

EDITOR

Susan J. Bunting
Lincoln College

ADVISORY BOARD

Staff

To the Reader

In publishing ANNUAL EDITIONS we recognize the enormous role played by the magazines, newspapers, and journals of the *public press* in providing current, first-rate educational information in a broad spectrum of interest areas. Many of these articles are appropriate for students, researchers, and professionals seeking accurate, current material to help bridge the gap between principles and theories and the real world. These articles, however, become more useful for study when those of lasting value are carefully *collected, organized, indexed,* and *reproduced* in a *low-cost format,* which provides easy and permanent access when the material is needed. That is the role played by ANNUAL EDITIONS. Under the direction of each volume's *academic editor,* who is an expert in the subject area, and with the guidance of an *Advisory Board,* each year we seek to provide in each ANNUAL EDITION a current, well-balanced, carefully selected collection of the best of the public press for your study and enjoyment. We think that you will find this volume useful, and we hope that you will take a moment to let us know what you think.

Sex lies at the root of life, and we can never learn to reverence life until we know how to understand sex.

—*Havelock Ellis*

A century ago Havelock Ellis, one of the first sexologists, uttered the objective printed above. Since then, generations of sexologists, sex educators, and books like this one have worked toward that goal. Readers of this edition of *Annual Editions: Human Sexuality 98/99* might wonder if this goal has been accomplished, and they would not be alone. Today many sexuality specialists, as well as others who study sociocultural trends, note that how sexuality is approached, understood, and experienced seems to have changed in some noteworthy ways. Yet in other important ways, sexuality and people's perceptions and experiences have not changed.

While we are all born with basic sexual interests, drives, and desires, human sexuality is a dynamic and complex force that involves psychological and sociocultural dimensions in addition to the physiological ones. Sexuality includes an individual's whole body and personality. We are not born with a fully developed body or mind, but instead we grow and learn; so it is with respect to our sexuality. A great deal of our sexuality is learned. We learn what "appropriate" sexual behavior is, how to express it, when to do so, and under what circumstances. We also learn sexual feelings—positive feelings such as joy and the acceptance of sexuality, or negative and repressive feelings such as guilt and shame.

For much of the past, sexuality received little attention in scientific research and even less within higher education communities. Sex education was perceived as unnecessary, dangerous, or a king of education inappropriate for the public education setting. The last century has seen changes in these areas. Prime examples include marked changes in the don't-talk-about-it dictum and the resultant explosion of books and articles on sexuality topics available to the public. In addition, the last 30 years have ushered in changes with respect to the traditional double standard including greater sexual freedom for women with reverberations in gender roles, and more acknowledgement, understanding, and acceptance of the sexuality of people who deviate in some way from the traditional sexual images—those who are handicapped, the young, the aged, the non-married, and those who make or are born into less common sexual or relationship choices. However, without the proper understanding referred to in our initial Ellis quote, this expansion in sexual freedom can lead to new forms of sexual bondage rather than to the increased joy and pleasure of healthy sexuality.

Annual Editions: Human Sexuality 98/99 is organized into six sections. *Sexuality and Society* notes historical and cross-cultural views and analyzes our constantly changing society and sexuality. *Sexual Biology, Behavior, and Orientation* explains the functioning and responses of the human body and contains expanded sections on sexual hygiene, diseases and conditions affecting sexuality and functioning, and guides to preventive and ongoing sexual health care. *Interpersonal Relationships* provides suggestions for establishing and maintaining intimate, responsible, quality relationships. *Reproduction* discusses some recent trends related to pregnancy and childbearing and deals with reproductive topics, including conception, contraception, and abortion. *Sexuality through the Life Cycle* looks at what happens sexually throughout one's lifetime—from childhood to the later years. Finally, *Old/New Sexual Concerns* deals with such topics as sexual abuse, rape, sexual harassment, and legal and ethical issues regarding sexual behavior. It closes with a focus on the future of sex, especially the building controversy about sexual freedoms.

Also, new to this edition of *Annual Editions: Human Sexuality 98/99* are selected *World Wide Web* sites that can be used to further explore the topics. These sites will be cross-referenced by number in the *topic guide.*

The articles in this anthology have been carefully reviewed and selected for their quality, currency, and interest. They present a variety of viewpoints. Some you will agree with, some you will not, but we hope you will learn from all of them.

Appreciation and thanks go to Loree Adams for her suggestions and expertise; to Bruce Boeck, Mychele Kenney, and Sue LeSeure for their willingness to act as two-way sounding boards; to Monica Shutt for her organization and assistance, to Ollie Pocs for inspiration, and to those who have submitted articles and reviewed previous editions. We feel that *Annual Editions: Human Sexuality 98/99* is one of the most useful and up-to-date books available. Please let us know what you think. Return the postage-paid article rating form on the last page of this book with your suggestions and comments. Any book can be improved. This one will continue to be—annually.

Susan J. Bunting
Editor

Contents

UNIT 1

Sexuality and Society

Eight selections consider sexuality from historical and cross-cultural perspectives and examine today's changing attitudes toward human sexual interaction.

A. HISTORICAL AND CROSS-CULTURAL PERSPECTIVES

B. CHANGING SOCIETY/CHANGING SEXUALITY

The concepts in bold italics are developed in the article. For further expansion please refer to the Topic Guide, the Glossary, and the Index.

UNIT 2

Sexual Biology, Behavior, and Orientation

Eleven selections examine the biological aspects of human sexuality, sexual attitudes, hygiene and sexual health care, and sexual orientation.

The concepts in bold italics are developed in the article. For further expansion please refer to the Topic Guide, the Glossary, and the Index.

vi

UNIT 3

Interpersonal Relationships

Seven selections examine the dynamics of establishing sexual relationships and the need to make these relationships responsible and effective.

The concepts in bold italics are developed in the article. For further expansion please refer to the Topic Guide, the Glossary, and the Index.

vii

UNIT 4

Reproduction

Six articles discuss the roles of both males and females in pregnancy and childbirth and consider the influences of the latest birth control methods and practices on individuals and society as a whole.

The concepts in bold italics are developed in the article. For further expansion please refer to the Topic Guide, the Glossary, and the Index.

UNIT 5

Sexuality through the Life Cycle

Seven articles consider human sexuality as an important element throughout the life cycle. Topics include responsible adolescent sexuality, sex in and out of marriage, and sex in old age.

The concepts in bold italics are developed in the article. For further expansion please refer to the Topic Guide, the Glossary, and the Index.

ix

UNIT 6

Old/New Sexual Concerns

Ten selections discuss ongoing concerns of sexual abuse, violence, and harassment, gender roles and issues, and sex in the media.

The concepts in bold italics are developed in the article. For further expansion please refer to the Topic Guide, the Glossary, and the Index.

x

AE: HUMAN SEXUALITY ARTICLE LIST

The following list of article titles, article numbers (in parenthesis), and page numbers are listed alphabetically for convenience and easy reference:

The concepts in bold italics are developed in the article. For further expansion please refer to the Topic Guide, the Glossary, and the Index.

1

Topic Guide

This topic guide suggests how the selections in this book relate to topics of traditional concern to students and professionals involved with the study of human sexuality. It is useful for locating interrelated articles for reading and research. The guide is arranged alphabetically according to topic. Articles may, of course, treat topics that do not appear in the topic guide. In turn, entries in the topic guide do not necessarily constitute a comprehensive listing of all the contents of each selection. **In addition, relevant Web sites, which are annotated on pages 4 and 5, are noted in bold italics under the topic articles.**

TOPIC AREA	TREATED IN	TOPIC AREA	TREATED IN
Abortion	2. Tradition or Outrage? 17. Roll Over, Ward Cleaver 30. Drug-Induced Abortion *(1, 2, 6, 7, 18, 20, 22, 23, 24)*	**Gender/ Gender Roles**	2. Tradition or Outrage? 3. Adventures in the Skin Trade 5. Sexual Pleasure Unscripted 6. Storm Troopers in the Culture War 7. Time for Partnership 8. We Are Men. Hear Us Roar 11. Orgasm Wars 12. Testosterone Rules 13. Risky Sex 17. Roll Over, Ward Cleaver 18. Bisexuality 19. Portrait of a New Man 20. 1997 Body Image Survey Results 21. Woman's Guide to Flirting 22. Men for Sale 23. 'It' Doesn't Just Happen 34. Raising Sexually Healthy Kids 37. Men and Sex at 20, 30, 40 38. Joy of Midlife Sex 40. Town That Closed Its Eyes 42. Lock Up Your Sons! 44. Wings of Desire *(3, 4, 5, 6, 7, 8, 9, 12, 16, 17, 18, 19, 27, 30, 33)*
Abuse	2. Tradition or Outrage? 12. Testosterone Rules 36. Breaking through the Wall of Silence 40. Town That Closed Its Eyes 41. Healing the Scars 42. Lock Up Your Sons! 43. Cyndi Potete's Fire and Rain 46. Do Ask, Do Tell *(3, 5, 15, 18, 27, 31, 32, 33)*		
Aging	12. Testosterone Rules 15. Are Women the Weaker Sex? 28. Rethinking Birth Control 37. Men and Sex at 20, 30, 40 38. Joy of Midlife Sex 39. Everything You Always Wanted to Know about Sex after 50 *(1, 2, 11, 15, 25, 26, 28)*		
AIDS	(*See* STDs [Sexually Transmitted Diseases])	**Homosexuality/ Bisexuality**	3. Adventures in the Skin Trade 17. Roll Over, Ward Cleaver 18. Bisexuality 35. Could Your Precious Child be Gay? 36. Breaking through the Wall of Silence 46. Do Ask, Do Tell 49. Sex in the Future *(7, 9, 10, 11, 12, 15, 19, 30, 33)*
Birth Control/ Contraception	27. Protecting against Unintended Pregnancy 28. Rethinking Birth Control 29. How Reliable Are Condoms? 30. Drug-Induced Abortion 49. Sex in the Future *(2, 6, 18, 20, 24)*		
Females/Female Sexuality	2. Tradition or Outrage? 3. Adventures in the Skin Trade 5. Sexual Pleasure Unscripted 10. Your Sexual Landscape 11. Orgasm Wars 13. Risky Sex 15. Are Women the Weaker Sex? 17. Roll Over, Ward Cleaver 18. Bisexuality 20. 1997 Body Image Survey Results 21. Woman's Guide to Flirting 34. Raising Sexually Healthy Kids 38. Joy of Midlife Sex 39. Everything You Always Wanted to Know about Sex after 50 41. Healing the Scars 42. Lock Up Your Sons! 44. Wings of Desire 47. Porning of America *(3, 5, 6, 7, 8, 12, 18, 19, 33)*	**Legal/Ethical Issues**	1. Sweden Looks Anew at Ways to Reach and Teach 2. Tradition or Outrage? 3. Adventures in the Skin Trade 4. Shot in the Dark 6. Storm Troopers in the Culture War 14. AIDS: Crushing HIV/the Second Key 15. Are Women the Weaker Sex? 16. Horizontal Fitness 17. Roll Over, Ward Cleaver 30. Drug-Induced Abortion 31. Infertility, Inc. 35. Could Your Precious Child Be Gay? 36. Breaking through the Wall of Silence 40. Town That Closed Its Eyes 41. Healing the Scars 43. Cyndi Potete's Fire and Rain 44. Wings of Desire 45. AIDS Exception 47. Porning of America 49. Sex in the Future *(3, 5, 7, 8, 19, 22)*

TOPIC AREA	TREATED IN	TOPIC AREA	TREATED IN
Males/Male Sexuality	2. Tradition or Outrage? 6. Storm Troopers in the Culture War 7. Time for Partnership 8. We Are Men. Hear Us Roar 12. Testosterone Rules 17. Roll Over, Ward Cleaver 18. Bisexuality 19. Portrait of a New Man 20. 1997 Body Image Survey Results 22. Men for Sale 43. Raising Sexually Healthy Kids 37. Men and Sex at 20, 30, 40 40. Town That Closed Its Eyes 41. Healing the Scars 42. Lock Up Your Sons! 47. Porning of America *(4, 9, 10, 11, 12, 16, 17, 18, 19, 30)*	**Sex Education**	1. Sweden Looks Anew at Ways to Reach and Teach 4. Shot in the Dark 10. Your Sexual Landscape 23. 'It' Doesn't Just Happen 24. Better Sex in Three Days 27. Protecting against Unintended Pregnancy 28. Rethinking Birth Control 33. Age-by-Age Guide to Nudity 34. Raising Sexually Healthy Kids 36. Breaking through the Wall of Silence 39. Everything You Always Wanted to Know about Sex after 50 46. Do Ask, Do Tell 49. Sex in the Future *(2, 18, 27, 28, 30, 33)*
Media	5. Sexual Pleasure Unscripted 17. Roll Over, Ward Cleaver 20. 1997 Body Image Survey Results 25. Celibate Passion 35. Could Your Precious Child Be Gay? 36. Breaking through the Wall of Silence 39. Everything You Always Wanted to Know about Sex after 50 42. Lock Up Your Sons! 43. Cyndi Potete's Fire and Rain 46. Do Ask, Do Tell 47. Porning of America 49. Sex in the Future *(29, 32)*	**Sexual Dysfunction**	5. Sexual Pleasure Unscripted 9. Recipes for Lust 10. Your Sexual Landscape 11. Orgasm Wars 16. Horizontal Fitness 19. Portrait of a New Man 20. 1997 Body Image Survey Results 23. 'It' Doesn't Just Happen 24. Better Sex in Three Days 26. Healing Power of Intimacy 32. Making Love Again 34. Raising Sexually Healthy Kids 38. Joy of Midlife Sex 39. Everything You Always Wanted to Know about Sex after 50 41. Healing the Scars 49. Sex in the Future *(1, 2, 4, 9, 10, 11, 15, 18, 19)*
Pregnancy	15. Are Women the Weaker Sex? 17. Roll Over, Ward Cleaver 27. Protecting against Unintended Pregnancy 28. Rethinking Birth Control 31. Infertility, Inc. 32. Making Love Again 48. Was It Good for Us? 49. Sex in the Future *(20, 21, 24)*	**Sexual Harassment**	*(See* Abuse)
		STDs (Sexually Transmitted Diseases)	1. Sweden Looks Anew at Ways to Reach and Teach 4. Shot in the Dark 10. Your Sexual Landscape 13. Risky Sex 14. AIDS: Crushing HIV/the Second Key 18. Bisexuality 29. How Reliable Are Condoms? 43. Cyndi Potete's Fire and Rain 45. AIDS Exception 49. Sex in the Future *(1, 2, 6, 9, 10, 18, 19, 30, 31, 32, 33)*
Rape	*(See* Abuse)		
Sex and Love	8. We Are Men. Hear Us Roar 9. Recipes for Lust 11. Orgasm Wars 13. Risky Sex 22. Men for Sale 23. 'It' Doesn't Just Happen 24. Better Sex in Three Days 25. Celibate Passion 26. Healing Power of Intimacy 34. Raising Sexually Healthy Kids 37. Men and Sex at 20, 30, 40 38. Joy of Midlife Sex 44. Wings of Desire 48. Was It Good for Us? 49. Sex in the Future *(11, 12, 14, 15, 16, 17, 18, 19, 27, 28, 29)*	**Therapy/ Counseling**	8. We Are Men. Hear Us Roar 9. Recipes for Lust 11. Orgasm Wars 23. 'It' Doesn't Just Happen 24. Better Sex in Three Days 26. Healing Power of Intimacy 32. Making Love Again 35. Could Your Precious Child Be Gay? 36. Breaking through the Wall of Silence 41. Healing the Scars 49. Sex in the Future *(1, 2, 11, 15, 18, 30, 33)*

Selected World Wide Web Sites for
Annual Editions: Human Sexuality

All of these Web sites are hot-linked through the *Annual Editions* home page: *http://www.dushkin.com/annualeditions* (just click on a book). In addition, these sites are referenced by number and appear where relevant in the Topic Guide on the previous two pages.

Some Web sites are continually changing their structure and content, so the information listed may not always be available.

General Sources

1. National Institutes of Health (NIH)—*http://www.nih.gov/*—Consult this site for links to extensive health information and scientific resources. The NIH is one of eight health agencies of the Public Health Service, which, in turn, is part of the U.S. Department of Health and Human Services.

2. SEICUS—*http://www.siecus.org/siecus/*—Visit the Sexuality Information and Education Council of the United States(SIECUS) home page to learn about the organization, to find news of its educational programs and activities, and to access links to resources in sexuality education.

Sexuality and Society

3. Human Rights Report: India—*http://www.usis.usemb.se/human/india.html*—Read this U.S. Department of State USIS (U.S. Information Service) report on India's human-rights practices for an understanding of the issues that affect women's mental and physical health and well-being in different parts of the world.

4. National Organization of Circumcision Information Resource Centers (NOCIRC)—*http://nocirc.org/*—This is the home page of the NOCIRC, which describes itself as "a nonprofit educational organization committed to securing the birthright of male and female children and babies to keep their sexual organs intact." It disseminates material about male and female circumcision.

5. Prostitution in Thailand and Southeast Asia—*http://www.links.net/dox/ProsThai.html*—This thought-provoking site provides a number of perspectives on "Prostitution in Thailand and Southeast Asia" (subtitled "How to Keep Millions of Good Women Down"). Justin Hall's site addresses such concerns as oppression, forced prostitution, and the spread of HIV/AIDS.

6. Q Web Sweden: A Women's Empowerment Base—*http://www.qweb.kvinnoforum.se/index.htm*—This site from a Swedish organization will lead you to a number of pages addressing women's health issues and discussing societal issues related to sex. It provides interesting cross-cultural perspectives.

7. SocioSite: Feminism and Woman Issues—*http://www.pscw.uva.nl/sociosite/TOPICS/Women.html*—Open this University of Amsterdam Sociology Department's site to gain insights into a number of issues that affect both men and women. It provides biographies of women through history, provides an international network for women in the workplace, and provides links in masculinity and men's issues, gay studies, family and children issues, and more.

8. Why Are There So Few Female Computer Scientists?—*http://www.ai.mit.edu/people/ellens/Gender/pap/pap.html*—Open this Massachusetts Institute of Technology site for a discussion by Ellen Spertus of why there are so few female computer scientists, and to gain understanding into the debate about how society treats males and females differently.

Sexual Biology, Behavior, and Orientation

9. Bibliography: HIV/AIDS and College Students—*http://www.sph.emory.edu/bshe/AIDS/college.html*—This Emory University site contains an in-print bibliography of articles dealing with HIV/AIDS and college students. Some 75 articles addressing sexual behaviors and behaviors related to HIV/Aids, primarily from academic and professional journals, are listed.

10. The Body: A Multimedia AIDS and HIV Information Resource—*http://www.thebody.com/cgi-bin/body.cgi*—Open this site to find out the basics about AIDS/HIV, learn about treatments, exchange information in forums, gain insight from experts, and help and get help.

11. Healthy Way—*http://www.ab.sympatico.ca/Contents/Health/GENERAL/sitemap.html*—This Canadian site meant for consumers will lead you to many links related to sexual orientation. It also addresses aspects of human sexuality over the life span, general health, and reproductive health.

12. Hispanic Sexual Behavior and Gender Roles—*http://www.caps.ucsf.edu/hispnews.html*—This research report from the University of California at San Francisco Center for AIDS Prevention Studies describes and analyzes Hispanic sexual behavior and gender roles, particularly as regards prevention of STDs and HIV/AIDS. It discusses gender and cultural differences in sexual behavior and expectations and other topics of interest.

13. James Kohl—*http://www.pheromones.com/*—Keeping in mind that this is a commercial site with the goal of selling a book, look here to find topics of interest to nonscientists about pheromones. Links to related material of a more academic nature are included. Check out the diagram of "Mammalian Olfactory-Genetic-Neuronal-Hormonal-Behavioral Reciprocity and Human Sexuality" for a sense of the myriad biological influences that play a part in sexual behavior.

14. Johan's Guide to Aphrodisiacs—*http://www.santesson.com/aphrodis/aphrhome.htm*—"The Aphrodisiac Home Page" provides links to information about a multitude of substances that some believe arouse or increase sexual response or cause or increase sexual desire. Skepticism about aphrodisiacs is also discussed.

Interpersonal Relationships

15. American Psychological Association—*http://www.apa.org/psychnet/*—By exploring the APA's "PsychNET," you will be able to find links to an abundance of articles and other resources related to interpersonal relationships throughout the life span.

16. Bonobos Sex and Society—*http://soong.club.cc.cmu.edu/~julie/bonobos.html*—This site, accessed through Carnegie Mellon University, includes an article explaining how a primate's behavior challenges traditional assumptions about male supremacy in human evolution. Guaranteed to generate spirited debate.

17. The Celibate FAQ—*http://mail.bris.ac.uk/~plmlp/celibate.html*—This site consists of Martin Poulter's definitions, thoughts, and suggested resources on celibacy, created, he says, "in response to the lack of celibate stuff (outside religious contexts) on the Internet," and his perception of the Net's bias against celibacy.

18. Go Ask Alice—*http://www.columbia.edu/cu/healthwise/about.html*—This interactive site provided by Healthwise, a division of Columbia University Health Services, includes discussion and insight into a number of personal issues of interest to college-age people and those younger and older. Many questions about physical and emotional health and well-being in the modern world are answered.

19. Sex and Gender—*http://bioanth.cam.ac.uk/pip4amod3.html*—Use the syllabus, lecture titles, and readings noted in this site as a jumping-off point to explore more about sexual differentiation in human cultures as well as the genetics of sexual differentiation and the biology of sex roles in nonhumans.

Reproduction

20. Ask NOAH About Pregnancy: Fertility & Infertility—*http://www.noah.cuny.edu/pregnancy/fertility.html*—New York Online Access to Health (NOAH) seeks to provide relevant, timely, and unbiased health information for consumers. At this site, the organization presents extensive links to a variety of resources about infertility treatments and issues.

21. Childbirth.Org—*http://www.childbirth.org/*—This interactive site about childbirth options is from an organization that aims to educate consumers to know their options and provide themselves with the best possible care to ensure healthy pregnancies and deliveries. The site and its links address a myriad of topics, from episiotomy to water birth.

22. The Issue of Abortion in America—*http://caae.phil.cmu.edu/caae/Home/Multimedia/Abortion/IssueofAbortion.html*—Open this Carnegie Mellon University Center for the Advancement of Applied Ethics site to learn about a CD-ROM that is being developed regarding "The Issue of Abortion in America." Reading the pages of this site will give you an introduction to important historical and social perspectives, legal issues, medical facts, and philosophical arguments related to the abortion debate.

23. Medically Induced Abortion—*http://medicalabortion.com/index.htm*—Access this home page of physician Richard Hausknecht to read his very detailed *New England Journal of Medicine* article about medical abortion using methotrexate and misoprostol. A bibliography is included. He also provides several links to media reports of the procedure.

24. Planned Parenthood—*http://www.plannedparenthood.org/*—Visit this well-known organization's home page for links to information on the various kinds of contraceptives (including outercourse and abstinence) and to discussions of other topics related to sexual and reproductive health.

Sexuality through the Life Cycle

25. American Association of Retired Persons—*http://www.aarp.org/*—The AARP, a major advocacy group for older people, includes among its many resources suggested readings and Internet links to organizations that deal with the health and social issues that may affect one's sexuality as one ages.

26. National Institute on Aging—*http://www.nih.gov/nia/*—The NIA, one of the institutes of the National Institutes of Health, presents this home page to lead you to a variety of resources on health and lifestyle issues that are of interest to people as they grow older.

27. Teacher Talk—*http://education.indiana.edu/cas/tt/tthmpg.html*—This home page of the publication *Teacher Talk* from the Indiana University School of Education Center for Adolescent Studies will lead you to many interesting teacher comments, suggestions, and ideas regarding sexuality education and how to deal with sex issues in the classroom.

28. World Association for Sexology—*http://www.tc.umn.edu/nlhome/m201/colem001/was/wasindex.htm*—The World Association for Sexology works to further the understanding and development of sexology throughout the world. Access this site to explore a number of issues and links related to sexuality throughout life.

Old/New Sexual Concerns

29. Cyber Romance 101—*http://web2.airmail.net/walraven/romance.htm*—This interactive site explores a very '90s topic: relationships forged on the Internet. Browse here to hear various viewpoints on the issue. Advice columnists and psychologists add their perspectives.

30. Men's Health Resource Guide—*http://www.menshealth.com/new/guide/index.html*—This resource guide from *Men's Health* presents many links to topics in men's health, from AIDS/STDs, to back pain, to impotence and infertility, to vasectomy. It also includes discussions of relationship and family issues.

31. Other Sexual Violence resources on the Web—*http://www.witserv.com/org/ocrcc/resource/resource.htm* —Open this useful site for "Links to Other Sexual Violence Pages on the World Wide Web." For example, it has a link to "Men Against Rape," a site maintained by the D.C. Men Against Rape organization, providing men's perspectives on sexual violence.

32. Sexual Assault Information Page—*http://www.cs.utk.edu/~bartley/saInfoPage.html*—This invaluable site provides dozens of links to information and resources on a variety of sexual assault-related topics: child sexual abuse, date rape, incest, secondary victims, and offenders. It also provides some material of interest in the pornography debate.

33. Women's Studies Resources—*http://www.inform.umd.edu/EdRes/Topic/WomensStudies/*—This site from the University of Maryland provides a wealth of resources related to women's studies. You can find links to such topics as body image, comfort (or discomfort) with sexuality, personal relationships, pornography, and more. The site also addresses political concerns.

We highly recommend that you review our Web site for expanded information and our other product lines. We are continually updating and adding links to our Web site in order to offer you the most usable and useful information that will support and expand the value of your Annual Editions. You can reach us at: *http://www. dushkin.com/annualeditions/.*

Sexuality and Society

Historical and Cross-Cultural Perspectives (Articles 1–4)
Changing Society/Changing Sexuality (Articles 5–8)

People of different civilizations in different historical periods have engaged in a variety of modes of sexual expression and behavior. Despite this cultural and historical diversity, one important principle should be kept in mind: Sexual awareness, attitudes, and behaviors are learned within sociocultural contexts that define appropriate sexuality for society's members. Our sexual attitudes and behaviors are in large measure social and cultural phenomena.

For several centuries, Western civilization has been characterized by an "antisex ethic" that encompasses a norm of denial and beliefs that sex is bad unless it is controlled or proscribed in certain ways. These restrictions have usually meant that sexual behavior should be confined to monogamous heterosexual pair bonds (marriages) for the sole purpose of procreation. Fear, myth, and lack of factual information or dialogue have maintained antisex and, many say, harmful beliefs, customs, and behaviors. In recent decades, changes in our social environment—widespread availability of effective contraception, the liberation of women from the kitchen, the reconsideration of democratic values of individual freedom and the pursuit of happiness, and increasingly open dialogue about sex and sexuality—have strengthened our concept of ourselves as sexual beings and challenged the long-standing antisex ethic. At the same time, some wonder if the style and extent to which our culture has incorporated messages about sex—indeed, sex sells!—is less than helpful or healthy or if our efforts to reverse the antisex ethic may be swinging too far.

As a rule, social change is not easily accomplished even where there appears to be a critical situation involved. In the past decade, HIV/AIDS has evolved, especially in the developing world regions of Asia and Africa, as a life-and-death situation that is intricately entangled with sociocultural beliefs, practices, and sexuality. Sociologists generally acknowledge that changes in the social environment and in behavior are likely to occur in the presence of interest groups that move the society to confront and question existing beliefs, norms, and behavior. Many of the articles in this section document changes in the social environment while highlighting the questions, confrontations, and different beliefs of different groups about what are or what should be our

social policies regarding sexuality. The articles also illustrate the diversity of beliefs regarding what was beneficial or detrimental about the past, and what needs to be preserved or changed for a better future.

The fact that human sexuality is primarily a learned behavior can be both a blessing and a curse. The learning process enables humans to achieve a range of sexual expression and meaning that far exceeds their biological programming. Unfortunately, however, sociocultural norms and practices can foreclose constructive learning experiences and contexts, often driving learning underground. Many feel that what is needed for the future is high-quality, comprehensive sex education to counteract the locker room, commercial sex, and trial-and-error contexts in which most individuals in our society acquire misinformation, anxiety, and fear—as opposed to knowledge, reassurance, and comfort—about themselves as sexual people. However, some continue to fear information-giving and sex education, even suggesting that such fact-giving and open dialogue are causes of ills ranging from declining morals to increasing illegitimacy to HIV epidemics and more. As we approach the twenty-first century, it seems that remnants of the antisex ethic persist, contributing to fear, anxiety, and uncertainty, and inhibiting the kind of sex education and dialogue that promotes the healthy expression of sexuality as a positive part of life.

A view of the past illustrates the connectedness of our values and perceptions of sexuality with other sociopolitical events and beliefs. Cross-cultural perspectives provide common human patterns and needs with respect to sexuality and other interpersonal issues. Several of the articles in this section describe and examine patterns of change in political, economic, medical, and educational spheres as they relate to sexuality, while exploring and challenging present sociocultural, educational, medical, and legal practices in several controversial areas. These areas include education in school, sex roles, AIDS, family planning, and contraception. Although the authors may not agree on the desirability of the changes they describe, or advocate the same future directions, they do emphasize the necessity for people to have information and awareness about a wide range of sexual topics. They also share another

belief: We as individuals and as a world society have a vital interest in the translation of social consciousness and sexuality into a meaningful and rewarding awareness and expression for all of society's members.

The first subsection, *Historical and Cross-Cultural Perspectives*, opens with an article about Sweden where in 1942 the first sexuality education in public schools was introduced. This country's successful efforts at increasing awareness, understanding, and acceptance of healthy sexuality as part of a healthy and happy life give us insight into how societies can change as we approach the dawn of a new century. The remaining three articles on sexuality-related issues in varied settings illustrate the complexity, urgency, and worldwide nature of many of today's sexuality issues. Each article challenges the reader to question why cultures dictate and/or proscribe certain beliefs, values, and practices and takes note of instances when these belief systems seem to help or harm the individuals and society involved. Several authors link misinformation about sexuality, long-standing traditions of inequality or submissiveness, or specific sociocultural practices or beliefs to dramatic, even life-and-death, personal, interper-

sonal, and societal consequences, giving this subsection a somber, even troubling, tone.

The four articles that make up the second subsection, *Changing Society/Changing Sexuality*, illustrate the varied, even conflicting, nature of the changes occurring in the sexual arena. Several selections deal with the continuing gender role changes that have affected societal, familial, and personal interaction between the sexes for several decades now. Drawing from authors, trends, and movements as diverse as feminism and the predominantly white male Promise Keepers, they illustrate the history, evolution, and key current issues regarding masculinity, femininity, and gender roles. Calls for an end to the tradition of divisiveness and the building of healthier, more cooperative relationships allowing for deeper intimacy come from widely different groups in this country and from several other countries.

Looking Ahead: Challenge Questions

What kind of sex education did you have in elementary school? In junior high? In high school? When do you think education about anatomy, physiology, and reproduction should start? Should the nature of the classes change as students get older? If so, how and why?

Have you ever spoken to a young person from another culture/country about sexuality-related ideas, norms, education, or behavior? If so, what surprised you? What did you think about their perspective or ways?

The worldwide AIDS epidemic differs in a number of ways from the state of AIDS in America. Should (and can) we, as Americans, do anything to help fight HIV/AIDS in other countries, and why?

What are your impressions of the women's and men's movements? Have you participated (or would you participate) in a feminist event like a Take Back the Night March? What was your reaction to the Million Man March? Promise Keepers? The Rules? The Code?

Is it harder or easier to be your gender today than it was for your parents' or grandparents' generations? Why? Do you think the changes in gender roles enhance or inhibit sexual relationships and intimacy? Why?

SWEDEN LOOKS ANEW AT WAYS TO REACH AND TEACH ITS YOUNG PEOPLE ABOUT SEXUALITY

Katarina Lindahl
International Director

Stefan Laack
Education Manager
The Swedish Association for Sex Education
Stockholm, Sweden

S weden was probably the first country in the world to officially introduce sexuality education in public schools. This occurred in 1942. Sweden now has a generation of grandmothers and grandfathers who have had sexuality education at school. Not the best, perhaps, but it was there, and this has helped create a positive atmosphere in Swedish society in relation to sexuality. In fact, there is little or no resistance to giving young people protection from unwanted pregnancies and STDs, including knowledge, access to contraception, professional and confidential counseling, and supportive laws.

But, after all these years, Swedes still feel a need to question and improve upon what they are doing to help young people with their sexuality so that they see it as a positive part of life.

For many years, the Swedish Ministry of Education distributed a thick book containing guidelines for teachers. It contained everything they needed to teach sexuality issues. But, in reality, few teachers read it, and even fewer used it in the classroom.

Why were the guidelines not used? Were they worthless? The answer is no. They were very useful. They pushed sexuality education forward. They gave a clear signal that sexuality education should be built on openness and respect—with both teachers and students ready to discuss sensitive issues.

Instead of guidelines, the Ministry of Education now sends a reference book to all schools. It contains examples of methods and subjects as well as literature and films. It is important to stress, however, that much of the sexuality

> *"Sexuality education should be built on openness and respect."*

education in schools today comes from exchanging experiences and learning with others. This concept extends from the classroom to other areas of life.

TRAITS OF A GOOD TEACHER

The best teacher of sexuality education is a person who feels comfortable talking about sexuality and who wants to educate. This person must also command trust and give respect. This could be a teacher, a coach, a clinician, or an administrator. As long as young people have faith in this individual, they will listen, ask questions, discuss issues, and learn.

People in many countries question sexuality education: "Why should we have it?" or "What are its goals?" or "They will learn when they get married." In Sweden, we have another view, and our experiences are positive. Sexuality education has, in fact, proved very effective in creating responsible sexual behavior as evidenced by low and decreasing figures on abortion, teenage pregnancies, and STDs.

Teenagers all over the world start having sexual relations before marriage. They have the right to enjoy their sexuality without feeling shame, guilt, or fear. They also need access to **information about preventing unwanted pregnancies and STDs. Studies in Sweden show that young people are generally not promiscuous. They also show that 90 percent of Swedish teens report a positive view of their sexuality, and that only three percent perceive their first experience in a negative light. But there are also young people who experience abuse and harassment, and they may be in any classroom. So we must open ourselves to them and, as educators, say: "I am a person who dares to talk about these things" or "You can come to me to discuss these issues." Teachers cannot create such a climate if they are dogmatic and moralistic.**

It is again important to stress that sexuality education does not take place just in the classroom. In a society that sees sexuality as a positive part of life, Sweden provides many other sources of information: the youth clinic, the newspapers, and, of course, family and friends. In fact, family and friends are the main sources of information for young people in Sweden.

When discovering their sexuality, young people are, at the same time, creating their own identity, free from parents and other close adults. A teenager thinks like this: sexuality is a part of my personality, something which I use to distance myself from the adult world. The effect is that teenagers are often silent when discussions on sexuality take place with their parents and other adults. They think to themselves that these people should not know about their sexual world, the world where they are individuals in their own right.

The task for sexuality educators is to break through the silence in which teenagers are surrounded. They cannot prevent them from making mistakes, but they can find ways to help them express what they have trouble articulating. If young people are given an "ah-ha" experience ("I know just what you mean.") and recognize themselves through the educator's conversation, they will become more receptive to new information. In their silence, teenagers often feel alone: "I am the only one who masturbates" or "I am the only one who has not slept with anybody" or "Everyone is better than me in getting dates." By articulating these thoughts and feelings, sexuality educators can prevent young people from feeling isolated.

There are two words that are the best guidelines for sexuality education: *normalization* and *individualization*. Adolescents are at a period in their lives where their bodies are changing from day to day. They need to know that their bodies and their experiences are normal. At the same time, they need to hear that they are unique and that they are special.

MEN NEED TO BECOME MORE INVOLVED IN EDUCATION

In Sweden, most visitors to clinics are women. Men rarely come. The Swedish Association for Sex Education started a clinic for young men in 1991 to answer questions about their needs and about issues relating to sexuality.

When asked where they had received information about the clinic, most young men mentioned their female partner, followed by a close friend, and the phone directory. Very few mentioned the Association's brochures or pamphlets. The clinic staff has learned that if it wants to inform young men about such a clinic, it must give the information to young women.

The most common reason why young men come to the clinic is a concern about STDs. Some have reason to worry, but the majority come "for safety's sake." A common reply is that they have met a new partner and want to make certain they are not infected prior to having a relationship. Only a few come with the outspoken aim of asking about sexuality. But after the examination and the tests, many are reluctant to leave. When asked if they have other questions, they talk about personal relationships, what women really want, and the anxiety about not satisfying a partner. They also ask questions like: "I ejaculate after three minutes. Isn't that too early?" or "My penis is five and a half inches when it is erect. Is that normal?"

Questions like these are difficult for boys and young men to discuss in a female-oriented environment. They need answers to which they can relate. To make this happen, men, too, have to take part in the basic work involved with sexuality education and contraceptive counseling.

MISTAKES WE MAKE AS SEXUALITY EDUCATORS

Sexuality educators sometimes make mistakes even with the best intentions. These include:

- *Talking at the Wrong Level.* Talking at the right level means talking about things that are important to young people and that will give them a chance to recognize themselves and to realize that what they feel is okay. Sexuality educators must realize that the subjects teenagers feel are important are not the necessarily the same as those for adults.

Many teenagers go through several phases before having sexual intercourse: desire; love at a distance; the first kiss; fantasies; masturbation; and petting. Sexuality educators have to realize that in each classroom there are young people with differing levels of sexual experience. Most are still far from sexual intercourse. They are still thinking about the wonderful boys or girls in the upper class or about the latest rock star. Some, however, are close to intercourse and have thoughts about it. It is not unusual for educators to talk about marriage, children, divorce, abortion, and STDs.

The risk is that some young people are not affected

by—and will not identify with—the information that they receive.

- *Placing Things in Too Favorable a Light.* Adults have a tendency to describe things the way they want them to be, not the way they are. For example, a teacher might describe all of the excellent features of a condom without talking about the difficulties in using them and the distaste that many young men have for them. When a male sexuality educator explains to boys what he feels is difficult about using condoms, he is able to personally relate to them, and they will be able to ask questions and talk about their feelings.

- *Focusing on Problems.* In sexuality education, it is easy to define problems. Yet young people very seldom look upon their sexuality as a problem. If they meet adults who start by talking about diseases and unwanted pregnancies, they will probably stop listening. Sexuality educators must help young people gain a perspective on their sexuality. This means taking into account that some individuals in a group may be wondering about their sexual identity. This also means considering the differences between male and female sexuality in terms of interpersonal relationships. Once young people have gained such

individual perspectives, they will be ready for information on unwanted pregnancies and STDs.

- *Teaching in the Abstract.* It is always important to be clear and concise. When information is unclear and hard to interpret, young people will often not ask questions and not listen. Educators must use words that are understandable and that are comfortable. Those who try to use the latest teenage jargon will appear phony.

CONCLUSION

Swedish citizens continue to have an ongoing public debate about the content and the methodology of the country's sexuality education programs. Above all, they believe that these programs must build upon an open and positive view of sexuality, and that all discussion must help young people personally identify with the information.

The two key words in sexuality education in Sweden are *normalization* and *individualization*—meaning that teenagers need to know that they are like everyone else while at the same time realizing that they are unique individuals. It is the responsibility of the teachers to help accomplish this.

women of the world

TRADITION OR OUTRAGE?

This woman risks **death** if she commits **adultery.** She could be lashed with a whip if she wears **makeup.** She is **forbidden** to travel without her husband's permission, Jan Goodwin investigates women **behind the veil**

A life destroyed by Islam

Parvin Darabi and her sister, Homa, were born and raised in Tehran in the 1950s. After receiving her Ph.D., Parvin moved to California and married an American. Homa, a doctor, married an Iranian. She and her husband spent ten years in the U.S. but returned to Iran in 1979, the year Khomeini came to power.

The call came at 6 A.M. My uncle in Iran wept as he spoke, while I sat in my home near Lake Tahoe in the gloomy predawn light, clutching the phone and trying to catch my breath. My sister Homa, who had been like my twin, had burned herself to death as a protest against the oppression of Iranian women.

The day before—February 21, 1994—while the rest of the family had been taking an afternoon siesta, Homa had gone to Tehran's crowded Tajrish Square. There, she yanked off her *chador*—the black, shroud-like garment that covers Iranian women from head to toe and that they are required by law to wear. Then she poured gasoline over herself. Shouting "Death to tyranny, death to oppression, long live freedom," she lit a match and was engulfed in flames.

My God, I asked myself, how could this have happened? And yet I knew. For a long time, Homa, a brilliant physician and a university professor, had been feeling helpless—trapped by the misogynistic rule of Iran's Islamic government. The last time I had seen her, she had told me it was "pure torture" for her to live there.

Homa and I grew up in Tehran, where our father owned a construction company. Our family was westernized in many ways—but very conservative in others. Homa and I were always being told that things we wanted to do—ride bikes, play sports, learn musical instruments—were not appropriate for girls.

From *Marie Claire*, March 1997, pp. 54-56, 58, 60. © Jan Goodwin. Reprinted by permission.

We were, however, both encouraged to get good educations. Homa chose to enroll in medical school at the University of Tehran. College campuses in Iran in the early 1960s were hotbeds of student activism; at the university, Homa began to speak out about her frustration with the position of Iranian women. It's terrible, she used to say, that a woman cannot petition for divorce, while a man can divorce his wife whenever he wants. She was also unhappy that Islam permits a man four wives of his own choice while a women has one marriage, arranged by her family.

She poured gasoline over herself, shouting "Long live freedom." Then she lit a match and was engulfed in flames.

Her own marriage was not arranged. My sister met her future husband, Manouchehre Keyhani, in medical school. His family was very different from ours—they were extremely religious. The women all wore veils and would never dream of disagreeing with their husbands. But Homa loved Manouchehre. He was good-looking, intelligent, hardworking, and, like her, passionate about medicine. In 1963, the year Iranian women won the vote, our parents agreed to the rare love-match. Homa and Manouchehre became husband and wife.

A year later, I finished my Ph.D. in engineering and moved to the United States. I married an American and settled with him in California. In 1968, Homa and Manouchehre followed me to the U.S., where they interned at a hospital in Maryland. Both my sister and I became American citizens. Manouchehre never did. He missed his homeland and so, shortly before the Islamic revolution in 1979, he and Homa returned to Iran. Right away Manouchehre became a supporter of Khomeini. I remember being horrified as I watched the news covering Khomeini's triumphant return to Iran after the fall of the Shah. Standing on the platform, directly behind the Ayatollah, was my sister's husband.

Once Khomeini came into power, Homa, just like all Iranian women, was forced to practice Islamic *hijab,* or veiling, whenever she left the house. She continued to teach at the University of Tehran, however, and every evening she ran her university medical practice. Then, in 1990, the university suddenly transferred her practice to a hospital run by an extremely conservative director. He objected to my sister's dress—a floor-length coat and large head scarf that had been acceptable to the ever-patrolling religious police—and ordered her to assume the strictest form of hijab: an enormous black sheet-like garment

with just a small hole cut in it for the eyes, nose, and mouth, and, over it, a chador. When Homa objected—"How can I examine patients dressed like that? It is impossible," she said—she was dismissed from the university.

After that, my sister again began speaking out about Islam's restrictions on women. The Ministry of Health got wind of what she was doing and the revolutionary guards placed a sign on her office door stating that the office was closed because the doctor wouldn't comply with hijab. Homa was devastated. She loved her work.

Shortly after this, my mother called me from Tehran, where she was visiting from the U.S. She said that the light had gone out in Homa—that my once joyful, charming sister now sat for hours without speaking, that she had lost a lot of weight and that her eyes were ringed with shadows. Alarmed, I flew to Iran. When I spoke with Homa, she said, "My life has been destroyed. They have taken everything. . . . You should see what these bastards in the government are doing—raping 9-year-old girls before they execute them. They are destroying the country." I wanted Homa to return to America with me, and I asked Manouchehre to get her an exit visa: A woman married to an Iranian—even if she is an American citizen—cannot legally leave Iran without her husband's written permission. Manouchehre refused. I consulted a lawyer, who insisted there was nothing anyone could do. Homa's U.S. passport was useless. In Iran, a woman's husband legally owns her, as he would any other piece of property.

I returned to the U.S. alone. The last time I spoke to Homa was in February, 1994, when she called to wish my son a happy birthday. Nine days later, she was dead.

Ten thousand people attended a memorial service for Homa in Tehran, and several thousand more—exiled Iranians—attended seven different services for her in cities across the U.S. Homa was always well-known and respected in her Tehran community. Now ordinary people began hailing her as a hero, an Iranian Joan of Arc. She suffered not only for her own cause but for the cause of many other innocent women in Iran.

As for me, I was determined that in the end my sister's death should have meaning. I'd never been political before, but I decided to give up my business to start a foundation in Homa's name that could campaign for the rights of Iranian women.

The Iranian authorities have summoned my male relatives and demanded that they now stop me from speaking out. Fortunately, however, I'm in America, and they have no jurisdiction over me here. And because of my sister, I will not remain silent.

An ayatollah's daughter

Aazam Alai Taleghani lives in Tehran. She is the daughter of the late Sayed Mahmoud Taleghani, one of Iran's highest-ranking ayatollahs. Her father was in prison or exiled throughout her childhood, for opposing westernization under the Shah. She herself was a member of parliament for four years under

Ayatollah Khomeini. Married, with four children, she is now head of the Islamic Women's Institute of Iran.

"I was raised in a very religious family. From my earliest childhood I wore the chador. I believe in hijab, veiling, because a woman should be viewed as a human being, not as a sexual commodity—which is what happens in the West. For me, the chador is a national uniform and has a symbolic meaning. But I have also suffered because of it. When I went to the university, in the days of the Shah, women were not wearing the chador." She remembers being mocked by the more westernized students and faculty.

But Taleghani does not think that women should be forced to veil; the Koran does not require it. "The decision to wear the chador should come from within. But covering is also historical, just as it is in other religions." Similarly, Taleghani is not happy with the law under which Iranian women who are improperly veiled are arrested and flogged. "I don't agree with this, and I have talked to the authorities about it. To treat a woman this way has a negative outcome, not a positive one."

Taleghani does support death by stoning for men or women who commit adultery, "even if, God forbid, it happened to my daughter. The law is the law. I would be devastated, of course, because she is my daughter." She adds: "Those who commit adultery feel so guilty, they want to be punished in this manner. They say, 'If you don't stone us as we deserve, then we will be consigned to hell.' "

Taleghani's marriage was arranged. "My father knew my husband's background very well. And I was able to evaluate him for myself, during conversations, when they brought him to our home. I also chose someone for my daughter. As parents, we are more aware of the emotional and mental status of a daughter, and so our choice is more beneficial."

Iranian men are permitted four wives. Taleghani believes that Iranian women benefit from this custom, since many of them were widowed by the war with Iraq in the 1980s. "In a society

---

"If my own daughter committed adultery, I would support death by stoning for her. The law is the law."

---

where there are many more women than men, [polygamy allows] women to have the chance to experience marriage."

In the U.S., she points out, married men have extramarital affairs. "You tell me which is better," she asks. "Muslim men have to marry their wives and then support them and their children. A Western man has no commitment, financial or otherwise, when he has an affair."

LEGAL OPPRESSION OF WOMEN

- Most Westerners would say Ayatollah Khomeini plunged Iranian women back into the Dark Ages—and since his death, things have not improved.
- Women are forbidden to wear Western dress. From the age of 7, all Iranian females must be covered from head to toe, preferably in black. In 1991, Iran's prosecutor-general stated, "Any woman who rejects Islamic dress is an apostate." Apostasy is punishable by death.
- Women caught wearing makeup or nail polish or with any hair showing can be arrested, declared corrupt, and given up to 72 lashes.
- In court, a woman's testimony has half the value of a man's.
- Inheritance laws permit a woman to receive only half as much as a man.
- A woman may not travel, work, attend college, join organizations, or leave her home for any reason, even to visit a relative, without her husband's permission.
- Unrelated men and women are forbidden to be alone together at any time. Married couples may not sit together on public transportation—or swim, ski, or play sports together. All schools are sexually segregated.
- Adultery, for women, is a capital offense, punishable by stoning to death. Article 116 of the Iranian penal law specifies that "stones used should not be big enough to kill the convict in the first or second blow..."
- A husband may divorce a wife without her consent, and without informing her beforehand.
- A woman is not considered a suitable guardian for her child. A divorced mother keeps custody of her son until he is 2, of her daughter until she is 7. Then her husband gets custody—and if her dies, the children go to their paternal grandfather.
- Because a virgin may not be executed, girls convicted of capital crimes are systematically raped before [the] sentence is carried out.
- Khomeini decreed that the age of majority for girls should be 9. They can marry at 9—and can also be executed for crimes "against the state," as many have been. (For boys, the age is 16.)

Asked about the regime's other restrictions on women, she replies, "Some laws work against a woman, others benefit her. Many such rulings do not come from our Holy Koran but from the different opinions of the *olama* (the predominantly male religious authorities)."

Taleghani feels, however, that Westerners are too quick to say that Iranian women are oppressed: "Particularly where motherhood is concerned, I think there is more respect for women here than in the West. In the home, the Iranian woman has more power. As for civil law and women's rights—we do have some difficulties, but we are working on them."

Taleghani takes issue with any comparison between conditions for women under the Iranian revolution and those in certain other Islamic countries, such as Afghanistan, where the Taliban fundamentalists have been severely and violently curtailing women's lives. She explains: "The Ayatollah Khomeini's intent was not to limit women. At the beginning of the revolution, he demanded that women come out and demonstrate and raise their voices. The Taliban, on the other hand, are forcing women to stay home and stay silent."

"Today, whether because of the war or the revolution, Iranian women are progressing much more than before and are better able to defend their rights. Of course, our freedoms are not Western freedoms. But academically, economically, and socially, women are becoming more active." Taleghani insists, however, that this is still not enough. "Women in Iran desire to go further. Our objective is to gain more rights and enter the higher ranks of society and the economy—regardless of gender, and each according to her own ability."

An Iranian in the U.S.

Ezam Monifee, 30, and her husband came here from Iran to study engineering. They live in the San Francisco Bay Area with their daughter. Ezam strictly observes hijab, always covering her hair and wearing long sleeves, a long shirt, and long skirts or loose pants when she goes out. No matter how frenetic her schedule, Ezam always makes time to bow down facing Mecca and pray five times a day.

"If you wear revealing clothes you attract a certain kind of male," Ezam says. "When a woman wears hijab, a Muslim man knows that she believes in herself, her family, and her Islamic traditions and he would never come close to her. In the West, it keeps American men from thinking bad things about me. They respect me, and I know I can never be anything to them but a coworker."

Ezam first wore hijab at the age of 12. "It was quite voluntary," she insists. "The Iranian revolution was just beginning, and I was reading a lot of Islamic books. I wanted to wear it. Now it's become a habit; I can't imagine not wearing it.

"We are always hearing that hijab is a symbol of women's oppression. But it doesn't prevent a woman from progressing with her life. Yes, I can no longer go to the beach or a swimming pool. And I would like to swim. I've tried to find an all-women's pool in this area, but there aren't any. So I have given it up." She also admits that hijab is not ideal wear in hot weather. But these things, she stresses, are not great hardships.

In the diverse community where she lives in the U.S., Ezam says, "no one comments on how I dress or behave. They know it is my religion. America is a free land." However, there are occasions when she is made aware of prejudice. During the Gulf War, she first heard the term "sand-niggers" used against Muslims. And blaming Muslims and calling them terrorists after incidents such as the Oklahoma bombing and the TWA disaster has become so prevalent, she's surprised when it doesn't happen. "You get used to it," she says. "To be honest, I even find myself thinking the same thing. When the media said that Iranians were responsible for the plane blowing up, I found myself thinking, 'It could be them.' But I know the Iranian government is trying so hard to change their image in the West, to make it work—they would never kill innocent people."

Just as she has learned to live with prejudice, Ezam has learned not to try to explain her religion. When she's entertaining American friends and it's time for her to pray, she excuses herself and leaves the room. "I don't tell them what I am doing," she says. "And if we are driving somewhere, my husband just stops the car, and we get out and pray on the grass by the side of the road. I've even prayed in crowded American airports. I'm proud of that. It means you believe in something, and practice it. Praying calms me down and comforts me. The moment when I talk to my God is the most special time. I wouldn't want to miss it."

Adventures in the
skin trade

The world's oldest profession has become Cuba's ticket to the global economy

By Coco Fusco
Ms. Magazine

She has the tawny complexion, oval face, aquiline nose, and sinuous body of a young Josephine Baker. The strobe lights twirling around Havana's Café Cantante catch her long neck and limbs as she twists her hips and rib cage in opposite directions, her yellow baby-doll dress swinging from side to side. Her look, her age, her hip clothes are telltale signs that she's a *jinetera,* the popular term for a Cuban woman who exchanges a range of services— including sex—for money from foreigners. The Café Cantante is a chic watering hole for the country's cultural elite— and for male tourists on the prowl.

Magazines all over Europe have been running stories in recent years about Cuba as a sex tourist's paradise. The exile Cuban press in Miami has been accusing Fidel Castro's government of being the country's number one pimp. During its annual meeting in January 1996, the United Nations Committee on the Elimination of Discrimination Against Women held a marathon session in which a Federation of Cuban Women spokesperson fielded questions about the condition of women in Cuba, including this "new wave" of *jineteras.* I'm in Havana to find out what this renewed international scrutiny is about.

By the 1940s, tourism had emerged as one of Cuba's largest industries. The Mafia takeover of hotels and casinos guaranteed that prostitution would play a prominent role in Havana's nightlife, and Cuba became known as little more than a whorehouse for visiting Americans and the higherups in President Fulgencio Batista's corrupt government.

Castro came to power promising to change all that. One of the first acts of the revolutionary government was to reeducate hundreds of prostitutes and offer them jobs as clerks, bus drivers, and waitresses. Many supporters of the revolution believed that women would have a better life under socialism. Now they, as well as the exiled opposition, see the reemergence of prostitution as a sign that socialism has failed Cuban women.

Well, yes and no. The truth is that *jineteras* have always been a part of the postrevolution landscape. When I began visiting the island over a decade ago, it wasn't unusual to find a few exceptionally well-dressed women circulating in hotel cabarets and at embassy functions. Cuban friends warned me that they were sex workers operating with the approval of the Ministry of the Interior—and that they reported on foreigners' activities.

What has changed since then is the Cuban economy. As the country totters on the brink of ruin, brought about by the withdrawal of Soviet subsidies and the U.S. trade embargo, the average Cuban makes $10 a month, while a beer in a club costs $7. Suddenly, doctors and teachers, as well as carpenters and shoemakers, are looking for a way to earn dollars—the only currency with value. And the number of women offering themselves to foreigners as temporary partners or potential wives is spiraling upward. The Ministry of Tourism projected one million tourists by the end of 1996. Among them are planeloads of men from Spain, Italy, Germany, Canada, and even the United States, men whose buying power and social status are multiplied tenfold upon arrival in a cash-starved country. It's no secret that many Cubans see the *pepes* (foreign johns) as replacements for a paternalistic government that can no longer provide the necessities of life. One of the top salsa hits on the is-

From *Utne Reader,* July/August 1997, pp. 66-69, 107-109. Originally "Hustling for Dollars" from *Ms.* magazine, September/October 1996, pp. 62-70. © 1996 by Ms. Magazine. Reprinted by permission.

land when I arrived advised Cuban women to find a "papiriqui con mucho juaniquiqui"—a sugar daddy. From the singers, the cabdrivers' quips, and the bawdy folk art I encounter around Havana, I also sense that on the street these women are seen as heroic providers whose sexual power is showing up the failures of an ailing macho regime. As Paco, a young hustler I met, explained, "Everything is upside down now. The men are at home with aprons, cooking and taking care of the kids, while their wives are on the street working."

Nestled around the Havana port area, La Habana Vieja, one of the city's poorest neighborhoods, draws the most tourists. I comb the streets, hoping to get the perspective of prostitutes who were in the business before the recent explosion. By the time I reach the Plaza de la Catedral, with its bustling craft market, Paco has latched on to me. He is a thin, small-framed, mischievous-looking 24-year-old with short hair, crisply ironed jeans, and imitation Ray Ban sunglasses. We stroll toward the Malecón, the waterfront boulevard that wraps around half the city. Eventually, he introduces me to Margarita and Helen, women in their late 20s who have been working the streets for more than 10 years. Margarita has a young son whom she supports; Helen lives alone.

When they started, Margarita explains, their main clients were merchant seamen and foreign technicians. Possessing dollars was illegal then, so they would get African students to buy consumer goods for them in the dollar shops. They were careful, and still are, not to be too ostentatious and incur envy that might lead someone to inform on them. They've been lucky so far and have never been arrested, but they have friends in jail.

They say that at least two-thirds of the young women in the barrio are *jineteras.* When I ask what the men think about it, they both laugh. "They see the *gallego* [Spaniard] coming in with a girl, and they don't see him," says Helen. "They see a chicken, beans, rice—a full fridge."

What about the dangers? The only case of violence they could think of was in 1993, when a *jinetera* was impaled on a mop by a European tourist who then threw her body from the balcony of his hotel. The murderer was out of the country before the body was found. Health risks? They claim that they insist on condoms, and that health is the one thing that the government still has under control. Knowing about the declining conditions in Cuba's hospitals, and chronic shortages of medicine, I wonder if they are just hoping to convince themselves that the old revolutionary promises are still kept. No one I spoke to during my trip wanted to accept the idea that an epidemic of sexually transmitted diseases, including but not limited to AIDS, was in the making.

When I ask them if they think about getting out of the business, Helen tells me a story that illustrates the dilemma facing Cuban women who have been socialized to believe in their equality but now face a polarized world that leaves them little room to maneuver. "I got married once," she said with a wry smile. "I thought I'd go to Spain and start a new life. But he was nuts, crazy. He wanted to keep me at home all day. I lasted two months, and then I realized that I had to get out.

I had no money and no place to go, so I had to come back here. He's so mad that he still won't give me a divorce."

Both Margarita and Helen said that some *jineteras* triumphed in Europe, but others were stuck, forced by pimps to work long hours seven days a week. At least in Cuba, they could survive working a few times a month.

To get to any sort of truth about *jineteras,* you have to plow through the myths that make discussions of *mulatas* (mixed-race women), tourism, and prostitution in Cuba so complicated. The *mulata* has been linked with illicit sex from colonial times onward. Many mixed-race women were the "love children" and mistresses of white men. According to an adage from the Caribbean plantations, white women were for marrying, black women for work, and *mulatas* for sex. That legacy, told and retold through songs, poems, and novels, has made the *mulata* a national symbol of sorts, and now the country's tourism campaigns are using that symbol as a way to make perfectly clear just what Cuba has to offer male tourists.

When I first visited postrevolutionary Cuba, I was impressed by the sexual assertiveness of the women I met. The stigmas attached to having an active sex life outside marriage were disappearing among women of my generation. More than 30 years of free birth control, sex education, coed boarding schools, and a social system that reduced parental control had provided greater sexual freedom and set the island apart from most other Latin American countries, as well as most Cuban-exile communities. This amounted to more than just increased liberalism about sex: In a country where consumer pleasures were few and far between, casual sex had become the most desirable leisure activity for the younger generation. Some Cuban intellectuals also see the increasing openness about extramarital sex and lesbian, gay, and bisexual activity as an unspoken revolt against the socialist emphasis on productive labor and the revolution's puritanical morality.

That a tropical socialist utopia could be known as a site of "sexual liberation" in the late 1980s and then transformed into an impoverished island ripe for sexual exploitation in the 1990s is one of the more painful signs of what entering a global postindustrial economy will mean for Cuba. One of the most glaring aspects of Cuba's reinsertion into the capitalist orbit is the way in which racial divisions have become more apparent. Cuban blacks are far less likely than whites to have wealthy relatives sending dollars from abroad. And now that tourism is the main source of hard currency, Cuba's image of itself as a modern industrial nation is in tatters. To lure foreigners, the government is showcasing "traditional" Afro-Cuban religious rituals and art, "traditional" Afro-Cuban music, and, of course, Afro-Cuban women. Those are the sorts of racist clichés that used to drive many educated Cubans up the wall. The prospect of developing a modern society with a diversified economy was linked in their minds with no longer having to service a First World lust for exotica.

I grab a cab one night with a Cuban journalist friend named Magaly and head out for El Comodoro, a hotel in Havana's swank Miramar district. The Habana Club disco at the Comodoro is the capital's most famous den of iniquity. Being there is like taking a trip out of Cuba to a teeny-

The hypocrisy reaches the highest levels. In 1992 Castro said that Cuban women were jineteras not out of need, but because they liked sex.

bopper club in Rome or Madrid. It's a labyrinth of chrome and vinyl, with Euro-pop dance music blaring so loud that I get hoarse trying to have a conversation.

Magaly and I stand at the railing of the sunken round dance floor. She shows me how the girls position themselves in full view while they dance, so they can attract a *pepe.* These are the most expensive *jineteras,* Magaly explains—they can afford to pay their own way into the club. The men tend to look a little older than those on the street, which I attribute to the high cost of entry and drinks, and the steeper prices charged by many of the *jineteras.* Over at the bar, a dozen overweight, middle-aged men are having their heads massaged by teenage girls.

As squalid as this is, what irks me as I discuss the *jinetera* issue with privileged Cubans like Magaly is their snobbery. She and I get into an argument when I point out that few Cubans seem willing to see a parallel between the *jineteras* and the many artists, musicians, and professionals with exportable skills who are also looking for opportunities to socialize—and occasionally have sex—with foreigners, in the hopes of getting grants or jobs outside the country, or even a marriageable mate. When the women involved are part of the elite, everyone looks the other way. It's poor women of color who take the heat. And the fact that *jineteras* of color are now marrying Europeans at an unusually high rate makes them objects of envy in a country where many people are desperately looking for any means possible to emigrate.

The hypocrisy reaches the highest levels. In 1992 Castro seemed happy to tolerate prostitution. He commented that Cuban women were *jineteras* not out of need, but because they liked sex. They were among the healthiest and best-educated hookers in the business, he added. This was interpreted by many Cuba watchers as an invitation to male tourists to take advantage of the sexual prowess of the revolution's children. Three years later, Federation of Cuban Women leader Vilma Espín denounced *jineteras* as decadent trash. Deputy tourism minister Miguel Bruguera claimed that Cuba "rejected" prostitution and sought to promote "healthy, family tourism." These pronouncements are part of an offensive that includes police sweeps, stiffer penalties for prostitutes, and a crackdown on hotel guards who accept bribes. I even heard rumors of work camps where jailed prostitutes were supposedly being sent.

The rhetoric and repression mask significant economic concerns. In the early 1980s, Castro denounced peasant farmers when they started to prosper in private markets, then a few years later lambasted artists who were selling their work without state intermediaries. Whenever an authorized private practice gets big enough to threaten the state's control over the economy, the government launches a cleanup campaign, and many people land in jail.

These days, the profits of Cuba's emerging class of self-employed vendors, beauticians, cabdrivers, and private restaurateurs are heavily taxed. But freelance *jinet-*

eras don't pay anything to the state. Thousands of dollars of bribes pass among *chulos, jineteras,* cops, and hotel guards each day. That underground economy is encroaching on a tourist industry funded primarily by the Cuban government.

"What bothers the government now isn't that women are selling themselves," insists political scientist Mariá de los Angeles Torres, an expert on Cuban affairs at De Paul University in Chicago. "It's that the business is now out of their hands. The state has been involved in promoting sex tourism for years." Torres recalls that in 1991, when Cubans were supposedly not allowed past hotel lobbies, the Comodoro Hotel offered special certificates—for a price—to male guests, authorizing those "with intent to marry" to take Cuban women to their rooms.

Indeed, who can and who does profit from prostitution is a key issue. The range of profitable activities in Cuba has dwindled over the past seven years. When the country entered what is now called its Special Period in 1993—and faced the worst food shortages and highest black market rates in decades—Cubans without outside resources had two choices: work in and around tourism and make dollars, or earn a pittance in pesos and watch their families suffer. Jobs in tourism are not plentiful enough to employ the many Cubans in need of dollars: only 2 percent of working Cubans are employed in legitimate jobs in hotel construction, maintenance, tourist entertainment, and sales. In 1993 I spoke with the granddaughter of a respected *santero* (a priest of the Afro-Cuban Santeria religion). She burst into tears when she told me that all the women in her office were turning tricks after hours. "You see my daughter and my grandparents, how thin they are," she cried. "But I just can't do it. I think about it, but I can't."

While the hardship that leads many women to sex work is real, the image of the *jinetera* selling herself for a pound of meat doesn't explain the range of motivations for the women involved. The desire for nonproductive leisure and consumerism is also an important—and explosive—factor. When the government began to push tourism in the 1980s, it created a zone of pleasure that was off-limits to most citizens. Area Dólares (the Dollar Area), as it was called, reminded many Cubans of the race and class segregation that kept them out of clubs and beaches before 1959. Present-day tourism has generated enormous resentment in a mostly working-class populace who watch a government that lectures about the socialist work ethic offer pleasure, leisure, and the country's finest resources to the party elite and visiting capitalists.

The Union of Communist Youth tried to stem the growing tide of disenchantment among Cuba's under-25 majority during the early 1990s with street parties and concerts. But those activities can't compare with the lifestyle that dollars can buy. The 1994 law that legalized possession of dollars facilitated access to "el hi-life," offering respite from power shortages, over-crowded housing, interminable lines, and lousy TV fare. "What would I do with a Cuban boyfriend on a Saturday night?" a *jinetera* asked me. "Wait for a bus for two hours, and then go home to an apartment with no privacy? These guys might be old and gross, but at least when I'm with them, I sit in a nice place with air-conditioning, listen to good music, and have a real drink. That helps me forget about bad breath and a big belly."

On a windy Sunday night, I go out looking for teenage *jineteras* at the new and very pricey Maliá Cohiba Hotel. It's an oversize high-rise, full of marble and glass, too many indoor fountains, and $400-a-night rooms. At the door, a guard gestures for me to stop. I tell him in my best imitation of gringo Spanglish that I am visiting from America, and he whispers an apology and lets me through.

I step outside and spot two teenagers chatting up a short, 50ish man in a gray suit. One girl is wearing over-the-knee spike-heel leather boots and has a per-oxide-blond Afro. The other, wearing a smoky-blue long dress, has long, dark unstyled hair and a lot of acne. When the man steps inside, three cops descend on the girls. The ensuing exchange looks calm, and within minutes the cops have let the girls go. I approach the girls and invite them out to eat.

Katy and Sussy tell me they are 18, but they look about 15. They say they've been in the business for four years, and they claim that the current clampdown is so tight that most hotel guards won't take the usual $25 bribe to let a girl upstairs, now that the penalty is two years in prison. An old vagrancy law has been resurrected and is being used against the *jineteras,* who get three warnings before they face up to eight years in prison, recently increased from four years.

Katy, the faux-blond *mulata,* does most of the talking. I ask if she's supporting anyone. "We're helping the country!" she tells me, reiterating the common line of those defending the *jineteras'* right to engage in sex work. "I'm too used to this life to give it up," she adds. "I'm used to having money, and I love to go to the clubs."

How much does she charge? "I won't work for less than $50," she says, "but some girls are ruining things by taking $20 or $30." She says she has seen as many as three clients a day. And both girls insist that they go to school, though they don't see any point to it. I ask Katy if she'd like to get out of the country. She explains that regulations don't permit someone her age to marry and leave. (The legal age is 21.) She did visit Italy, where her older sister lives with her Italian hus-band, and liked it, but decided not to overstay her three-month visa. Her sister got her started as a *jinetera.* "She told me that she didn't want me to 'become a woman' with a Cuban man who would mistreat me," Katy says. "She found me a nice Italian guy. He spent a month here with me, and then left me $500. He's waiting for me to be old enough for us to get married."

Between the lines I hear old and new Cuban morali-ties converging: There's postrevolution pragmatism in planning how to lose your virginity before marriage, and how to get around immigration restrictions; the older belief is that white male foreigners protect women of color from the archetypically controlling, even abusive, Caribbean male. But in reality, there's no one protecting Katy or Sussy.

I ask the girls what they think about having sex with old men. Sussy blurts out, "We just have to suck 'em a long time," and then goes back to munching on her french fries. I feel I am watching the saddest part of Cuban socialism's last chapter—the island's own ver-sion of a Generation X, kids without any dream of a future beyond the next purchase. Despite the hopes of many Cubans that the ideals of equality between the sexes and races, of freedom from hunger and want, might become reality under a revolutionary govern-ment, Cuba is being pushed back in time. *Mulatas* are once again the focus of sexual exploitation and sexual mythology. But the *jinetera* can't be boiled down to merely a tale of victimization, for she is also a symbol of the Cuban people's frustration with state interven-tion, the cruel realities of the embargo, and the pressure to join the global economy. What is so disheartening is that, as is so often the case, women are bearing the brunt of society's malaise.

Coco Fusco is an interdisciplinary artist, academic, and critic.

A Shot in the Dark

Are AIDS vaccines ready for the real world?
The United States government says no.
But in Thailand, where desperation
is higher, the world's first
large-scale trial will
soon begin.

Jon Cohen

Jon Cohen covers AIDS for *Science* and is writing a book about AIDS vaccine research. Despite having several thousand dollars worth of equipment stolen from his hotel room safe, Cohen says he loved Thailand. Luckily the thieves weren't aesthetes—they took Cohen's notebooks out of his briefcase before stealing it.

ONE EVENING LAST September three dozen AIDS experts gathered in a meeting room of the Pang Suan Keaw Hotel in the town of Chiang Mai, northern Thailand. As a storm brewed outside, they began to lay the groundwork for one of the most significant medical undertakings of our time: a full-scale human trial of an AIDS vaccine. Although over the past ten years 36 AIDS vaccines have been injected into more than 2,000 people, none has yet received the kind of real-world test that can show whether it actually works. Now these researchers were preparing to launch such a trial by the beginning of 1997. And they would do it in Thailand, one of the nations hardest hit by the worldwide explosion of AIDS.

If the participants had been in an ar-gumentative mood, of if they had been meeting elsewhere perhaps, they could have seized on any of a large number of contentious issues—the most obvious being that the two vaccines under consideration, made by the California-based companies Genentech and Biocine, had been rejected for human trials in the United States just 15 months earlier. The National Institutes of Health (NIH) had decided that these vaccines were too questionable to justify the government's spending millions of dollars testing them on Americans. But no one here, in this room in Chiang Mai, saw fit to raise the point. They all understood that Thailand, struggling to deal with a raging epidemic of HIV infections, has an urgent need to try *something*—even something that has only an outside chance of working. As many as 1 million of Thailand's 60 million residents are already infected with HIV, and anyone who travels through the country these days can see the deep scars AIDS is causing—not only because of the steadily mounting death toll but because of the lives utterly wrecked.

And so, as the rain fell and the wind rose in the dark outside the Chiang Mai hotel, a representative from Biocine faced no hostile questions as she addressed the group. Rather, the gathered officials—from the Thai government, the World Health Organization (WHO), and the U.S. military—all listened attentively as she went into the details of launching large-scale Thai trials of an AIDS vaccine. It was clear that everyone in the room thought this approach made sense. Then, suddenly, there was a clap of thunder and the room went black.

"Just keep talking," someone said in the darkness.

And they did—this assembled brain trust of AIDS vaccine experts just went on talking in the dark. By now it is a condition anyone involved in AIDS vaccines is used to.

AS SOON AS researchers first offered convincing proof, in April 1984, that HIV causes AIDS, the search for a vaccine began. Genentech, a darling of the biotechnology industry, was one of the first companies to take up the challenge. Across San Francisco Bay, another zealous biotech firm, Chiron, also assigned a team of scientists to the problem. In 1987 Chiron hooked up with the Swiss pharmaceutical giant Ciba-Geigy to form Biocine, and the next year Biocine's HIV vaccine was injected into a few dozen volunteers in Switzerland. In keeping with vaccine-development tradition, the first tests aimed only at determining whether the vaccine was safe and whether it triggered basic immune responses, such as the production of antibodies. Similar small-scale tests of a Genentech vaccine began in 1991.

Both companies exploited genetic engineering to get around the vexing problems posed by old-fashioned approaches to a viral vaccine. Most of these contain a harmless version of the whole virus: the polio vaccine designed by Jonas Salk, for example, contains "killed," or inactivated, poliovirus, while the more commonly used vaccine devised by Albert Sabin contains weakened but still viable strains of the pathogen. Both approaches have their dangers. It's possible while trying to prepare a vaccine made of inactivated viruses to let a few live ones slip through. Just such a mishap once occurred with an early batch of the Salk vaccine, and more than 100 children were inadvertently paralyzed by polio. A botched inactivated-HIV vaccine would almost certainly mean death for many.

A weakened-virus vaccine could be even more dangerous. Researchers might, for example, misjudge how weak to make the HIV virus. What if it could still cause AIDS, although perhaps in 20 years instead of the usual 10? Even a properly weakened virus might be risky. HIV belongs to a group of viruses that insert their own genetic code into a host's DNA, and there is evidence that the insertion alone can cause cancer. And finally, there was always the possibility that once injected into people, the weakened virus would replicate and in some cases produce mutated, stronger strains.

The Biocine and Genentech vaccines employ the same basic strategy for evading these dangers. While many of the details of the two vaccines differ, each, instead of relying on whole HIV, is fashioned from just a part of the virus. HIV looks something like a ball studded with little gearshift knobs. It uses these knobs, made of a protein known as gp120, to make its way into white blood cells. Biocine and Genentech produced engineered versions of gp120 and used these alone in their vaccine. Since the rest of the virus is missing, the vaccine cannot possibly cause HIV infection, but it can, the companies hope, prime the immune system to make antibodies to gp120. Theoretically, if HIV infects a vaccinated person, his or her immune system will at-

tack the gp120 knobs and disable them, leaving the virus disarmed. Theoretically.

IN 1988, WHEN the first Swiss volunteer received an injection of the Biocine vaccine, Thailand was just learning that it had an AIDS problem. For three years the country had been regularly testing visa applicants for HIV, in addition to testing members of high-risk groups, such as injecting drug users, male and female prostitutes, blood transfusion recipients, and men who visited sexually transmitted disease (STD) clinics. By 1987 fewer than 100 HIV-infected people had surfaced out of 200,000 tests. But in 1988 the numbers began to change. In one methadone clinic, for example, the HIV rate jumped from 1 percent at the beginning of the year to more than 32 percent by September. By 1990, 44 percent of injecting drug users surveyed in Bangkok were infected.

A second wave of infection began in 1989: rates among female prostitutes went from 1 percent to more than 40 percent in some places. And in the far larger population of heterosexual men who visited STD clinics, a third wave struck: the rate went from two-tenths of a percent in 1988 to 5 percent by 1991—a prevalence 50 times higher than that among heterosexual men in the United States.

Many researchers, though, saw something odd in the pattern of these numbers. Among drug users, the infection rate was fairly uniform throughout Thailand. But among female prostitutes and heterosexual men, the outbreak was far worse in the north, in cities like Chiang Mai, than in the south, in cities like Bangkok. Among 21-year-old men drafted into the Royal Thai Army, for example, 10 percent of the conscripts from the provinces around Chiang Mai were infected, compared with 1 to 3 percent elsewhere in the country.

AIDS experts around the world had by this time begun to pay attention to Thailand's raging epidemic. Among them were researchers attached to the United States Army. The Army has a long tradition of vaccine research—its intent is chiefly to protect its far-flung soldiers from local diseases. But there is another motivation at work here: the Army believes it is possible that AIDS could kill so many people in developing countries that these nations could become destabilized and that the United States might ultimately be pulled into the wars that would follow.

In December 1990, Colonel Donald Burke, head of the U.S. military's AIDS research program, attended an AIDS meeting on one of his visits to Thailand. There he heard reports of the peculiar, and perplexing, patterns of new Thai cases. "It appeared to be a very hot heterosexual epidemic in the north," says Burke. "I had no reason at all to expect that. Why, of all places, Chiang Mai?" Was sexual activity different in the north? Did HIV get help in the north by cofactors, such as sexually transmitted diseases, that increased the infection rate? Or was the virus that was infecting heterosexuals in the north different from the one infecting drug users? "It could have been any one of these," Burke says.

Burke soon discovered, however, that STD rates were no higher in the north than in the south. Not only did this finding make the cofactors explanation unlikely, but it also cast doubt on the popular notion that Thai men in the north had sex with prostitutes more frequently than did men in the south. Thus Burke was left with an explanation that, while it made more sense to him, was more disturbing: what was different about northern Thailand was not the behavior of heterosexuals infected with the AIDS virus but the behavior of the virus itself.

The quickly mutating AIDS virus has evolved into several different subtypes distributed around the world. "HIV is like the buffalo" is how Somboon Suprasert, a nurse who works with AIDS patients in Chiang Mai, puts it. "The buffalo from Thailand, India, Bangladesh, and Burma—their habits are not the same. But they're all buffalo." In 1990, when Burke was looking at the pattern of Thai infections, there were four HIV subtypes under scrutiny: A, B, C, and D. In the United States and Europe the overwhelming majority of AIDS victims carry subtype B.

To find out what was going on in Thailand, Burke collected 20 blood samples from HIV-infected soldiers at Kawila Hospital, which is located on a Thai army base in Chiang Mai, and had the blood analyzed. He quickly discovered that while the drug users in Thailand were carrying subtype B, the heterosexuals in the north were infected with a subtype that had never been seen before—now called subtype E. (The list has since gone up to I.)

Some hints have since emerged as to why E would be so potent in heterosexuals: in test-tube studies led by Max Essex at Harvard, subtype E viruses infected cells from the vaginal lining more easily than did subtype B viruses. But whatever the mechanism, this heterosexual epidemic of subtype E has given the AIDS epidemic in Thailand a different look from those in the United States and Europe, where HIV has hit gay men and drug users the hardest. Ninety percent of HIV-infected Thais are heterosexuals. At Kawila Hospital, long, dark wards are filled with hundreds of soldiers lying in clunky metal-frame beds, withering from AIDS. Here in Thailand, explains Colonel Sakol Eiumtrakul, who heads the hospital, "HIV is a problem of the family. Every family can have HIV if a man has sex with a prostitute who is infected." Recent surveys back up his point: 96.5 percent of HIV-infected Thai military recruits in the north said they had had sex with a prostitute, and 38 percent of prostitutes in the same area are infected.

Simple numbers alone, of course, do not show the true face of AIDS here.

PRATOOM THAJORN is a nurse and social worker in San Patong, a district 20 kilometers outside Chiang Mai that some AIDS researchers believe has the highest rates of HIV infection in all Thailand. As she travels from one village to another in the driving rain, it becomes clear that HIV assaults the Thai family from every angle.

Pratoom begins with a visit to the home of Deng Boonyarat, a 68-year-old water buffalo tender who died of AIDS two days before. "He didn't have any money for prostitutes or for any risky behavior," Pratoom explains; this man was infected by a blood transfusion. Pratoom is sitting on a woven mat in his wood shack on stilts, a bare lightbulb hanging from the ceiling, and idyllic posters of mansions in bucolic settings tacked to the walls. As his disease progressed, she says, he had to sell his animals to pay for medical care. He died broke, and his family, with less than $7 to their name, could not afford to have him embalmed, let alone to put on a funeral with a traditional meal for all the mourners. But as his body sat packed in ice to keep it from rotting, the villagers donated nearly $800; his family would in the end be able to feed 300 people at his funeral. Today it is Pratoom's turn to help: another social worker she has brought along hands the family an envelope stuffed with money.

"You have the enemy around here and you give me the pistol. One day you tell me, don't fire that pistol! It will burst and it will harm you."

Pratoom drives over rutted muddy roads through rice fields to reach another clutch of shacks on stilts. Again the client is a 68-year-old man, but this one is not infected with HIV. Rather he is taking care of his 30-year-old daughter and his 25-year-old son, both of whom are infected. They have the thin limbs and sunken faces of people who have progressed to full-blown AIDS. The father, who has pustules on his limbs from his own battle with tuberculosis, explains that both his children moved in with him because their spouses had died of AIDS. His son, who has a 5-year-old boy himself, appears to have dementia and wanders aimlessly about the little village. The daughter says that though her 10-year-old son is uninfected, AIDS is taking a heavy toll on him. "He doesn't want to get married, because he's seen both his uncle and his father get sick from AIDS," she explains.

On the other side of Chiang Mai, a Buddhist monk, or *phra*, named Phongthep Dhammagaruko offers another form of care for people with AIDS. Phra Phongthep runs the region's only hospice for AIDS patients who are in the last stages of the disease, many of whom have been rejected by their families and have nowhere else to live. Although his traditional yellow robe and clean-shaven head give him the look of another time, Phra Phongthep is very much a monk of the late twentieth century. He is using every tool he can in his fight against the disease—including a supply of medicine for opportunistic infections associated with AIDS.

Phra Phongthep desperately wants people to understand just how grave the situation in Thailand is. To that end he has put together an elaborate slide show,

with a written text, to illustrate the problem. One slide shows a former hospice resident being cremated. The man's charred hand reaches out from the fire. "It looks as though he's beckoning people to join him if they persist in their unsafe behavior," says Phra Phongthep. The man, he points out, is being burned on a log fire in an open field. Customarily Thais use a crematorium, but like many crematoriums around the country, the local one has been used so much in recent years that it is broken.

THAILAND ENTERED the AIDS vaccine race in 1991. That fall, the World Health Organization announced that it had selected Thailand, along with Rwanda, Brazil, Uganda, and Zaire, as a finalist for hosting a trial. The U.S. Army, with a project of its own, simultaneously revealed that Thailand was its first choice. Meanwhile the National Institute of Allergy and Infectious Diseases (NIAID), one of the institutes that make up the NIH and the world's largest supplier of funds for AIDS vaccine research, had its eye on Zaire and the United States.

With any vaccine, a long road runs between the decision to prepare for efficacy trials and the actual launch of those trials. Countries must ready all the components that fall under the vague rubric "infrastructure"—everything from laboratories to paved roads to telephone lines. Staff must be hired and trained. Epidemiologists and behavioral scientists must identify the groups that will make the best volunteers. At the same time, the country's political climate must remain relatively stable (unrest in Rwanda and Zaire knocked them out of contention).

21

And even though researchers may already have put the vaccines through preliminary, small-scale trials in the United States or Europe, the potential large-trial hosts have to repeat some of the same tests to make sure that the vaccines are safe with their own people and produce a similar immune response.

By April 1994 the United States had moved further than any other country down the road to efficacy trials. That month, a group of leading AIDS vaccine researchers met at NIAID's behest and decided the government should find out whether the Genentech and Biocine vaccines would work.

Staging trials in U.S. populations would, without question, be difficult. Among the problems was that the new infection rates in the people at greatest risk were relatively low compared with the rates in groups in places like Thailand. This meant that even a two- or three-year trial involving thousands of people might yield data that were too weak to prove conclusively whether a vaccine worked.

Moreover, to many researchers the data that already existed on gp120 vaccines were not inspiring. Although the vaccines had prevented HIV infections in chimpanzees, those experiments involved only a handful of animals, and the tests were done under highly artificial conditions. To make matters worse, chimpanzees are widely considered to be an iffy animal model. It is next to impossible for a chimpanzee to get AIDS after infection with HIV; in ten years of experiments, only one chimp has succumbed. Monkeys, on the other hand, do develop AIDS from a close relative of HIV called SIV. But researchers had little convincing evidence of success with vaccines based on the SIV surface protein.

If the animal data presented a murky picture, test-tube studies made the situation even more confusing. Researchers achieved encouraging results when they took antibodies produced in vaccinated humans and put them in a lab culture of HIV: the antibodies neutralized the virus. It appears, though, that HIV in the body is significantly different from HIV in a test tube. When researchers mixed these same antibodies with HIV freshly extracted from patients, the antibodies had virtually no effect.

Still, despite some reservations, the NIAID group was nearly unanimous in its recommendation that the vaccines move into efficacy trials to assess their true

worth. But the recommendation was just that—the final decision rested with NIAID director Anthony Fauci.

A month later, in May, the vaccines' prospects were damaged when the U.S. media made much ado about a handful of gp120 vaccine recipients who had subsequently become infected with HIV. It mattered little to critics that these cases involved people who had not received their complete number of doses, or that the trials had been too small to measure the efficacy of the vaccine. In the wake of the hubbub, at a NIAID meeting in June, Fauci reconsidered the question of staging efficacy trials. This time the debate attracted a horde of journalists.

With television cameras whirring, scientists from Genentech and Biocine made their cases for staging the trials. Representatives from prominent AIDS activist groups told the panel that their communities were wary of testing the vaccines, given their hazy effects. The NIAID group's April recommendation was scrutinized in detail. At the end of the day, the panel voted to put efficacy trials on indefinite hold until more promising vaccine candidates moved through the pipeline. Fauci quickly announced that he concurred.

Why did Fauci reject the April recommendation? Critics charge that he was afraid of the political repercussions of spending millions on trials that had become high profile and that might well fail. Supporters contend that sound logic prevailed. Whatever the reasons, the decision incensed many longtime vaccine testers. "I thought it was atrocious," says epidemiologist Kenrad Nelson of Johns Hopkins. "The only way to determine whether a vaccine works is to test it. It's impossible from the data they had in hand to determine whether a vaccine would work."

Thai scientists were dismayed as well. Before Fauci's June meeting, they had sent him a letter expressing their worry that if Fauci decided not to conduct the U.S. efficacy trials, Biocine and Genentech might substantially reduce their efforts in developing countries. And they wanted the NIAID panel to emphasize to the world one point: "Given the explosive character of the epidemic in Thailand . . . we feel that the parameters for choosing whether or not to proceed with vaccine trials, including efficacy evaluation, are substantially different here."

"In Thailand they like consensus—they don't like to go against the current,"

says Jose Esparza, who until recently headed AIDS vaccine development at WHO. "Taking a different position from the United States is not easy for a small country like Thailand. They admire U.S. science and can't just ignore it."

And as a result, the Thais were deeply stung by Fauci's decision. "You have the enemy around here and you give me the pistol," says Prasert Thongcharoen, an AIDS expert at Mahidol University in Bangkok. "One day you tell me, don't fire that pistol! It will burst and it will harm you." Prayura Kunasol, who at the time headed Thailand's Department of Communicable Disease Control, was equally beside himself about the decision. "I was not happy with that," he says. "It demonstrated selfishness."

But in the end, the Thais, who themselves have a long tradition of vaccine development, resolved to go it on their own. "We Thai people have to do for our Thai people," says Prayura. "We have to be self-reliant."

In October 1994, WHO tried to bolster Thailand's decision by convening a group of experts and asking whether vaccines such as the ones made by Genentech and Biocine merited trials in hardhit developing countries. The answer was a qualified yes, although the experts warned that vaccine developers needed to take into consideration the subtypes at large in the trial population. The gp120 protein varies among subtypes, and no one knew for certain whether a vaccine for one subtype could help a person infected with another.

Thailand did not follow the prescription. When NIAID torpedoed the vaccine trials in the United States, Genentech found itself stuck with 300,000 doses in its refrigerators—300,000 vaccines tailored for subtype B, the one prevalent in the United States. Until that point, the company had been working with Thailand on setting up a subtype E vaccine trial among heterosexuals. After Fauci's rejection, however, Genentech suddenly switched gears. The biotech firm decided instead to use its B vaccines among Thai drug users (who had been reported to be infected with subtype B). In February 1995, Genentech launched a trial on 31 recovering drug users in Bangkok. If the vaccine appears as safe and able to stimulate immune responses in this population as it did in 561 cases in the United States, the researchers hope to begin an efficacy trial in 2,500 Thai drug users by the end of this year.

But even as Genentech and the Thais prepared their trial, the nature of the epidemic was changing. Last September Thai and American researchers reported that while in 1989, 97 percent of Thai drug users were infected with subtype B, by 1993 only 56 percent were. The rest were carrying subtype E, which is now spreading like wildfire through the drug users just as it had in the heterosexual population.

Is there any chance a vaccine designed for one strain will work for a different one? John Moore, an investigator at New York's Aaron Diamond AIDS Research Center, recently conducted some intriguing research on the subject. He and his co-workers tested samples of five HIV subtypes and of the antibodies that people exposed to each subtype had produced. They mixed each virus subtype with each group of antibodies, known as a serotype, and waited to see if the serotypes in the different combinations had a greater or lesser ability to neutralize the viruses. They found no clear pattern.

Such a result leaves researchers arguing whether the glass is half empty or half full. The backers of the vaccines look at Moore's data and claim that exposure to a vaccine from one subtype can prime the immune system equally well against any other subtype. Moore, a notoriously gloomy critic of the Biocine and Genentech vaccines, thinks otherwise: "If there were a single serotype that strongly neutralized several isolates, that argument might be valid," he argues. "But however badly the serotypes from infected people do, serotypes from vaccinees do much worse, even against the serotypes from the same subtype. So if the vaccines do badly against the same subtype, why would they do better against a different subtype?"

Biocine's vaccine study, however, could ultimately render the subtype issue moot. While the company is starting small trials with a synthetic version of subtype B's gp120 protein, it has recently developed a subtype E version that should be ready for tests this fall. Biocine hopes to mix the two in a single vaccine, and if all goes well, it will start efficacy trials on this cocktail at the end of 1997.

For critics like Moore, however, even Biocine's preparation seems unlikely to work. Not only does a vaccine for one subtype not work well against another subtype, they argue, but the vaccines don't work well, period. Moore points to a recent study of his in which he analyzed volunteers from the earlier American gp120 trials who had become infected with HIV. Twelve of them had received three or four doses of the vaccine, and all but one had high levels of gp120 antibodies. "Everything I know about the performance of the current generation of gp120 subunit vaccines reinforces my belief that Tony Fauci made absolutely the right decision in not approving efficacy trials in the United States," Moore declares.

D ESPITE THE naysayers, it looks as though in the end the Thais will stage real-world tests of at least one of these vaccines. "The Thais are going to make decisions for efficacy trials by themselves, and they're not going to be confused by a paper by John Moore," says Esparza. But even if efficacy trials of the Biocine or Genentech vaccine do get the final go-ahead, the trials won't be easy. For starters, finding the best people to participate will be a challenge, to say the least. Ethics demands that the volunteers be told how to avoid contracting HIV, but if they take the education to heart, their infection rates may become too low to prove whether the vaccine is effective. At the same time, the volunteers have to be reliable enough to show up for their full series of shots and then come for follow-up visits, which could easily take three years. Finding a few thousand people who fit such a bill won't be easy.

And even if everything goes as planned—which would be a first—there remains the question of who will pay for a trial, which could cost $10 million. Both companies say they'll chip in, but they can't afford to fund everything. WHO and the Thai government have verbally committed themselves to helping pay for trials, but no other countries or foundations have offered help, despite the reality that, for now, the Thai vaccine trials are the only real game in town. Since Fauci's June 1994 decision, the development of new vaccines has slowed to a trickle, with a handful of new formulations currently only in their first trials in a few dozen people apiece.

The vaccine trials will need not only money but time, and that is something Thailand has little of. The nation is just beginning to see the impact of HIV on its society: only 6,000 people have died so far, but by the year 2000 some 100,000 people will be dying annually, and the rate will keep climbing. Even if the trials do start soon, it will take several years to see whether these AIDS vaccines work. As Colonel Sakol puts it, "From the history of many infectious diseases that kill a lot of people, we know that scientists win. But it takes a lot of time. Now we're taking the first step."

> While some people spin wheels debating whether feminists are pro- or anti-sex, feminists are creating a real sexual revolution: reenvisioning sex and sexuality, affirming our right to pleasure, giving voice to women's experiences and our stories of lust and desire.

s e x u a l   p l e a s u r e

UNSCRIPTED

BY REBECCA CHALKER

Although people talk more openly about sex today, for most people "real sex still means heterosexual intercourse," observes Naomi McCormick, president of the Society for the Scientific Study of Sexuality. She says, "Unfortunately, everything else is considered foreplay, afterplay, or just fooling around." But thanks to an explosion of feminist activity, the concept of sex and sexuality is expanding and being dramatically transformed. Sex becomes whole-body, body-aware, and body-comfortable and always includes our minds and spirits. Needless to say, it's adult and consensual (if it involves a partner or partners), sensual and very erotic. It carries no requirements for height, weight, or physical abilities, and one is never too old. It expands the possibilities beyond the boundaries of latex when it comes to safer sex; includes but doesn't require hands, toys, or genital contact; and isn't obsessively fixated on having orgasms.

Key to it all is breaking free of the narrow definition of sex based on genital contact and a reproduction-driven script that focuses on intercourse, and male-centered performance criteria. Sexuality is "so much more than body parts, reproduction, and physiology," says Debra Haffner, president of the Sexuality Information and Education Council of the United States. As she points out, "It includes attitudes, emotions, gender roles, and relationships, as well as intimacy and pleasure."

This view of sexuality encompasses a broad continuum of activities that may provide sexual pleasure—a dream, a thought, a conversation, cuddling, kissing, sensual massage, dancing, oral/genital stimulation, and intercourse. Although it may be a goal, orgasm is not necessary for sex to be intensely erotic and meaningful, nor is intercourse any more important than other forms of sexual expression.

We all can (and many of us already do) have completely satisfying sexual experiences by exploring the realm of the senses nongenitally, and by embracing masturbation as a natural, completely rewarding route to sexual pleasure, rather than a mere remedial aid, or something we do only during the "dry" times.

As lesbians well know, people can be totally sexual without intercourse. For those who are heterosexual, the goal is not to eliminate intercourse but to allow more opportunities for women and men to explore their erotic powers. Studies show that many women never experience orgasm solely through penetration. (In Susan Quilliam's book *Women on Sex*, more than 93 percent of the women she interviewed said they could not reach orgasm through penetration alone.) And research shows that engaging in longer, more varied sexual sessions can lead to higher levels of arousal, deeper levels of intimacy, and stronger "sexual bonding."

In expanding our concept of sexuality, the whole body becomes an erogenous zone, and foreplay gives way to "outer-

"The liberated orgasm is an orgasm you like, under any circumstances."

course," as an end rather than a means. Outercourse involves reexploring all the above- and below-the-waist-pleasures many of us discovered on couches and car seats during that panting, juicy time when "going all the way" was taboo. For sex therapist Ruth McConnell, her own experiences led to her outspoken advocacy: "My high school boyfriend and I wanted to save intercourse for marriage, but that didn't stop us from having ecstatic sex. We explored ourselves and each other and learned how to fantasize and kiss and touch in very imaginative ways." Those intense sessions "left us feeling like we'd been transported to hyperspace."

Focusing on outercourse is a sure way to discover the joys of ever-heightening states of arousal and other routes to release. For heterosexual partners this is especially important, given that most women take far longer than men to become completely aroused. Outercourse requires men to control their ejaculations, offering both partners an opportunity to fully reach their sexual potential. Touch, taste, talk, fantasy, play—partnered outercourse offers an evolving repertoire that reflects mood, moment, circumstance, and ability.

But our sexual pleasure does not require the presence of a partner and need not rely on physical stimulation of any kind. Women who have "been there and done that" know it can simply be a matter of "thinking off." As psychologist Gina Ogden points out, "our ability to reach orgasm solely through fantasy challenges the idea that sexual pleasure is centered in the genitals and depends on physical stimulation." In studies that Ogden conducted, more than 60 percent of the women said they could come to orgasm at will, solely through fantasy. Ogden, who coined the phrase "thinking off," has found that women use a variety of methods. Some create elaborate, graphic stories that they can get lost in. Others—like one woman who told her, "I go totally inside and empty my mind. It's quiet and light"—use a more meditative approach. A number of Ogden's clients talk about becoming

their own lovers and getting off on themselves. As one woman said about this secret garden, "It's something that nobody can take away from me as long as my mind is active."

Hands on or off, self-pleasuring is a vital part of our sexuality. And deserving most of the credit for helping women break free of the taboos about masturbating are feminists, especially Betty Dodson, whose Bodysex workshops enabled many to overcome shame or squeamishness. The first Kinsey Report found that only about 40 percent of women masturbated; in the latest the total had risen to 70 percent. In Susan Quilliam's more recent book, 81 percent of the women surveyed stated that they masturbated regularly.

Many women say that "masturbation is more than simply pleasure. It is also an expression of newfound sexual independence," Quilliam reports. And she notes that many of them say they enjoy masturbating in semi-public places. Her findings illustrate just how well feminists have succeeded in redefining masturbation, from being considered as only a tool for learning how to have orgasms or for filling a void until the next lover, to being accepted as a primary means of self-pleasure and stress reduction and an ongoing component of one's sense of well-being.

While our minds and spirits are the ultimate erogenous zones, and every inch of our bodies a potential source of pleasure, we have an extensive sexual anatomy (which all women must have the right to claim and keep intact). That women have an extensive, important sexual anatomy is undisputed today. But until the 1960s, when psychiatrist Mary Jane Sherfey debunked Sigmund Freud's theory that it was an "atrophied penis," the clitoris had been one of this century's best-kept secrets in many societies. Comparing male and female sexual anatomy, point by point—an exercise which "western" researchers had not done since the mid-nineteenth century—Sherfey found that the key difference between the clitoris and the penis was that the various parts were rearranged

One of the more hotly contested debates concerns whether women can ejaculate. Reports have generally been dismissed as tales told by women trying to cover up the fact that they'd "wet the bed." Many sexologists and physicians continue to label it "urine" (despite the fact that there is no telltale ammonia smell), "vaginal secretions," or even "leftover bathwater" (à la Masters and Johnson). Beverly Whipple is one of several sex researchers who have conducted studies on female ejaculation, and her findings, while not definitive, are intriguing. Whipple and others have analyzed women's "ejaculate" and found that it is chemically similar to men's ejaculate. They've also identified tiny glands embedded in the dense tissues surrounding the urethra that may be the source of this fluid.

So, if all women have these glands, why don't we all ejaculate when we climax, just like men do? Researchers speculate that the amount of fluid varies, as it does in men, and may at times be so small as to not be noticed; may be confused with other vaginal secretions that occur during arousal; or, during heterosexual sex, may be mistaken for a man's ejaculate.

Does any of this matter? Some people find preposterous the idea that women may have prostate glands. But as Whipple says, "Women who experience this have reported secretly suppressing orgasms out of fear of wetting the bed." She notes that some women have had unnecessary surgery to cure "incontinence." Knowing that ejaculation may be perfectly normal is an important step in owning and accepting our sexuality.

and adapted to fulfill the particular needs of reproduction.

Building on Sherfey's work, the Federation of Feminist Women's Health Centers, in *A New View of a Woman's Body,* provided a broader definition of the entire clitoris [a definition that some sexologists consider too broad]. According to the federation, the glans, or tip, of the clitoris is merely the most sensitive part of an extensive system that includes erectile tissues that fill with blood and become highly sensitive to touch and vibration when women are sexually excited, muscles that contract in spasms, and glands that produce sexual secretions. Clitoral tissues and muscles surround the walls of the vagina. When stimulated as tension builds in the muscles, spasms occur that release the blood trapped within the tissues, causing the pleasurable sensation of orgasm.

Contrary to the popular misconception, the "G spot" is not a spot in the vagina. It's erectile tissue that surrounds the urethra (just as it does in the penis) and runs along the "roof" of the vagina. During sexual arousal it becomes engorged (you can feel it through the vaginal walls), is very sensitive, and when stroked heightens the feelings of pleasure. For some women, specifically stimulating this area may help them to reach orgasm.

Although many of us have come to expect having orgasms as part of good sex, for others it remains an elusive goal. It has been reported that about one third of women do not have orgasms at all, one third have them part of the time, and one third experience them fairly consistently. But we also know that some women do not recognize when they are having an orgasm. And although we know that our orgasmic range varies, no one has investigated why this is so. Marilyn Fithian and William Hartman of the Center for Marital and Sexual Studies in Long Beach, California, report that even among orgasmic women, some appear to be easily orgasmic while others have to work at learning how to have orgasms, and how to have them regularly.

Research shows that there are few physiological reasons why women cannot have orgasms. For example, Beverly Whipple and her colleague Barry Komisaruk have been studying orgasms resulting from genital and nongenital stimulation in women who have severe spinal cord injuries. Whipple says, "In the past, reports of orgasms by women who have this type of injury have been labeled 'phantom orgasms.'" She says that many women she has worked with experience sexual arousal and response, and say that they have 'felt' an orgasm.

As Barbara Seaman boldly declared in *Free and Female,* the first feminist sex-advice book, "The liberated orgasm is an orgasm you like, under any circumstances." This statement seems as fresh and on the mark today as it was almost 25 years ago. In the 1970s, feminists embraced information about how to achieve orgasm reliably, because women had been denied that right and knowledge for so long. But today some feminists are questioning the impact that the intensive focus on women's orgasm has had on our sexuality. Naomi McCormick believes that many therapists have put too much pressure on women to have orgasms, due to Masters and Johnson's model of performance. As a result we often feel pressed to "achieve orgasm" as proof of our sexuality. Therapist JoAnn Loulan suggests that this occurs because we look at orgasm as a commodity or goal, and forget about the pleasure along the way. Because Loulan believes that this pressure is so strong, she feels compelled to warn her clients against "the tyranny of orgasm." Among heterosexuals, that tyranny is often the result of male expectations. Susan Quilliam says, "Men nowadays see female orgasms as a proof of male sexuality and so pressure women to climax."

British psychologist Lynne Segal asserts, "There's more to women's emotional life than the most efficient route to orgasm." What's missing from the discussion, according to Segal, is "the story of desire." She criticizes early feminists for failing to account for "the often troubling, irrational, or perverse nature of sexual desire and fantasy," yet she also acknowledges that "it is difficult to capture and define the essence of desire." She's right—lust, desire, and love are more elusive and intriguing aspects of our sexuality. But the work done on female orgasms and the emotional and psychological aspects of our sexuality should not be mutually exclusive. Although the "story of women's desire and lust" is difficult to analyze, it is being told, through the flowering of women's erotica. An ever more diverse group of feminists, in addition to offering up frank womanish sex talk, are sensualizing and liberating the genre from what had too often been a detailing of exploits and technique. Now, in publications such as *Yellow Silk* and *Libido,* and books like *Pleasures,* the *Herotica* series, and *Erotique Noire,* desire and lust, as women experience them, are being shared. For hands-on advice there is now a treasure trove of books by a bevy of feminist sexologists, and an expanding crew of outspoken "sexperts" who share their insights and opinions.

Despite the attempts of fundamentalists and right-wingers to turn back the clock, there's a real woman-friendly sexual revolution in progress. As a result of the work of a growing group of feminist scholars and sexologists who are exploring the psychological and social aspects of sexuality, the way women's sexuality is viewed is being changed. Feminists are throwing away the script, challenging the old sexual order, reenvisioning sexuality and sex, and reminding women and their partners of more inventive, exciting, and egalitarian alternatives.

Rebecca Chalker is the coauthor of "A Woman's Book of Choices" (Four Walls Eight Windows) and is the coeditor of "A New View of a Woman's Body" (Simon & Schuster).

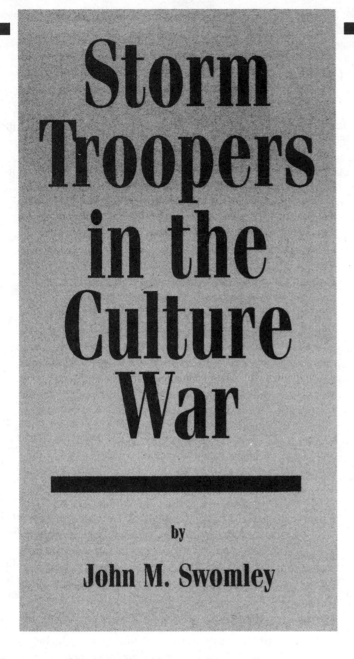

Storm Troopers in the Culture War

by

John M. Swomley

Promise Keepers, now described as the "third wave of the religious right," following Jerry Falwell's Moral Majority and Pat Robertson's Christian Coalition, is no longer a novelty or just another revival movement. Much has become clear about this group that was earlier shrouded in mystery. And as more information about PK's true mission is revealed, concern about the group's influence grows.

There are at least three major facets to Promise Keepers. The first of these is implicit in its religious origin, leadership, and goal. PK originated in a charismatic group of Vineyard Christian churches that feature emotionally charged services, rock music, and what John Wimber, an influential Vineyard leader, calls "power evangelism." PK's top officials—President Randy Phillips; cofounder, chief executive officer, and former University of Colorado head football coach Bill McCartney; and cofounder and pastor James Ryle—are members of the Valley Vineyard Church in Boulder, Colorado.

PK's stated goal is to be the instrument of "biblical unity" or "breaking down the walls" of denominational and doctrinal distinction by building a new denomination or para-church. According to its fact sheet:

PK is not a membership or dues-paying organization, but is part of a larger movement of Christian men becoming more active throughout their local churches. . . . Through stadium conferences, educational seminars, resource materials, and local churches . . . Promise Keepers seeks to unite Christian men . . . believing that accountable relationships among men are critical in helping one another. . . . PK is not a political or partisan organization, nor is it affiliated with any denomination. Finally, Promise Keepers does not promote a self-help or self-improvement philosophy, but encourages men to commit every aspect of their lives to Jesus Christ.

Obviously, PK does not want to alert existing churches and denominations to its intent to supplant them, but it has developed a centralized headquarters with thirty-six regional offices serving all fifty states and about 16,000 local groups; "indepen-

From *The Humanist*, September/October 1997, pp. 8-13. © 1997 by John M. Swomley. Reprinted by permission.

dently run spin-offs" in Australia, New Zealand, and Canada; a daily radio program; and other features of a "nondenominational" organization—including a fundamentalist theology based upon biblical inerrancy.

Promise Keepers competes with the Southern Baptists in targeting Jews for conversion. It speaks of this as "the next frontier in reconciliation" and recently convened a meeting of Messianic Jewish leaders in Atlanta, Georgia. According to its July 1997 *Promise Keepers News*, PK claims "approximately 150 Messianic Jewish congregations and nearly 200,000 Messianic believers across the United States." Justin Kron, a Messianic Jew, is PK's Illinois field representative.

Promise Keepers has also begun efforts to penetrate Roman Catholic churches. For example, in Buffalo, New York, where Catholics are the largest denomination, PK organized a Roman Catholic mass as part of its Rich Stadium conference in June 1997. Although not well attended despite its prior publicity (only about fifty men took part), the mass was designed to prepare Catholic men for participation in the PK conference. That same afternoon, Catholic clergy were among other local clergy at a PK luncheon.

The key to PK's para-church is in its local groups, which meet weekly. In its literature, PK says, "Since 1996 more than 120,000 men have been trained by Promise Keepers to lead small groups of men in local communities." Each group is led by a "key man" chosen by the national organization. One of the seven promises of a Promise Keeper requires active participation in a small group of other men who monitor all aspects of each other's behavior, including their sexual relations, family life, business practices, and financial affairs. The key men report to "ambassadors" who, in turn, report to headquarters.

Olin Henneman is PK's Upstate New York field representative, whose territory includes most of the state, from Newburgh and Poughkeepsie west to Buffalo and Jamestown. Henneman says his job is "to start and assist task forces for PK, training men to become ambassadors, who make up the task forces and cover the community." Ambassadors then train key men "to represent PK with men and local churches [in] prayer and in a relationship with them by phone or contact." He says PK provides no donations to local churches, but local churches "sometimes donate to Promise Keepers."

Henneman says there are different levels of key man training: "Key man level one is more or less discussing the characteristics of a man, and why a man does things, and why he's different than women, and why his feelings are certain ways versus why women feel certain ways. We talk about what the Promise Keepers vision is and goals, and how to discuss these items with other men in his church." He says key man level two training is actually showing and teaching men how to start a men's ministry and small groups.

Henneman says PK likes to have two key men in each church, sometimes three if a church is large enough. As of June 1997, he reports there were 192 key men in some 250 Upstate New York churches, with another 100 "waiting for certification." "With our relationship now with the Assemblies of God churches and a couple of other denominations that have agree-

ments with Promise Keepers," he says, "we will be training key men in each church."

Ultimately, PK wants to have a key man in each of the nation's 400,000 churches, using the military ideas of discipline and male bonding in small groups. "The goal," says Bill McCartney, "is to go into every church whether they like us or not."

Because it's more convenient to have the small groups operate among men in the same church, Promise Keepers has gone to great lengths to solicit cooperating pastors. For example, it spent $4,609,726 in scholarships, transportation, lodging, and meals to get pastors to attend its 1996 pastors conference in Atlanta. That doesn't include the larger sum of $14,957,088 PK spent on field ministries, working with pastors and churches before, during, and after conferences. A special effort was made to pay the expenses of black pastors to and in Atlanta, according to some who were invited to a preconference breakfast in Kansas City.

McCartney's threat "to go into every church" is producing some results. One Methodist bishop told me that he did not want to oppose Promise Keepers; he wanted to work with the organization to keep men in his denomination's churches. An uninformed bishop, pastor, or layperson may see positive values in Promise Keepers. However, it's important to note that, unlike most existing denominations and churches, there is no democracy within the organization. A small group of self-appointed men in the Vineyard churches controls the entire effort, including its theology, finances, and personnel.

When I mentioned this on a radio talk show with a PK state coordinator, he denied the lack of democracy by stating that there is a Promise Keepers board of directors representing various denominations. The denominations do not elect the board members, however; they are Promise Keepers selected by the Vineyard Fellowship leaders to give the appearance of being drawn from different denominations.

Furthermore, the men behind Promise Keepers believe essentially in a theology of political power achieved through religion. This is summed up in their concept of a Christian nation led by a military messiah. As McCartney declared, when he called upon 39,000 pastors in Atlanta to "take this nation for Jesus," "whoever stands with the messiah will rule with him." And this political power is afforded to only male Christians under Vineyard Fellowship-type leaders.

The concept of a Christian nation or a theocracy ruled from the top is based on fundamentalist ideology or selected verses from the Bible which justify such rule. For example, the Jesus of the New Testament repudiated a politics of domination when he said, "You know that those who are supposed to rule over the Gentiles lord it over them and their great men exercise authority over them. But it shall not be so among you; for whoever would be great among you must be your servant" (Mark 10:43–44). But such teaching has no place in PK's vision of building a Christian nation.

The Seven Promises of a Promise Keeper

© 1994

1. A Promise Keeper is committed to honoring Jesus Christ through worship, prayer, and obedience to God's Word in the power of the Holy Spirit.
2. A Promise Keeper is committed to pursuing vital relationships with a few other men, understanding that he needs brothers to help him keep his promises.
3. A Promise Keeper is commited to practicing spiritual, moral, ethical, and sexual purity.
4. A Promise Keeper is committed to building strong marriages and families through love, protection, and biblical values.
5. A Promise Keeper is committed to supporting the mission of his church by honoring and praying for his pastor, and by actively giving his time and resources.
6. A Promise Keeper is committed to reaching beyond any racial and denominational barriers to demonstrate the power of biblical unity.
7. A Promise Keeper is committed to influencing his world, being obedient to the Great Commandment (see Mark 12:30–31) and the Great Commission (see Matthew 28:19–20).

Neither does Jesus as the "Prince of Peace," who repudiated war and armed might. The Vineyard Fellowship people, as well as other religious right leaders, have replaced him with their concept of a military messiah speaking the language of war. Promise Keepers speaks of an "army of God," while Pat Robertson's Regent's University is training people to rule until Jesus comes again. (A *regent* is one who rules in place of the king.)

The concept and language of war has been used by other right-wing leaders who helped PK get started, notably James Dobson of Focus on the Family and Bill Bright of Campus Crusade for Christ. Bright has had a "military ministry" to the armed forces while Dobson, in his book *Children at Risk,* promotes the idea of a "civil war," saying, "Bloody battles are being fought on a thousand fronts, both inside and outside the government." Except for those of the organized right-wing militias, these have largely been culture wars fought at abortion clinics by violent groups such as Operation Rescue and Missionaries for the Pre-born or by the Christian Coalition for control of government or public schools or against the secular state or homosexuals.

Now, however, there is a mass movement—Promise Keepers—that not only speaks of organizing an army of men but has hired retired military officers to help it organize in the armed forces. One of those officers, Richard Abel, a retired air force brigadier general, has been conducting "wake-up calls" with hundreds of active duty soldiers. Another is Jim Pack, a retired Green Beret colonel who was a psychological warfare specialist at Fort Bragg, North Carolina, and is now PK manager of the Texas region. A third officer, Chuck Stecker, a retired Special Forces lieutenant colonel, has been organizing PK within the military with the aid of some military chaplains. Addressing a 1996 conference of military chaplains in Atlanta, Stecker said:

I believe with all of my heart that the military structure that we know and love so well is perfect for the accountable relationship which God is calling us to in Promise Keepers. That same structure, whether it be at the squad level for the army and right up or whether it be at the detachment level, squadron level, and so forth, is exactly what we need. I believe that accountable relationships build readiness. Quite frankly, and having served in a Ranger battalion, if a squad leader did not know where his soldiers were, his Rangers, he was not doing his job. And in order to be able to know those things he had to be in accountable relationships with them in order to develop that.

McCartney has been relating this military approach to the thousands of PK accountability groups in churches. In a 1995 Promise Keepers video entitled *The Next Step: From the Stadium to the Small Group,* he said, "Many of you feel like you have been in a war for a long time, yet the fiercest fighting is just ahead. God has brought us here to prepare us. Let's proceed. It's wartime." He said the clergy must become "the commissioned officers," led in effect by Promise Keepers: "We have a great army that we are assembling. They're Christian men of this nation. However, our leadership, our clergy are not in uniform. Our clergy are divided. . . . There's no *unity of command.* . . . There is tremendous division in our clergy. We have to assume that responsibility."

A third major facet of Promise Keepers is evident in its immediate political target. Although PK leaders have consistently denied that it has a political agenda, their various public statements and their list of enemies clearly define them as the army of the far right. For example, the single most important issue for all the far-right-wing Catholic and Protestant groups is the legal right of women to reproductive freedom. That includes access to abortion, which the far right defines as including the use of any contraceptives after intercourse that prevent implantation in the uterus.

In the July 1997 *Promise Keepers News*, PK doesn't blame the violent crime in the United States and high prison population on such things as drugs or a lack of job opportunities for inner city youth; rather, it points the finger at abortion. In preparing its members for the upcoming October 4 "Stand in the Gap" gathering in Washington, D.C., it states, "The legal undermining of the sanctity of human life, from the pre-born to the old and infirm, represents a rejection of America's two-century-old tenet that mankind is made in God's image, and is a repudiation of morality as a factor in court decisions." This is pure right-wing propaganda and part of PK's anti-woman philosophy. It's also no secret that McCartney has spoken to rallies held by Operation Rescue.

Of course, there is no legal or court authorization to undermine the life of the old and infirm—now or in the past. References to this, then, are expressions of the religious right's objection to death with dignity. As for abortion, there was no law against it when the United States was formed. Such laws,

The Christian Right Regroups

As we approach the 1998 elections, political pundits and commentators are already making their predictions as to who will be the winners and who will be the losers, based on their analyses of the 1996 general election. Many pundits agree that the Christian right figured heavily in the 1996 defeat of presidential hopeful Robert Dole. They also point to the resignation of Ralph Reed as head of the Christian Coalition and the sale of Pat Robertson's share of the Family Network as further proof that the Christian right is losing its effectiveness in national-level politics.

Recent events, however, suggest that the right is merely reconfiguring its political strategy, with the 1998 elections as its first major target. The Family Network sale for $1.9 billion allows Robertson to cash out at a relatively high premium for his investment in the telecommunications business, thus allowing him to focus his energies on more time-sensitive objectives. More importantly, the money from the sale can be used to fund right-wing political activities and perhaps lessen the negative image the Christian Coalition has with a growing number of voters.

One such activity could be in the form of backing the Promise Keepers' "Stand in the Gap" march on Washington, D.C., slated for this October. The event, sponsored by the fundamentalist men's ministry, has been compared to Louis Farrakhan's Million Man March—only this time the goal is to galvanize and cement the convictions of the Christian right with a key constituency: disaffected white males who played a crucial role in electing Republicans in the 1996 general election.

The Christian right can also take advantage of the sentiment expressed at the recent Southern Baptist Convention. Representing one of the largest denominations in the United States, Southern Baptists passed resolutions condemning Disney for what was called its pro-homosexual social agenda, along with several resolutions supporting the posting of the Ten Commandments in public buildings and the passage of a Religious Liberty Amendment to the Constitution in order—they said—to save the Judeo-Christian heritage of America. The Christian right registers its greatest strength in the South. If it can reignite its constituency there—in particular, states such as Arkansas and Kentucky where Democratic senators are retiring—then the goal of achieving a veto-proof Republican majority in the Senate and, thereby, advancing the Christian right agenda, will be one step closer.

Such an achievement would be a great prize toward the right's campaign to institutionalize such issues as public aid for religious schools and prayer in public schools and to destroy the freedoms gained in such areas as abortion and affirmative action. No, the Christian right has not given up the fight; it's just realigning its troops in preparation for different battles.

Steve Watkins is an English instructor in the Dallas Community College District and is currently working on his Ph.D. at the University of Texas at Arlington.

when adopted in the nineteenth century, were chiefly to protect women from unsafe surgery. Moreover, there has never been legal sanctity of life in the United States—nor for Native Americans, black slaves, sweatshop workers, child laborers, wartime conscripts, unwanted immigrants, interred Japanese Americans, and various others.

Promise Keepers cannot even speak of "sanctity of life" as a biblical principle. There is no such phrase in the Bible, a book which describes children killed for the sins of the fathers and adults killed for numerous violations of Mosaic law. In the Bible, God actually orders the slaughter of thousands, including pregnant women. God even commands abortion under certain circumstances; there is no "unborn" child. Throughout the Bible, human life is defined as *nephesh,* or one who breathes. Furthermore, although abortion was widely practiced throughout the ancient world, no condemnation of it as sin appears in the Bible.

Yet despite all this, the July PK article blames men who "have remained idle as 34 million unborn children have been legally slain, allowing the debate to become an issue of a woman's right to choose rather than a man's responsibility to practice sexual purity." In other words, women are not created in "the image of God" with the freedom to make decisions regarding their lives, their health, and the welfare of children already born. It is men, specifically "promise keepers," who are to determine the destiny of American women.

Promise Keepers' political agenda has always called for men to make or keep women submissive to male leadership and control in the family and elsewhere. Its leaders abhor what they call the "feminization of the church." Tony Evans, one of PK's most popular speakers, tells men to reclaim their role—without compromise—as head of the house and tells women they should submit for "the survival of our culture."

PK's right-wing agenda, however, is not always so blatantly set forth to the men who attend the group's stadium events. On the matter of race, for example, stadium speakers use cover terms like *racial reconciliation.* According to Mandy Carter, field representative for the National Black Lesbian and Gay Leadership Forum, PK says "nothing about concrete measures to right the historic inequities imposed on people of color." She went on to speak about the publicized embraces by whites of blacks at stadium events: "We are concerned that Promise Keepers calls for racial harmony but does not speak to its 96 percent white membership about the racial advantage that whiteness gives them in this society. Institutionalized racism is not healed by hugs."

Carter is also concerned about the "men only" aspect of Promise Keepers. "In communities of color, survival has depended on men and women working in partnership toward a vision of self-determination and leadership," she said. Actually, in todays' society, the overwhelming number of working-class families survive only because both husband and wife work outside the home and require partnership, not domination, in household activities.

Sensitive to such criticism, PK leaders have been talking recently about men "serving" their families, but they have not changed their patriarchal emphasis or their determination to prevent equal rights for women. A good illustration of this is the way they solicit support from and pander to male pastors while excluding women pastors from clergy events.

Instead of insisting on an equal participation of women and men in the family, Promise Keepers uses gimmicks at stadium events to indicate that, while men remain in charge, they also serve. In Buffalo this past June, PK arranged for a Des Moines, Iowa, psychologist to wash the feet of his wife and two daughters on stage. That event, which is not likely to be repeated frequently in Buffalo homes, was publicized in the *Buffalo News.* The local newspaper, however, ignored a warning by the National Coalition Against Domestic Violence—which represents more than thirteen hundred battered women's groups as well as state domestic violence and sexual assault coalitions—that PK's emphasis on "men regaining 'rightful' control of the family" threatens to undermine "years of hard work to change outdated laws and social attitudes." One conference speaker, the Reverend David Castro, did make passing mention of such issues in his altar call for the confession of sexual "sin," but there was no significant emphasis or subsequent media notice.

In Buffalo and at other stadium events, sex was promoted as one of the leading problems facing men, and this theme was reiterated throughout PK conferences and materials. Sex has always been profitable, either as an industry or as a means for frightening people into joining some moralistic movement. And Promise Keepers is certainly making its money. It not only charges fees of $60 to $70 to enter a stadium event but sells books, tapes, clothing, food, and other items. In the public inspection copy of its 1996 Internal Revenue tax return, PK lists $16,413,431 as gross sales of such inventory and a total revenue of $87,419,179. Savings and cash investments are shown at $8,309,138 and inventories it could sell at $4,187,354. A few of its leaders made salaries over $80,000. Its president received $132,512 plus benefits and expenses.

As a nonprofit organization, PK claims that none of its funds are used, directly or indirectly, for political purposes. But, this only means that it has not engaged in partisan politics or the support of candidates; it does *not* mean that it refrains from taking stands on or promoting positions on issues like abortion, homosexuality, and related far-right hot buttons.

In fact, PK's stadium speakers, in their own low-key way, condemn various political practices. And its big financial backers include such right-wing political activists as former presidential candidate Pat Robertson, Focus on the Family's James Dobson, the Family Research Council's Gary Bauer, and religious right media mogul Stephen Strang, while former Jerry Falwell and Pat Robertson media adviser Mark DeMoss—whose family's foundation pours millions of dollars into right-wing causes—serves as PK's national spokesperson. CEO Bill McCartney served on the board of directors of the homophobic Colorado for Family Values and was quoted in the July 28, 1994, *Boulder Camera* as saying, "We will not compromise. Wherever truth is at risk, in the schools or legislatures, we are going to contend for it." And no group marches on the nation's capital—as Promise Keepers plans to do this fall with up to one million men—without a political agenda. As "Stand in the Gap" organizer Raleigh Washington said, "There's no way the group can restrict itself when it comes to public policy. We are producing leaders in this organization. They will enter the political sphere."

I n any appraisal of Promise Keepers, it is essential to note that many fundamentalists and evangelical Christians do not approve of the group. In a recent resolution, the Fellowship of Fundamental Bible Churches said, "Promise Keepers' teachings are a strange mixture of truth and error. Its methods for promoting those teachings are questionable." It urged Christians "to be wise, to be warned, and to beware of this false movement."

European writer Jewel van der Merwe asks:

conference in New York—scheduled to precede October's march on Washington—was cancelled.

On another front, the July 1, 1997, *Denver Post* reported that Promise Keepers announced widespread cutbacks and is laying off paid staff at all levels. In the article, McCartney calls the cutbacks "painful" but gives no figures. (As of July, PK said it had 452 full-time staff and an estimated annual budget of $87 million, which is lower than outside estimates but $10 million less than PK's own figures for 1996.)

Promise Keepers' Growth Ministry

Year	Staff	Stadium Event Attendance	Budget
1993	22	50,000 at one stadium	$4 million
1994	150	278,600 at seven stadiums	$26 million
1995	300	727,342 at thirteen stadiums	$64 million
1996	360	1,100,000 at twenty-two stadiums	$97 million
1997	452	1,250,000 at twenty-four stadiums and march on Washington (estimated)	$87 million (estimated)

Is Promise Keepers creating a new folk religion? The large mass rallies, the exaltation of emotion over reason, the lack of doctrinal integrity, the taking of oaths [the seven promises PK men are told to keep], the focus on fatherland and fatherhood, and the ecumenical inclusion of aberrant esoteric doctrines, bears a disconcerting similarity to an era which gave rise to one of the most dreadful armies in history.

Criticism of Promise Keepers is increasing, but almost all appears in the alternative press like *The Humanist*, the *Nation*, and a few religious journals. Even so, the word is getting out. As a result of the growing criticism, PK is experiencing financial difficulties. Stadium events are not as well attended as in previous years. In Buffalo, 30,000 to 40,000 men were expected, but PK reported only 20,000 in attendance. In Chicago, only about 22,000 attended the PK conference at Soldier Field; in Kansas City, Missouri, attendance was only 38,000; and in Denver—PK's home base—attendance estimates were down 11,000 to 20,000 from what had been expected. In addition, PK's Shea Stadium

The "official" explanation for the difficulties is that PK followers are saving their money to attend "Stand in the Gap." However, some critics say PK's call for "racial reconciliation" may be causing problems. Others believe many men are being turned off by the expectations PK has for long-term recruits.

Whatever the explanation, Promise Keepers is still one of the most formidable religious right-wing groups to watch. The danger to America is not from majority acceptance of this movement but from public apathy and the media's acceptance of its publicity handouts. Any disciplined religious movement can exercise control over government and social organizations if people do not expose it, organize counter movements, and educate their fellow citizens about the importance of separation of church and state. Freedom of and freedom from religion are dependent upon a secular—not a theocratic—state.

John M. Swomley is an emeritus professor of social ethics at St. Paul School of Theology in Kansas City, Missouri. He is also president of Americans for Religious Liberty and serves on the national board of the American Civil Liberties Union.

A time for partnership

Riane Eisler

Today's questioning of sex roles and relations is part of a broader movement towards greater democracy and egalitarianism

Men are from Mars, proclaims a recent book title, and women are from Venus. This two-planet image vividly expresses the lingering belief that women and men are fundamentally and unalterably different.

But if it were true that women and men are inherently so different, how is it that their differences differ so much from one time and place to another? For example, in Victorian England the mark of real femininity was a "ladylike" paleness and weakness, whereas in Kenya real femininity was traditionally proved by a woman's ability to do very hard work on behalf of her family. In the Samurai Age of Japan, real masculinity was proving oneself a fierce warrior, whereas among the Hopi Indians of North America men were supposed to be peaceful, agreeable, and non-aggressive.

Not only that, but over the last decades the roles and relations of women and men have been changing at a very rapid pace. For example, large numbers of women have in many Western nations begun to do things that were once considered exclusively men's work, such as the work of doctors, plumbers, engineers, lawyers, welders and university professors—all highly-paid professions and trades from which women were once barred. Similarly, men have begun to redefine fathering to include some of the "women's work" of feeding, diapering, and otherwise caring for and nurturing babies.

Moreover, even against enormous resistance, women's and men's relations have gradually become more egalitarian. At the same time, although more slowly, once firmly entrenched beliefs that men, and what men do, are more important than women and what women do, have also begun to change—with such commonplace remarks as "hope next time it's a boy" increasingly considered offensive by both new mothers and fathers.

For some people, both women and men, these changes are a source of hope for a more humane, less violent, less unjust future: one where one kind of person (be it a person of a different race, nationality, religion or sex) is no longer viewed as of a lower order than another. But for others, these changes are a source of

RIANE EISLER, of the United States, is co-founder of the Center for Partnership Studies in California. She is the author of many articles and books, notably *The Chalice and The Blade: Our History, Our Future* (Harper and Row, San Francisco, 1990), which has been widely translated. Her most recent work is *Sacred Pleasure: Sex, Myth and the Politics of the Body* (Harper and Row, San Francisco, 1995).

Reprinted with permission from *The UNESCO Courier,* September 1995, pp. 5-7.

confusion and fear, yet another complexity to be dealt with in a far too rapidly changing world.

Women, men and human relations

It is certainly true that our world has been changing very fast over the last few hundred years, so fast that, in the words of the futurologist Alvin Toffler, it has put some people in "future shock". Rapid technological and economic changes have destabilized not only established habits of work, but long-standing habits of thinking and acting. This has been the source of much dislocation and stress. But as modern history drastically demonstrates, technological and economic change has also opened the door for questioning much that was once taken for granted—be it the once supposedly divinely-ordained right of kings and princes to absolute authority, or the once also supposedly divinely-ordained right of men to absolute authority in the "castles" of their homes.

The questioning we see all over the world today of sex roles and relations is thus part of a much larger questioning. It is also part of a much larger movement for change: the global movement toward more democratic and egalitarian relations in *both* the so-called private and public spheres.

In fact, once we examine the constant interaction between the private and public spheres, it is possible to see patterns or connexions that were invisible in older studies, because these focused almost exclusively on the public or men's world from which women and children were excluded. These patterns or connexions show something that once articulated seems self-evident: that the way a society organizes the roles and relations of the two halves of humanity—which is what men and women are—profoundly affects everything in our lives.

For example, how these roles and relations are organized is a critical factor in how a society structures the family. Societies where women's and men's roles are rigidly circumscribed, which are generally also rigidly male-dominated societies, are by and large also societies where we see a generally authoritarian, top-down family structure. Even more specifically, it tends to be a family where men rule over women and parents rule over children, with this rule ultimately backed up by fear and force. On the other hand, societies where women's and men's roles are more flexible and there is more equality between women and men tend to have more democratic families, with less socially condoned use of fear and force.

Moreover, societies characterized by more rigid male dominance (where sex roles are also more rigid) are generally also more authoritarian.

For example, with the rise to power of Hitler in Germany and the imposition of a brutally authoritarian and very violent regime, there was much emphasis on returning women to their "traditional" roles in a male-dominated family. Conversely, in the Scandinavian nations, strong emphasis on sexual equality has gone along with both political and economic democracy, as well as with social priority given to activities stereotypically associated with women such as child care, health care and environmental housekeeping.

A new view of the past

Further light is shed on these connexions by archaeological studies such as those of the Lithuanian-American archaeologist Marija Gimbutas, the British archaeologist James Mellaart, and the Greek archaeologist Nicolas Platon. These studies indicate that, contrary to what we have been taught, the earliest cradles of civilization were not authoritarian, male-dominant and chronically warlike. There are strong indications that these prehistoric societies (for example, Catal Huyuk in Turkey, which dates back approximately 8,000 years) were more peaceful and egalitarian societies in which, significantly, women were not dominated by men.

Thus, Platon notes that in the highly technologically developed Minoan civilization that flourished on the Mediterranean island of Crete approximately 3,500 years ago the influence of women is evident, and that this was a remarkably peaceful and prosperous society in which "the whole of life was pervaded by an ardent faith in the goddess Nature." As we can still see today from their beautiful nature-celebrating art, the Minoans also seem to have had a great respect not only for women but for our Mother Earth: what we today would call an ecological consciousness.

So here again we see the variability of women's and men's roles and relations, and how these roles and relations are affected by, and in turn affect, social structure. We see that stereotypically "feminine" values such as nurturance and non-violence can be embraced by men, and that women can take on stereotypically "masculine" roles of social and religious governance. Most important, we see that neither war nor the war of the sexes is inevitable.

But I want to emphasize an important matter. There is no evidence that, because women in these societies seem to have held high social and religious positions, men were dominated by women. In other words, these societies were neither matriarchies nor patriarchies. They conformed more to what I would call a partnership rather than a dominator model of social organization: a form of organization that offers a viable alternative to the

(UN photo/L. Barns)

Sex roles and relationships are being reassessed today. The larger movement that underlies this trend is the creation of a world in which basic principles of partnership become primary.

complex tensions that are inherent in relations based on domination and subordination.

*G*ender equity and quality of life

Indeed, if we re-examine modern history from this larger perspective, we see that underneath its many complex currents and cross-currents lies a powerful movement towards a partnership social organization, countered by strong resistance to it. We see that all the modern progressive movements have basically been movements challenging different forms of domination backed by force and fear. This is the common thread in the eighteenth- and nineteenth-century rights of man, anti-slavery, anti-monarchist, socialist, pacifist and feminist movements. In the same way, the twentieth-century anti-colonialist, anti-war, participatory democracy, women's rights and economic justice move-

ments are not isolated phenomena. They are all part of a much larger movement: the movement to create a world in which—be it in our global family of nations or in our individual families— principles of partnership rather than domination and submission are primary.

Moreover, we see that the contemporary movement toward gender equity is an integral part of this larger partnership movement. This should not surprise us, since the domination of one half of humanity by the other is a basic model for all forms of domination. Conversely, the equal valuing of the two halves of humanity teaches children from early on to value diversity, rather than seeing it as a reason for ranking "superior" people over "inferior" ones.

This is why those parts of our world where the movement to raise the status of women has been most successful are also more generally democratic. Even beyond this, a recent statistical survey of eighty-nine countries conducted by the Center for Partnership Studies indicates that if the movement towards sexual equality continues, we can also predict a generally higher quality of life for all.

This study, entitled "Gender Equity and the Quality of Life", shows the Scandinavian nations on the average with both the highest gender equity and the highest quality of life. It also verifies that there is a strong correlation between, on the one hand, such gender inequity indicators as substantially lower female than male literacy, high maternal mortality, and low female participation in government and, on the other, indicators of a generally lower quality of life for all such as high infant mortality, a high number of refugees fleeing a country, and a high ratio of Gross Domestic Product going to the wealthiest as opposed to the poorest 20 per cent of the population. Furthermore, the study indicates that areas where the movement for women's rights has made the least progress also tend to be those where human rights ratings are generally lower.

In short, the way in which a society structures the relations between women and men is of profound personal, social and economic significance. It is encouraging that many governments worldwide are beginning to pass laws to equalize the position of women and men, following the provisions of the United Nations Convention on the Elimination of All Forms of Discrimination against Women. This will obviously vastly improve women's quality of life. But it is also essential if we are to move to a world of greater partnership and peace, not only between men and women but between the diverse nations, races, religions and ethnic groups on our planet.

We Are Men.

Hear Us Roar

Who says women are better at love?

Note to all women about to read this article:

There's nothing here that would interest you. We men will just talk amongst ourselves as you make your way to another page. Maybe we'll share a nice cup of cappuccino while we wait. You know, get in touch with our feelings and all.

by Jim Killam

ARE THEY GONE? Good. This meeting of the Loyal Order of Confused Guys, Lodge No. 6723, will now come to order.

Guys, we have a problem. Everywhere we turn, society is telling us we need to become more "womanlike" in order to relate better to women. You can't watch a TV show or read a story to your kids without seeing some doofus husband totally mess up his marriage and family before his wife swoops in and saves the day with her superior relational skills. Even in the workplace, guys are considered cavemen when we don't relate to women the way other women do. Basically, guys are considered inferior just for being, well, guys.

Sure, we'd all agree that men and women approach life and relationships differently: Men just want to get the job done—focusing on tasks and goals. Meanwhile, women are intensely interested in the process of getting there. But who decided that the female approach is the correct one and that men are just a bunch of sex-crazed, relationally impaired bozos?

To find some answers, I rounded up four of the most regular married guys I know—Doug, Jim, John and Keith—each married at least ten years. We spent the better part of a Saturday morning hammering away at this problem. Not only did we reject the "men need to become women" idea, we also came up with a Guy Manifesto that made sense even when I read it to my wife.

But I'm getting ahead of myself. First, let's agree that popular culture, and even some Christian authors and speakers, are sending men a one-sided message: namely, that we need women to give us a clue.

"We're being sold a bill of goods," says Keith, a graphic designer. "For years, I just went along with it. Then all of a sudden I said, 'How come nobody's up there telling women that it's not so important to talk about the process?' Why does that sound absurd, but telling men they need to change sounds reasonable? I'm not saying I don't want to understand my wife better. But why are we being told that we've all got to move over to the women's side and communicate like them?"

Couselor H. Norman Wright, the highly regarded author of scads of books on Christian marriage, agrees that men don't have to turn into women. But he does feel we need to step outside of our male nature from time to time.

"Both men and women are called to change," he told me. "But men tend to be more defensive. They don't realize that they can stay the way they are and add to it another way to relate. . . . They can expand.

"If you go to Scripture," he adds, "1 Peter talks about consideration and understanding as part of the biblical model of leadership. The changes are for *our* benefit."

In other words, men become more Christlike and have better marriages as we work to understand what makes our wives tick. And the same is true for our wives in relation to us. Change is a two-way street.

What does this mean for men? Sometimes, it's as basic as understanding what our wives want. Women frequently tell us they want us to talk to them more . . . but on *their* terms. For instance, when they tell us about a problem, they're probably not looking for us to propose a solution. They just want someone to empathize with them.

"Don't give suggestions or advice," Wright counsels. "Listen and reflect her feelings. For example, your wife tells you about a problem and you respond with, 'That sounds like it's really important to you.' And

you do that without looking at your watch and without one eye on the TV."

Okay, we could give that a try. But let's admit that it's not as easy as it sounds. Guys spend most of their time in a goal-oriented mindset, whether it's at work, fixing things around the house or watching a baseball game.

"My wife will come in and I'm already doing something," says John, a physician. "And she wants to go into *her* mode and talk about something. I just can't switch that fast."

Basically, *guys* are considered inferior just for being well, guys.

"I can do it," adds Jim, a counselor. "But I have to have absolutely nothing else in my mind. Lots of times that's about 9:30 or 10 at night. I'm ready to be process-oriented, but my wife is asleep already."

Can We Talk Here?

Willard F. Harley, Jr., author of *His Needs, Her Needs* (Revell), says conversation is a basic emotional need for most women. But it's nowhere near the top of the list for most men. That's why we can afford to bend more than our wives in this area. We could gently suggest, though, that our wives think more carefully about their timing.

"All day at work I have to listen to what people are saying," says Jim. "Then I get home and ask a simple question and my wife gives me ten times more detail than I want. The problem is, how do I tell her I don't

want that kind of detail without her getting mad at me or feeling hurt?"

That may simply be a matter of understanding how each spouse relates.

"For the first five years of our marriage," Keith says, "I'd come home and Karen would say, 'How was your day?' And I'd say, 'Fine.' That would drive her crazy. Now we've developed our own language to where that makes perfect sense. She understands that if I felt like talking about it I'd talk about it. Or at 10 o'clock that night I might say, "You know what happened today?'"

Difficult as it is to overcome the barriers of timing and detail, there's an even tougher obstacle. Of course, I'm talking about the male and female approaches to sports.

Take figure skating. Please. Most guys I know can't watch skating with their wives without commenting on the judging (it's totally rigged). They also can't help but voice their wish that the skaters would fall more (it'd be better drama). And it's impossible not to comment on those sequined outfits some of the male skaters wear ('nuff said).

"The judges drive me crazy," Keith says. "In basketball, the ball goes in the hoop and it's two points. In skating, the top two skaters can finish the competition with one ahead by a tenth of a point. But it doesn't necessarily matter because of what some announcer calls 'the organic nature of the judging.'

"The skater who everybody thought was behind actually wins. My wife is watching the process of skating and how pretty it is, and I'm going, 'That can't happen. How could *she* have won?'"

According to Harley, it's better for husbands not to watch figure skating than to make fun of it while watching. But, he adds, the more compatible you become with your wife, the more you'll enjoy watching skating with her—not because of the skating, but because you love doing things together. The same goes for your wife watching the World Series or the Super Bowl with you.

Finding things you *both* enjoy is a process, but Norm Wright agrees it's a necessary task. And it requires a few adjustments. For example, go ahead and enjoy watching the World Series with your wife. Just don't expect her to "connect on the level you're at." Also, he advises, "a guy should then be willing to learn something *his wife* enjoys." Oops.

In my marriage, that would be shopping. I have the ability to actually enjoy shopping with my wife, but I have to shift into that mode. And no children can be present—it has to be a date-like atmosphere. I have to set aside a solid two hours to do nothing but shop. Otherwise, the female approach to shopping drives me crazy. My friend Jim is the same way.

"My wife assumes if you go buy a gift for somebody, it doesn't matter if you find what you want in the first minute," he says.

"You have to shop for like an hour before it's an important gift."

In contrast, most guys I know employ the search-and-destroy technique.

"I'll go through hardware catalogs and ads for three weeks," says Doug, a sales manager. "And all of a sudden at 9 o'clock some night I'll jump up and say, 'I'm ready.' I walk in the store, I buy it, I walk out. Ten minutes."

So what makes the woman's method better? Actually it isn't. It's just different. For some couples, shopping can become a form of recreational companionship, which, according to Willard Harley, is a basic need for most husbands. It's entirely possible to go shopping together and have fun doing it . . . even if one of you shops and the other hunts.

The key is to give each other's feelings, preferences and needs equal weight. Then, instead of always going off in separate directions, find a few things you can do together. In the process, you'll create a lifestyle that benefits both of you.

This works best when you understand that your basic emotional needs differ from your wife's. Harley says men want these things most from their wives: sexual fulfillment, recreational companionship, physical attractiveness, domestic support and admiration. Contrast that to what most women want: affection, conversation, honesty and openness, financial support and family commitment.

Of course, these aren't exactly the same for every man or every woman. So how do you find out what your wife needs? Ask her. How does she find out what you need? Tell her.

Here's one reward: The better we relate emotionally to our wives, the better they'll meet *our* major needs. And don't let our confused culture mandate how you act. Women don't want their husbands to behave like cavemen, but they don't want wimps, either.

"You always hear about differences being so bad," says Doug. "That's why we're in this androgynous state. We were created differently for a reason. Acknowledge that and then find fulfillment in those differences. I will function in my created role, as God intended."

Okay, it's time for Keith to recite the Guy Manifesto—not to be confused with the big-band leader from the forties.

"I'm a Christian male and I'm not going to shirk from what that means. I'm not going to apologize for having a tendency to communicate this way. I'm not going to apologize for being naturally competitive. But, I'm not going to ignore my responsibility to understand my wife's needs and desires, either."

He is man. Hear him roar.

Meeting adjourned.

Jim Killam is a free-lance writer and journalism instructor at Northern Illinois University.

Sexual Biology, Behavior, and Orientation

The Body and Its Responses (Articles 9–12)
Hygiene and Sexual Health Care (Articles 13–16)
Human Sexualities and Orientation (Articles 17–19)

Human bodies are miraculous things. Most of us, however, have less than a complete understanding of how they work. This is especially true of our bodily responses and functioning during sexual activity. Efforts to develop a healthy sexual awareness are severely hindered by misconceptions and lack of quality information about physiology. The first portion of this unit directs attention to the development of a clearer understanding and appreciation of the workings of the human body.

Over the past decade and a half, the general public's awareness of, and interest and involvement in, their own health care has dramatically increased. We want to stay healthy and live longer and know that to do so, we must know more about our bodies, including how to prevent problems, recognize danger signs, and find the most effective treatments. By the same token, if we want to be sexually fit and to continue being sexually functional as we age, we must be knowledgeable about sexual health care. *Annual Editions: Human Sexuality 98/99* has an expanded section that can help readers do what they need to do today to be healthy, happy, sexy older men and women in the twenty-first century.

As you read through the articles in this section, you will be able to see more clearly that matters of sexual biology and behavior are not merely physiological in origin. The articles included clearly demonstrate the psychological, social, and cultural origins of sexual behavior as well.

Why we humans feel, react, respond, and behave sexually can be quite complex. This is especially true regarding the issue of sexual orientation. Perhaps no other area of sexual behavior is as misunderstood as this one. Although experts do not agree about what causes our sexual orientation—homosexual, heterosexual, or bisexual—growing evidence suggests a complex interaction of biological or genetic determination, environmental or sociocultural influence, and free choice. In the early years of this century,

sexologist Alfred Kinsey's seven-point continuum of sexual orientation was introduced. It placed exclusive heterosexual orientation at one end, exclusive homosexual orientation at the other, and identified the middle range as where most people would fall if society and culture were unprejudiced. Since Kinsey, many others have added their research findings and theories to what is known about sexual orientation. John Money, a Johns Hopkins University researcher, who for the last 30 years has done research and writing on what he calls the sexology of erotic orientation, asserts that we should consider orientation as even more multidimensional than Kinsey's continuum. He stands with others who suggest that we pluralize our terms in this area: human sexualities.

That the previous paragraph may have been upsetting, even distasteful, to some readers emphasizes the connectedness of psychological, social, and cultural issues with those of sexuality. Human sexuality is biology, behavior, and much, much more. Our sexual beliefs, behaviors, choices, even feelings and comfort levels, are profoundly affected by what our culture prescribes and proscribes, which has been transmitted to us by the full range of social institutions and processes. This section begins our attempt to address these interrelationships and their impact on human sexuality.

The subsection *The Body and Its Responses* contains four informative and thought-provoking articles that illuminate the interplay of biological (especially hormonal), psychological, cultural, and interpersonal factors that affect sexual functioning. It also addresses such physiology and sexual functioning issues as female orgasm and includes intriguing current findings on chemical and sensual aphrodisiacs or lust-enhancers.

Hygiene and Sexual Health Care contains fact-filled articles that address male and female sexual health concerns, including AIDS and other sexually transmitted diseases,

ing more visible in the public eye via popular magazine stories (even features) and popular television and movies (even in starring roles). Both of these dynamics have challenged a culture that has often been called fundamentally homophobic (or homosexual-fearing). The closing article challenges cultural perceptions about transsexuals (people who believe their sexual organs/gender assignment is incorrect and seek to change to the other gender). What impact the new research findings in sexual orientation and greater public discussion of human sexuality(ies) will have on society and its members is uncertain. Many hope they will usher in a new level of understanding of human sexuality, intimacy, and ourselves.

Looking Ahead: Challenge Questions

How do you rate yourself with respect to knowing how your body works sexually on a scale from one (very uninformed, not even sure of correct names for my parts and processes) to five (well-informed and can troubleshoot sexual health conditions and figure out how to improve sexual response)? What has held your score down or increased it?

If you or your sexual partner were experiencing a sexual problem, would you prefer it have a physical, an emotional, or an interactional cause? Why?

Do you feel comfortable talking to your doctor, your friends, your partner about your sexual functioning and health-related concerns? Why or why not? Do you want this to change? How?

It is rare for people to wonder why someone is heterosexual in the same ways as we wonder why someone is homosexual or bisexual. What do you think contributes to a person's sexual orientation? Do you think it is possible for people not to feel threatened by sexual orientations different from their own? Why or why not?

that affect health, sexual functioning, and interest in sex. The final article in the subsection deals with techniques for maintaining sexual vibrancy into the later years of life.

The *Human Sexualities and Orientation* subsection features articles that dramatically demonstrate the changes that have occurred during the last decade with respect to homosexuality and bisexuality in the United States. In the past few years, growing numbers of scientific findings have identified biological, genetic, and hormonal differences between heterosexual and homosexual people. In addition, more gay, lesbian, and bisexual people have publicly acknowledged their orientation and are becom-

Recipes for Lust

Scientists had long dismissed aphrodisiacs as worthless.

Then studies revealed that some actually do what folklore and herbalists

claimed. Here's a guide to what works—and what doesn't.

BY MICHAEL CASTLEMAN

Old beliefs die hard—especially when they promise to add zing to our sex lives. The rhinoceros has been hunted to near-extinction partly because its powdered horn is believed to boost virility. (It doesn't.) And the legendary "Spanish fly"—actually made by pulverizing a Mediterranean beetle—is merely a urinary tract irritant that can be poisonous in large doses.

So until recently, scientists insisted that nothing ingested, inhaled, or injected could possibly have the amatory effect promised in that old rock song, "Love Potion #9," whose narrator "started kissing everything in sight" after downing an herbal brew. The sad fact is that there are many more ways to kill sexual interest than enhance it. But while science has still not identified anything that charms reluctant objects of desire into ripping off their clothes, a surprising number of herbs, drugs, and foods have physiological effects that just might make reluctant paramours more receptive to erotic invitations.

The reputations of most alleged aphrodisiacs can be traced to one of three sources: ancient myths, medieval medical theory, and traditional herbal medicine. The term "aphrodisiac" itself comes from Aphrodite, Greek goddess of beauty and love. In mythology, when Uranus, ruler of the heavens, was killed in a battle among the gods, his flesh fell into the sea and Aphrodite was created from it. Ever since the tale arose, products of the sea have been considered sex stimulants—especially oysters, whose fleshy moistness bears some fanciful resemblance to the female genitalia.

Such resemblances lie at the heart of the Doctrine of Signatures, a dubious medical philosophy that reigned in the Middle Ages. The idea was that God had blessed his children with natural remedies that announced their utility by their appearance, or "signature." Plants with heart-shaped leaves were prescribed for heart disease, yellow flowers were used to treat jaundice, and so on. Using the same "logic," plants with phallic parts—carrots, for example—were considered virility boosters, according to George Armelagos, Ph.D., a professor of anthropology at Emory University and author of *Consuming Passions: The Anthropology of Eating.* Similarly, anything soft and moist—peaches, oysters, ripe tomatoes—were linked to the vagina and considered aphrodisiacs for women. The theory held sway from China to Africa, where rhino horns looked phallic enough to spur the belief that they were sex stimulants. The head ornaments of other animals also gained reputations as aphrodisiacs—and gave us a term for feeling sex-starved, "horny."

Meanwhile, in herbal medicine any plant containing a stimulant gained a reputation as a sex enhancer. Before Arab caliphs visited their harems they sipped coffee, which of course contains caffeine. Montezuma and Casanova fortified themselves for sex by drinking another caffeinated beverage, hot chocolate. In addition, many herbs with action on the urinary tract gained reputations as aphrodisiacs, particularly irritants like Spanish fly and diuretics like saw palmetto.

BEYOND FOLKLORE

Until the early 1980s, most scientists had dismissed all traditional aphrodisiacs as quaint frauds whose powers had less to do with sex than suggestion. In some cases, they're right: Nothing even remotely libidinous has ever been discovered about the herb damiana, despite its scientific name,

Turnera aphrodisiaca. "It's very difficult to separate aphrodisiacs' effects on the mind from their effects on the body," notes Varro Tyler, Ph.D., a recently retired professor of pharmacognosy (natural medicine) at Purdue University. "Sexual enjoyment involves the mind as much as the body, so anything people consider arousing becomes arousing."

But with all due respect to the power of suggestion, researchers are now finding that several traditional aphrodisiacs do stimulate more than just the imagination:

•**YOHIMBE.** For centuries the bark of the West African yohimbe tree was reputed to restore erections to impotent men. And studies during the 1980s showed that a chemical in the tree's bark, yohimbine, indeed raises erections in some men by increasing blood flow to the penis. About 10 years ago the Food and Drug Administration (FDA) approved yohimbine as a treatment for impotence. The herbal extract is now available in five prescription drugs: Yocon, Ahprodyne, Erex, Yohimex, and Yovital. The herb quebracho also contains yohimbine.

However, some medical naysayers have continued to assail yohimbine as worthless. While a recent review of 16 studies shows that yohimbine *is* effective, the skeptics may be right about the yohimbine sold in health food stores. In 1995 the FDA sponsored a study of 26 over-the-counter yohimbine products, including Super Man and Hot Stuff. The yohimbine content of yohimbe bark is 7,089 parts per million (ppm), but the concentrations found in the tested products ranged from less than 0.1 ppm to 489 ppm, probably not enough to have much effect. If you want yohimbine's benefits, go with a prescription drug.

•**OYSTERS.** These shellfish are exceptionally rich in zinc, a mineral intimately related to male sexual health. Men with zinc-deficient diets are at high risk for infertility, prostate problems, and loss of libido. University of Rochester researchers have successfully restored sperm counts in infertile men using zinc supplements. Besides oysters, whole grains and fresh fruits and vegetables also contain this mineral.

•**WILD YAM.** This tuber's age-old reputation as a treatment for gynecological ailments was partially validated by the finding that it is a potent source of diosgenin, a chemical resembling female sex hormones. Though there's still little evidence that it boosts sexual desire, many herbalists tout wild yam salves for vaginal dryness, which makes intercourse uncomfortable for many women.

•**GINSENG.** The Chinese and Koreans insist that ginseng boosts sexual desire. Several Asian animal studies suggest that ginseng stimulates sexual function, and a Russian study shows it to be effective in treating impotence. But American scientists remain skeptical, including noted herbal medicine expert James Duke, Ph.D., author of *Ginseng: A Concise Handbook*.

•**CAFFEINE.** If your honey's thoughts turn to dreamland just as yours turn to dallying, a cup of coffee just might keep him or her awake long enough to make the most of the evening. University of Michigan urologist Ananias Diokno, M.D., found that compared to those who did not drink coffee, regular java drinkers were considerably more sexually active. But the finding may simply reflect caffeine's ability to keep the Sandman at bay until the end of the 10 o'clock news, rather than any boost in sexual desire per se.

•**CHOCOLATE.** Chocolate contains not only caffeine but also phenylethylamine (PEA), dubbed "the molecule of love" by sexual medicine specialist Theresa Crenshaw, M.D., author of *The Alchemy of Love and Lust*. A natural form of the stimulant amphetamine, PEA is actually a neurotransmitter. Both love and lust increase blood levels of PEA, but after a heartbreak the levels plummet. Although chocolate contains high levels of PEA, critics contend that it gets metabolized so quickly that it couldn't have much libidinous effect. Perhaps, but giving chocolates has become a worldwide courtship ritual. P.S.: The artificial sweetener, NutraSweet, also contains PEA. Maybe lovers should forget the champagne and toast one another with goblets of Diet Coke.

•**GINKGO.** Ginkgo is the latest arrival among sex-promoting herbs. It has no traditional reputation as an aphrodisiac, but research shows that it improves blood flow through the brain. Widely used in Europe to treat stroke and poor circulation in the brain, ginkgo also boosts blood flow into the penis. In one study, 50 men with erection impairment caused by poor penile blood flow were given 240 milligrams of a standardized ginkgo extract daily for nine months. Thirty-nine (78 percent) regained their erections, including all those who had previously been helped by impotence drugs.

HORMONAL HELP

Everyone knows testosterone is the primary male sex hormone. It's only a short leap to the notion that extra testosterone might give men a sexual boost. It does—but *only if you're deficient*. Few men are. "Testosterone has been one of the most abused and over-prescribed medications for male sexual dysfunction in medical history," insists Crenshaw. She compares the hormone to oil in a car: If you have enough, adding more doesn't make your car run better. In fact, extra testosterone may throw the body's hormonal circuitry out of whack, increasing irritability, aggression, blood pressure, and hair loss. But like a car low on oil, supplemental testosterone can restore sexual functioning in men who are truly deficient (See "Patching Up Testosterone," PSYCHOLOGY TODAY, February 1997).

Testosterone is not just for men, however. The ovaries produce it in small quantities, and the hormone is responsible for female libido. But at menopause women's testosterone production declines. Studies have shown that women who supplement replacement female sex hormones with a little testosterone feel more energetic and libidinous. Unfortunately, the hormone may also cause acne, aggressiveness, oily skin, and possibly liver damage. In other words, it should not be taken impulsively. But Crenshaw considers testosterone "promising" for carefully screened women who suffer unusual libido loss of menopause.

Another possible hormonal contributor to sex drive is dehydroepiandrosterone (DHEA), a precursor of both estrogen and testosterone. Recently DHEA has become the biggest supplement fad since melatonin, fueled by media hype that it improves mood, increases energy, prevents cancer and heart disease—and boosts libido.

Crenshaw calls DHEA a "natural aphrodisiac." Her studies show that in young women DHEA levels are "significant predictors" of sexual thoughts, desire, and masturbation. But she believes that the hormone may be less important for men, suggesting that guys "are so overwhelmed by testosterone that the DHEA effect is insignificant by comparison." However, another researcher says that DHEA doesn't do much sexually for either men or women. Samuel Yen, M.D., a professor of reproductive medicine at the University of California at San Diego, gave people 50 milligrams of DHEA a day for three months. They reported a greater sense of well-being, but no extra sex drive.

DHEA's safety is equally controversial. Some studies show that DHEA prevents liver tumors in animals, while other studies show that it causes them. If you opt for DHEA, it's available over the counter at many health food stores.

IN THE REALM OF THE SENSES

Mention "aphrodisiacs" and most people think only of herbs or drugs. But that view is as limited as the missionary position. "The most neglected ingredient of great sex is the backdrop," Crenshaw says. "Instead of making love on a deep-pile carpet by a roaring fire in a ski chalet with a magnificent view, people are in a dark bedroom on musty sheets when they're exhausted. For ordinary sex to become great, the setting is crucial. Arouse your senses—all five of them."

Take smell. What's the aroma of lust? Cinnamon, reports Alan Hirsch, M.D., neurologic director of the Smell and Taste Research Foundation in Chicago. Hirsch fitted male medical students' penises with gauges that detected erection and then exposed them to dozens of fragrances. The only one that got a rise was the smell of hot cinnamon buns. But other aromas can also add sensuality to sex. Try scented candles on your night table, flowers, or a new perfume.

Lovers should also remember to think visual. Many sex therapists recommend X-rated videos as aphrodisiacs. Most men need little convincing, but many women consider traditional male-oriented pornography demeaning. Some years ago, former porn starlet Candida Royalle launched Femme

Productions to produce X-rated videos aimed specifically at women. Femme videos feature plenty of "action," but the characters also have loving relationships and some emotional complexity.

According to two recent studies, Royalle's female sensibility is a major turn-on for women. University of Connecticut psychologist Donald Mosher, Ph.D., showed 395 college students one of six X-rated videos—three traditional male-oriented tapes, and three Femme programs. Most men found both types equally arousing. Women, however, clearly preferred the Femme programs, reporting considerably more intercourse afterward than those who watched the traditional pornography.

A similar study at the University of Amsterdam delved deeper, as it were, into the participants' sexuality. In addition to filling out a survey, female undergraduates were fitted with tampon-like devices that measured vaginal engorgement, an indication of sexual arousal. In the survey arm of the study, the women greatly preferred the Femme programs. But both types of videos elicited similar vaginal reactions, suggesting that feelings of sexual arousal are often more subjective than objective.

For a free catalog of Femme videos, call 1-800-456-LOVE. Another source of woman-oriented erotic videos is The Sexuality Library; call (415) 974-8985.

Finally, lovers shouldn't forget their sense of touch. "Every square inch of the body is a sensual playground," sex therapist Louanne Cole says. "It's sad that so many lovers explore only a few corners." To discover the sensuality of the whole body, try a hot bath or shower together using a fragrant herbal soap. Bathing is a wonderfully arousing prelude to lovemaking. The warmth relaxes muscles made tense by the daily grind. And soaping and drying each other can be a marvelous whole-body turn-on. For extra enjoyment, drape your towels over a radiator or pop them into the dryer so they'll be warm when you use them.

AROUSED BY INTIMACY

Okay, so you've got a roaring fire in the hearth, cinnamon-scented candles, a pot of ginseng tea, and a plate of oysters on the coffee table. Now what? Next try the board game, "An Enchanted Evening." It's a delightfully sensual aphrodisiac-in-a-box.

"An Enchanted Evening" began in 1979 as a kiss-and-make-up offering from then-37-year-old Barbara Jonas of Scottsdale, Arizona, to her husband, Michael. Today, it's one of the nation's best-selling adult board games. (It's available at game stores and lingerie shops nationwide, or call 1-800-776-7662.) "An Enchanted Evening" begins with each player writing a secret wish for later than evening. Then you roll dice and draw game cards. Some are "talk" cards that ask open-ended questions designed to celebrate your relationship: "You have lunch with a long-lost friend who asks, 'What attracted you to your spouse?' What did?" Others are "touch" cards with deliciously ambiguous directions: "Kiss your spouse in a place that's soft

BEWARE
THE SEX KILLERS

If you want to rev up your sex life, first make sure you don't shut it down. Many everyday items can interfere with pleasure in the sack:

•**ALCOHOL.** In *Macbeth,* Shakespeare wrote that this substance "provokes the desire, but takes away the performance." Truer words were never penned. When people of average weight drink more than two beers, cocktails, or glasses of wine in an hour, alcohol interferes with erection in men and impairs sexual responsiveness in women. Drink too much, and all you'll do in the prone position is pass out.

•**TOBACCO.** Smoking narrows the blood vessels, impairing blood flow into the penis in men and increasing their risk of erection impairment. In women, the same mechanism limits blood flow into the vaginal wall, decreasing lubrication.

•**ANTIDEPRESSANTS.** Antidepressants work—but at a price. All except one (see below) carry a considerable risk of sexual side effects: loss of desire and difficulty reaching orgasm in both sexes, impaired erections in men, and lubrication problems in women. Currently the most popular antidepressants are the selective serotonin reuptake inhibitors (SSRIs): Prozac, Zoloft, and Paxil. According to Jamie Grimes, M.D., chief of outpatient psychiatry at the Walter Reed Army Medical Center in Washington, D.C., SSRIs cause sex problems in more than half of those who use them. Sex-impairing side effects also occur among older antidepressants like Elavil, Tofranil, and Nardil.

If you take an antidepressant what can you do to preserve sexual function? Jacob Katzow, M.D., a Washington, D.C., psychiatrist, says a lower dose might reduce sexual side effects while preserving antidepressant benefits. Or try a "drug holiday." Anthony Rothschild, M.D., a psychiatrist at MacLean Hospital in Belmont, Massachusetts, had 30 couples—each with one member taking an SSRI and reporting loss of sexual function or desire—go drug-free on weekends, from Thursday morning to Sunday at noon. Among the 20 taking Paxil or Zoloft, half reported better sexual functioning and more desire over the weekend, and only two said they felt more depressed. But of the 10 taking Prozac, only one reported sexual improvement, probably because Prozac takes longer than other SSRIs to clear from the blood.

Another option is to ask your physician about switching to Wellbutrin (bupropion). For reasons that remain biochemically unclear, it has no sex-impairing side effects.

•**OTHER LEGAL DRUGS.** An enormous number of prescription and over-the-counter medications—even the antihistimines people take for allergies—can cause sexual impairment. "If a drug label says, 'May cause drowsiness,'" says sexual medicine specialist Theresa Crenshaw, M.D., "it can impair sexual desire or performance." John Morganthaler, director of the Sex/Drug Interaction Foundation in Petaluma, California, estimates that up to 20 percent of all sex problems are caused by drug side effects or interactions. He recommends asking your doctor and pharmacist about this possibility every time you get a prescription.

•**ILLICIT DRUGS.** There's a good reason why narcotics and tranquilizers are called "downers." That's what happens to the sexual interest of people who use them. But "uppers" are no better. Amphetamines and cocaine stimulate sexual desire, but impair orgasm, making sex decidedly frustrating. With regular use, desire fades as well.

The most sexually unpredictable illicit drug is marijuana. Some say it enhances lovemaking. Chemically, it just might. Pot increases blood levels of phenylethylamine, a neurotransmitter associated with love and lust. But marijuana makes other people withdraw or become anxious or irritable, which can ruin sex.

Finally, all illicit drugs involve risk of involuntary intimacy with the legal system. Fear of possible arrest causes anxiety, and anxiety takes the joy out of sex.—*M.C.*

and warm." The first one around the board—if the players get that far—wins his or her wish.

"An Enchanted Evening" made a believer out of Marty Klein, Ph.D., a Palo Alto, California, marriage counselor. "When I first heard about it, I felt totally cynical. But I thoroughly enjoyed it. It encourages the kind of playful touch and supportive communication most couples stop sharing after a while. And it shows a profound understanding of how intimacy and sexual desire go hand in hand."

They do, indeed. Which just goes to show that the world's greatest sex-stimulant is that crazy, wonderful emotion called love. Without love's special magic, sexual enhancements can fall flat. But for couples who share that intimate, chemical bond, aphrodisiacs, defined broadly, can transform lovemaking from "eh" to ecstatic.

Michael Castleman is a San Francisco-based health writer. His latest book is Nature's Cures *(Bantam).*

Your Sexual Landscape

For too long, women and doctors have maintained an uneasy silence about what goes on below the beltline. It's time we got comfortable with our own anatomy—

our health depends on it

By Beth Howard

Vagina. There, I've said it. This simple three-syllable word is no tongue twister—but it leaves even the boldest of us sputtering.

And it's not just talking about vaginas that makes women nervous. Many of us can't bear to *look* at our anatomy. The vagina is the locus of our most profound feelings about intimacy. No wonder it's shrouded in mystery and shame, or that the men in our lives often know their way around our bodies better than we do.

Until recently even medicine was guilty of keeping the vagina under wraps. Research on vulvar-vaginal disorders (the vulva is the external genitalia) is nearly nonexistent, says Libby Edwards, M.D., a vulvar-disease specialist at the Carolinas Medical Center in Charlotte, NC. And medical training on the subject is notoriously scanty. Even the obvious specialties limit their scope. Gynecologists tend to focus on the internal reproductive organs; urologists on urinary tract problems. Most dermatologists stop short of the vulva. "Thanks to sexual taboos, this area has been virtually ignored," says Peter Lynch, M.D., chairman of dermatology at the University of California

at Davis and one of the field's few specialists in vulvar dermatology.

Medicine may be neglecting women, but we are often our own worst enemies when it comes to vaginal health. "*Vagina* is a dirty word. Women don't think about taking care of their vaginas," says Sharon Hillier, Ph.D., director of reproductive infectious disease research at Magee-Women's Hospital at the University of Pittsburgh. Add the shame factor, and you've got the setup for a stalemate: Doctors don't ask about vaginal problems, and women don't tell.

But times are changing. Spurred by new data about vaginal health, gynecological researchers have begun to advocate a newer, friendlier way of thinking about the vagina. Not simply a place for penises, babies and tampons, this four-inch-deep tunnel is also home to a variety of microscopic organisms that conspire to make it as delicately balanced an ecosystem as a tropical rain forest. When the system is running properly, friendly bacteria called lactobacilli constantly manufacture hydrogen peroxide, in effect churning out tiny bits of bleach to keep not-so-friendly organisms in check. Left to itself, the vagina is one of the cleanest surfaces on the body.

The idea of a naturally clean vagina is so at odds with women's beliefs and society's stereotypes that Dr. Hillier has embarked on a virtual vagina campaign. "The healthy vaginal ecosystem," she declares, "is an endangered habitat."

IRRITANTS AND INFECTION:
Preserving a Pristine Environment

As with other ecological disasters, we can blame ourselves when the vagina's natural balance is upset. We have unsafe sex, take antibiotics (which kill off healthy bacteria) or mistakenly use nonprescription yeast cures when we don't really have yeast infections.

Ironically the primary culprits are often products aimed at helping women feel "fresh." Douches, vaginal deodorants and scented panty liners contain chemicals that can irritate the

searchers reported in the *Journal of Infectious Diseases* last November that tampons did not adversely affect the vaginal ecosystem.

Not only can some vaginal products cause internal trouble, but they also can result in external redness or itching and derail sex. What to do: Stop using the product and let the ecosystem's natural cleanup squad restore things to normal. Vulvar irritation often comes in the form of dermatitis: dry, itchy skin that may be due to tight or chafing clothes combined with the moisture of normal vaginal secretions. The solution: loose-fitting clothes. Your doctor may prescribe a steroid ointment if the problem persists.

BACTERIA, VIRUSES AND YEAST:
Stopping an Ecological Disaster

The good news for women of all ages is that the vagina has a natural tendency to restore itself—to a point: Dis-

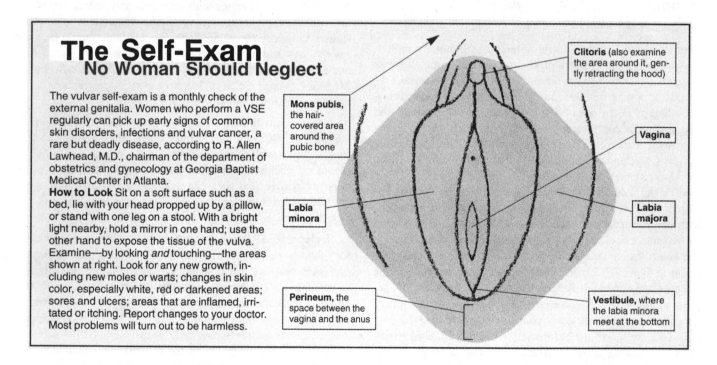

The Self-Exam
No Woman Should Neglect

The vulvar self-exam is a monthly check of the external genitalia. Women who perform a VSE regularly can pick up early signs of common skin disorders, infections and vulvar cancer, a rare but deadly disease, according to R. Allen Lawhead, M.D., chairman of the department of obstetrics and gynecology at Georgia Baptist Medical Center in Atlanta.

How to Look Sit on a soft surface such as a bed, lie with your head propped up by a pillow, or stand with one leg on a stool. With a bright light nearby, hold a mirror in one hand; use the other hand to expose the tissue of the vulva. Examine—by looking *and* touching—the areas shown at right. Look for any new growth, including new moles or warts; changes in skin color, especially white, red or darkened areas; sores and ulcers; areas that are inflamed, irritated or itching. Report changes to your doctor. Most problems will turn out to be harmless.

Mons pubis, the hair-covered area around the pubic bone

Labia minora

Perineum, the space between the vagina and the anus

Clitoris (also examine the area around it, gently retracting the hood)

Vagina

Labia majora

Vestibule, where the labia minora meet at the bottom

vaginal walls and disrupt the normal flora. A study of 182 women done at the University of Washington in Seattle found that women who routinely douched for hygiene were four times as likely as those who didn't to lose their healthful lactobacilli. "Douching can upset the ecosystem in much the same way as putting weed killer on the lawn can kill the underlying lawn," Dr. Hillier says. "It has no medical benefits," and it's actually associated with an *increased* risk for pelvic inflammatory disease.

Fortunately tampons seem to have little effect on the vagina. Today's less absorbent, natural-fiber tampons are far safer than the super-absorbent synthetic ones that spurred cases of toxic-shock syndrome in the early 1980s. Re-

charge combined with odor, particularly a fishy odor, is almost always a tip-off to the presence of an infection that can make intercourse painful and require medical attention. "Normal secretions are not foul or fishy," says David E. Soper, M.D., director of the division of benign gynecology at the Medical University of South Carolina in Charleston. The wise course of action is to become familiar with these sex stoppers before they strike. (For a list of common complaints, see "The Infection Connection."

The problem is, some women blame bad hygiene for their symptoms. Doctors are often party to the cover-up: In a recent survey by the National Vaginitis Association, nearly 50% of gynecologists said that even when they found evidence of the most common infection, bacterial vaginosis, they treated it only if patients complained of symptoms.

A vaginal infection won't always be diagnosed during a routine gynecological visit, notes Jill Maura Rabin, M.D., head of urogynecology at Long Island Jewish Medical Center in New Hyde Park, NY. The Pap smear is not designed to detect vaginal infections. That's why it's important to speak up about symptoms such as odor and discharge, especially because unchecked infections now appear to be more dangerous than previously believed. Bacterial vaginosis, for example, has recently been linked to a higher rate of pelvic inflammatory disease, pregnancy complications and postoperative infections.

Viruses present an altogether different threat to vaginal health and sexual pleasure, so it's also crucial to bring any herpes blisters or genital warts to a doctor's attention. (For information about how to examine yourself, see box on previous page.

AGE-RELATED DRYNESS:
Changes in the Terrain

Sometimes discomfort during intercourse is not a symptom of infection but the primary problem. Its most common cause is vaginal dryness. Some women develop premenopausal dryness due to a drop in estrogen or as a result of hysterectomy, chemotherapy or the use of antidepressants, antihistamines and some hormonal contraceptives. "And after menopause, nearly all women experience dryness," says Geoffrey Redmond, M.D., a Cleveland endocrinologist and author of *The Good New About Women's Hormones.*

When the ovaries stop producing estrogen, the vaginal lining gets drier and thinner, making it vulnerable to irritation, which can result in pain during sex. The vulva and the vagina also become less elastic, although regular stimulation—through either masturbation or intercourse—may reduce this change, according to Beverly Whipple, Ph.D., an associate professor in the department of nursing at Rutgers University in Newark, NJ.

For a quick fix, drugstores display a variety of slippery substances designed to keep your love life gliding happily along. Gels are used just before sex, while liquid moisturizers can be applied as often as needed. Choose a water-soluble product; oil-based ones can upset the vaginal ecology and erode latex used in diaphragms and condoms.

Lack of moisture puts a damper on intimacy. But the right lubricant can keep things gliding along.

The best solution for postmenopausal women, though, is estrogen replacement. "The minimal dose that protects women against heart disease and osteoporosis may not be enough to adequately relieve thin, dry tissue," says Dr. Redmond. You'll have to speak up if you want your doctor to fine-tune treatment. One offbeat solution is the Reality female condom. Anecdotal reports suggest some women are using it to protect thinning tissues during intercourse.

Menopause produces other vaginal changes. The vagina begins to narrow and shorten, and the rugae—tiny ridges that help the vagina expand at childbirth and enhance its gripping effect during sex—gradually disappear. For many women, pelvic muscle strength decreases with age. This may reduce the sensation of friction during intercourse. Some women turn to cosmetic surgery to tighten the vaginal opening, but "this should be a last resort," says Linda Brubaker, M.D., director of urogynecology and reconstructive pelvic surgery at Rush-Presbyterian-St. Luke's Medical Center in Chicago. For most women, exercises or physical therapy can strengthen the pelvic muscle.

Women who undergo a hysterectomy may notice that the vagina feels different during intercourse, because the cervix is routinely removed during the surgery, according to Dr. Whipple. Many doctors don't tell patients to expect this, and women may not realize that they can ask for cervix-sparing surgery. "Studies support the fact that if the cervix is left, women don't report a change in sexual response," she says.

If menopausal changes aren't to blame for sexual discomfort, the source may be vulvodynia or vaginismus, two painful problems that can affect women of any age. Vulvodynia is a set of chronic symptoms—burning, rawness, stinging or irritation of the vulva and the vaginal opening—with an unknown cause. (For more information, contact the National Vulvodynia Association in Silver Spring, MD, at 301–299–0775.) Vaginismus, an involuntary spasm of the vaginal muscles that occurs before or during penetration, also causes extreme pain. It's often related to fear or anxiety about sex.

Finding the Elusive G Spot

The G spot usurped the clitoris as the focus of sensual pleasure in the 1980s, when researchers reported that orgasm often results when a small area beneath the front of the vaginal wall is stimulated. It's easiest to find your G spot when you're kneeling. You or your partner can insert two fingers about halfway into the vagina and explore the front wall until you find a patch of tissue that begins to swell. (Use your other hand to press on the lower abdomen just above the pubic hair.) Stimulation produces a pleasant sensation for most women and often leads to orgasm, reports Beverly Whipple, Ph.D., an associate professor in the department of nursing at Rutgers University in Newark, N.J. Once you've located the G spot, you and your partner can try different positions to improve his contact with the area during lovemaking.

The Infection Connection

Here's how to cope with the most common vaginal infections that strike women in midlife:

The culprit	The symptoms	The cure
Bacterial vaginosis, an overgrowth of normal vaginal bacteria.	Thin grayish or white discharge that has a foul, fishy odor. Possible itching and irritation.	The prescription drugs metronidazole or clindamycin. Avoid nonprescription yeast drugs—they could make matters worse.
Yeast infection, an overgrowth of the *Candida* fungus.	Odorless white, cottage cheese–like discharge and itching.	If you're sure it's yeast, try an over-the-counter yeast fighter; otherwise, see your doctor. Eating yogurt that contains live *Lactobacillus acidophilus* cultures may reduce the risk of future infections.
Trichomonas, a parasite usually transmitted during sex.	Frothy, yellow-green fishy-smelling discharge; itching, painful urination or intercourse.	Prompt treatment with the prescription drug metronidazole for both you and your partner.
Herpes simplex virus, which can be transmitted sexually even in the absence of blisters.	Itching, stinging sores on the vulva or in the vagina.	There is no cure, but prescription antiviral drugs can reduce outbreaks and to some extent protect a partner from infection.
Human papillomavirus, which can be sexually transmitted.	Vaginal warts which may itch or burn after sex.	Certain types of HPV place women at above-average risk of cervical cancer, so most growths are surgically removed.

Whether it's the pain of vaginismus or the annoyance of a yeast infection, doctors are taking vaginal symptoms more seriously. "There is a transition from seeing them as a nuisance to seeing them as a threat to women's health and psychological well-being," says Dr. Hillier. As more physicians fight to clean up the vagina's public image, this under-appreciated part of our anatomy will no doubt be seen as less mysterious—and more marvelous.

Your next step? See the box for advice on how to use vulvar self-exams to get acquainted with your body. Debra Gussman, M.D., a Denver gynecologist, puts it this way: "If you don't know what you look like, how are you going to know everything's okay?"

Beth Howard lives in New York City and is writing a book about sexual wellness for women.

The Orgasm Wars

For years, scientists have been debating the function of female orgasm. Now they've finally figured it out. For women, the psychology of sexual satisfaction turns out to be much more sophisticated than most (male) scientists have been willing to concede. Of course.

**F. Bryant Furlow and
Randy Thornhill, Ph.D.**

F. BRYANT FURLOW is a research assistant and student of evolutionary biology at the University of New Mexico in Albuquerque. He is currently studying adult reactions to health cues in baby cries. An honors student, Furlow is also a science columnist for the *New Mexico Daily Lobo*. When not at the lab, Furlow and his girlfriend can be found watching kangaroo rats and sunsets in the desert.

RANDY THORNHILL, PH.D., is a professor of biology and a Regents' Professor at the University of New Mexico in Albuquerque. The recipient of Guggenheim and Japan Society for Promotion of Science Fellowships, as well as a Humboldt Prize, Thornhill has focused his research on behavioral ecology and the evolution of human behavior and psychology. Recently he has been scrutinizing human aesthetic judgments and the role of developmental stability in evolution.

Ever since Alfred Kinsey and Masters and Johnson made the subject of human sexual response safe for respectable scientists, laboratory studies of the physiologic "hows" of sexual arousal have flourished. Volunteers have been prodded, filmed, tape-recorded, interviewed, measured, wired, and monitored, quantifying for the annals of science the shortened breath, arched backs and feet, grimacing faces, marginally intentional vocalizations, and jumping blood pressure of human orgasm.

While physiological details abound, fewer scientists have attempted to answer the "why" questions about human orgasm. To those who view human behavior in an evolutionary framework, which we believe adds an invaluable perspective, male orgasm is no great mystery. It's little more than a physiologically simple ejaculation that is accompanied by a nearly addictive incentive to seek out further sexual encounters. The greater the number of inseminations a male achieves, the better his chances of being genetically represented in future generations.

Compared with the more frequent and easily achieved orgasm men experience, women's sexual climax has remained a mystery. After all, women do not need to experience orgasm in order to conceive. So what is the function of orgasm in females?

Darwinian theorists who made early attempts to address female orgasm proposed that orgasm keeps a woman lying down after sex, passively retaining sperm and increasing her probability of conception. Others suggested that it evolved to create a stronger pair bond between lovers, inspiring in women feelings of intimacy and trust toward mates. Some reasoned that orgasm communicates a woman's sexual satisfaction and devotion to a lover.

Most recently, evolutionary psychologists have been exploring the proposition that female orgasm is a sophisticated adaptation that allows women to manipulate—even without their own awareness—which of their lovers will be allowed to fertilize their eggs.

Male Nipples?

The diversity of evolutionary hypotheses reflects one general attitude: that the quickened breath, moaning, racing heart, muscular contraction and spasms, and nearly hallucinatory states of pleasure that orgasm inspires constitute a complex physiologic event with apparently functional design. But critics of adaptationist hypotheses have long argued that evolution is more slipshod than purposeful. A few, including Harvard evolutionist Stephen Jay Gould, have insisted that female orgasm probably doesn't *have* a function.

Women's romantic attachment does not increase the frequency of orgasm! Nor does experience.

Instead, Gould argues, female orgasm is incidental, caused by an anatomical peculiarity of embryonic development. In embryos, the undifferentiated organ that later becomes the penis in males becomes the clitoris in females. Antiadaptationists like Gould—whose thinking uncannily parallels Freud's belief that women spend their life in penis envy—hold that the clitoris is, biologically speaking, an underdeveloped penis; it can let women mimic male orgasm, but it has no functional relevance or evolutionary history of its own.

Well known for his emphasis on chance events and structural constraints as major players in the evolutionary process, Gould sees the supposed functionlessness of female orgasm as a classic illustration why scientists ought not automatically assume that a trait has adaptive significance. He criticizes other evolutionists for overemphasizing natural selection and functionality, and concludes that female orgasm is like the male nipple—nothing more than developmental baggage.

Many evolutionists have rejected

Reprinted with permission from *Psychology Today*, January/February 1996, pp. 42-46. © 1996 by Sussex Publishers, Inc.

Gould's notion that women's orgasms are developmentally contingent on men's. Unlike a male nipple, adaptationists have pointed out, the female orgasm *does* something. It inspires strong emotions that can affect bonding and sexual preferences, making women more likely to prefer the company of one mate over another.

Only during the past few years have studies begun to yield evidence that may resolve the baggage-versus-adaptation debate over women's orgasms.

Sperm Competition, with Women Judging

Clues for a reasonable adaptation hypothesis were readily available by the late 1960s, when *The British Medical Journal* published an exchange of letters about the muscular contractions and uterine suction associated with women's orgasm. In one letter, a doctor reported that a patient's uterine and vaginal contractions during sex with a sailor had pulled off his condom. Upon inspection, the condom was found in her cervical canal! The doctor concluded that female orgasms pull sperm closer to the egg as well.

Yet, it was only three years ago that two British biologists, Robin Baker and Mark Bellis, tested the so-called upsuck hypothesis. They were building upon ideas articulated by evolutionary biologist Robert Smith, who suggested that since women don't have orgasms every time out, female orgasm favors some sperm over others. Baker and Bellis sought to learn just how female orgasms might affect which of a lover's sperm is used to fertilize a woman's eggs.

They asked volunteers to keep track of the timing of their orgasms during sex, and, after copulation, to collect male ejaculates from vaginal flowback—a technical term denoting a distinct form of material that emerges from the vagina several hours after sex (scientists have devised a way to collect it). The team counted sperm from over 300 instances of human copulation.

They discovered that when a woman climaxes any time between a minute before to 45 minutes after her lover ejaculates, she retains significantly more sperm than she does after nonorgasmic sex. When her orgasm precedes her mate's by more than a minute, or when she does not have an orgasm, little sperm is retained. Just as the doctors' letters suggested decades earlier, the team's results indicated that muscular contractions associated with orgasm pull sperm from the vagina to the cervix, where it's in better position to reach an egg.

Baker and Bellis proposed that by manipulating the occurrence and timing of orgasm—via subconscious processes—women influence the probability of conception. So while a man worries about a woman's satisfaction with him as a lover out of fear she will stray, orgasmic females may be up to something far more clever—deciding which partner will sire her children.

Good Men Are Hard To Find

Meanwhile, other researchers were making discoveries about the nature of male attractiveness. Behavioral ecologists had noted that female animals, from scorpion flies to barn swallows, prefer males with high degrees of bilateral body symmetry, called developmental stability in the parlance of science.

Development, or the translation of genes into parts of the body, can be perturbed by stresses such as disease, malnutrition, or genetic defects. One measure of developmental *in*stability is deviation from bilateral symmetry in traits like hands, eyes, and even birds' tail feathers. Males whose immune systems are strong, and who forage well, develop with high symmetry, so females who choose symmetrical suitors are securing good genes for their offspring.

Evolutionary biologist Randy Thornhill and psychologist Steve Gangestad at the University of New Mexico in Albuquerque have tested whether humans also share this

Female orgasm is less about bonding with nice guys than subconscious evaluation of their lovers genetic endowment. Women have orgasm more often with men whose bodies are most symmetrical.

preference. And indeed they do. In their studies, women consistently identify as most attractive males whose faces (and other body parts) are most symmetrical.

But this, it turns out, is more than a matter of mere aesthetics. A large and growing body of medical literature documents that symmetrical people are physically and psychologically healthier than their less symmetrical counterparts.

Thornhill and Gangestad reasoned that if women's orgasms are an adaptation for securing good genes for their offspring, women should report more orgasms with relatively symmetrical mates. Collaborating for a second time, the two, along with graduate student Randall Comer, devised some very interesting studies to test this idea.

First they enrolled 86 sexually active heterosexual couples from among the undergraduates. The average age of the partners was 22 and the couples had been together an average of two years. Then the researchers had each person privately—and anonymously—answer questions about his or her sexual experiences.

The researchers took facial photographs of each person and analyzed the features by computer; they also had them graded for attractiveness by independent raters blind to the study. They measured various body parts to assess bilateral symmetry—the

Explosive Findings!

If we use his study's findings to understand how we humans are designed to behave in the sexual domain, says Randy Thornhill, Ph.D., then we are better equipped to deal with problems that arise in relationships. He points to the following results as among those we should take to heart:

- A woman's capacity for orgasm depends not on her partner's sexual skill but on her subconscious evaluation of his genetic merits.
- Women's orgasm has little to do with love. Or experience.
- Good men are indeed hard to find.

- The men with the best genes make the worst mates.
- Women are no more built for monogamy than men are. They are designed to keep their options open.
- Women fake orgasm to divert a partner's attention from their infidelities.

width of elbow, wrist, hand, ankle, and foot bones, and the length of the second and fifth fingers. Earlier studies had suggested all of these were associated with health.

Indeed, the hypothesized relationship between male symmetry and female orgasm proved to be true, the researchers recently reported in the journal *Animal Behavior* (Vol. 50, December). From data on sexual behavior provided by the women, those whose partners were most symmetrical enjoyed a significantly higher frequency of orgasms during sexual intercourse than did those with less symmetrical mates. Even the

> 'As uncomfortable as it may make many of us men, a woman's orgasm appears to be a more complex and discriminating comment about her lover's merits than are our own.'

data on sexual experience provided by the men showed the women had more orgasms with the most symmetrical men.

Of course, symmetry is a relative thing, and a relative rarity at that. No one is perfectly symmetrical, and very high symmetry scores were few and far between in this sample, as in others. In consolation, Thornhill and Gangestad point out that the differences they are measuring are subtle, and most require the use of calipers to detect.

What's Love Got To Do With It?

It's important to note what did not correlate with female orgasm during sex. Degree of women's romantic attachment did not increase the frequency of orgasm! Nor did the sexual experience of either partner. Conventional wisdom holds that birth control and protection from disease up orgasm rates, since they allow women to feel more relaxed during intercourse. But no relationship emerged between female orgasm and the use of contraception.

Nor can the study results be explained by the possibility that the symmetrical males were dating especially uninhibited and orgasmic women. Their partners did not have more orgasms during foreplay or in other sexual activities. Male symmetry correlated with a high frequency of female orgasm *only during copulation.*

The findings support evolutionary psychologists' "good genes" hypothesis: Women have orgasm more often with their most symmetrical lovers, increasing the likelihood of conceiving these men's children. Well, that's how it would have worked for millennia, before condoms and the Pill.

And it is for the precontraceptive stone age that our brains seem to be built; the agricultural and industrial revolutions are flashes in the geological pan, far too recent in evolutionary terms to have fundamentally changed the way we experience emotions or sex. To argue, as may champions of chance like Gould, that sexual attraction has remained completely arbitrary throughout evolution seems increasingly unwarranted.

Cheating Hearts

Here's the cruelest part of Thornhill and Gangestad's findings: The males who most inspire high-sperm-retention orgasmic responses from their sexual partners don't invest more in their relationships than do other men. Studies show that symmetrical men have the shortest courtships before having sexual intercourse with the women they date. They invest the least money and time in them. And they cheat on their mates more often than guys with less well-balanced bodies. So much for the beleaguered bonding hypothesis, which wants us to believe that women with investing, caring mates will have the most orgasms.

The women who took part in the study were no saints, either. They sometimes *faked* orgasm. Their fakery was not related to male symmetry. Faking, however, was more common among women who reported flirting with other men. Clearly earlier theories were not too far off the mark when they proposed that a man looks for cues of sexual satisfaction from his mate for reassurance about her fidelity. Faking orgasms might be the easiest way for the woman with many lovers to avoid the suspicions of her main partner.

Baker and Bellis found that when women do engage in infidelity, they retain less sperm from their main partners (their husbands, in many cases), and more often experience copulatory orgasms during their trysts, retaining semen from their secret lovers. Taken together, these findings suggest that female orgasm is less about bonding with nice guys than about careful, subconscious evaluation of their lovers' genetic endowment.

Exhibit B

Patterns of female orgasm point to one important conclusion about our evolutionary past—that sexual restraint did not prevail among women. But that's only part of the evidence. Exhibit B is male ejaculation.

Baker and Bellis found that the number of sperm in men's ejaculate changes, and it varies according to the amount of time that romantic partners have spent apart. The longer a woman's absence, the more sperm in her husband's ejaculate upon the couple's reunion. Males increase ejaculate size, it seems, to match the increased risk that a mate was inseminated by a competitor.

In an ancestral environment of truly monogamous mating, there would have been no need for females to have orgasm or for men to adjust ejaculate size. Both are adaptations to a spicy sex life.

Male Bias

Darwin proposed that female animals' preferences have shaped male ornaments such as peacocks' tails. But his audience—largely male scientists—laughed off his theory of sexual selection on the grounds that females (human or otherwise) are too fickle to exert the necessary selection pressure.

Today, evolutionary biology is no longer so completely a male discipline. But many male evolutionists nevertheless carry old biases. The notion that female orgasm is anything other than a developmental legacy leaving females able to imitate "the real thing" will be difficult for some to accept. But as uncomfortable as it may make many of us men—including male scientists—a woman's orgasm appears to be a more complex and discriminating comment about her lovers' merits than are our own.

It takes more than just a hormone to make a fellow's trigger finger itch.

TESTOSTERONE RULES

Face it, we all do it—we all believe in stereotypes about minorities. These stereotypes are typically pejorative and false, but every now and then they have a core of truth. I know, because I belong to a minority that lives up to its reputation. I have a genetic abnormality generally considered to be associated with high rates of certain socially abhorrent behaviors: I am male. Thanks to an array of genes that produce some hormone-synthesizing enzymes, my testes churn out a corrosive chemical and dump the stuff into my bloodstream, and this

BY ROBERT SAPOLSKY

probably has behavioral consequences. We males account for less than 50 percent of the population, yet we generate a huge proportion of the violence. Whether it is something as primal as having an ax fight in a rain forest clearing or as detached as using computer-guided aircraft to strafe a village, something as condemned as assaulting a cripple or as glorified as killing someone wearing the wrong uniform, if it is violent, we males excel at it.

Why should this be? We all think we know the answer: something to do with those genes being expressed down in the testes. A dozen millennia ago or so, an adventurous soul managed to lop off a surly bull's testicles, thus inventing behavioral

Robert Sapolsky is a neuroendrocrinologist at Stanford who studies the cellular mechanisms of stress-induced diseases. In 1987 he received a MacArthur genius award. Sapolsky last wrote for DISCOVER in March 1996 about the behavior and social interactions of aging baboons.

From *Discover*, March 1997, pp. 44-47, 50. Excerpted from *The Trouble with Testosterone: And Other Essays On the Biology of the Human Predicament* by Robert Sapolsky. © 1997 by Robert Sapolsky. Reprinted by permission of Scribner, a Division of Simon & Schuster.

endocrinology. It is unclear from the historical records whether the experiment resulted in grants and tenure, but it certainly generated an influential finding: that the testes do something or other to make males aggressive pains in the ass.

That something or other is synthesizing the infamous corrosive chemical, testosterone (or rather, a family of related androgen hormones that I'll call testosterone for the sake of simplicity, hoping the androgen specialists won't take it the wrong way). Testosterone bulks up muscle cells—including those in the larynx, giving rise to operatic basses. It makes hair sprout here and there, undermines the health of blood vessels, alters biochemical events in the liver too dizzying to contemplate, and has a profound impact, no doubt, on the workings of cells in big toes. And it seeps into the brain, where it influences behavior in a way highly relevant to understanding aggression.

Genes are the hand behind the scene, directing testosterone's actions. They specify whether steroidal building blocks are turned into testosterone or estrogen, how much of each, and how quickly. They regulate how fast the liver breaks down circulating testosterone, thereby determining how long an androgenic signal remains in the bloodstream. They direct the synthesis of testosterone receptors—specialized proteins that catch hold of testosterone and allow it to have its characteristic effects on target cells. And genes specify how many such receptors the body has, and how sensitive they are. Insofar as testosterone alters brain function and produces aggression, and genes regulate how much testosterone is made and how effectively it works, this should be the archetypal case for studying how genes can control our behavior. Instead, however, it's the archetypal case for learning how little genes actually do so.

Some pretty obvious evidence links testosterone with aggression. Males tend to have higher testosterone levels in their circulation than do females, and to be more aggressive. Times of life when males are swimming in testosterone—for example, after reaching puberty—correspond to when aggression peaks. Among many species, testes are mothballed most of the year, kicking into action and pouring out testosterone only during a very circumscribed mating season—precisely the time when male-male aggression soars.

Impressive though they seem, these data are only correlative—testosterone found on the scene repeatedly with no alibi when some aggression has occurred. The proof comes with the knife, the performance of what is euphemistically known as a subtraction experiment. Remove the source of testosterone in species after species, and levels of aggression typically plummet. Reinstate normal testosterone levels afterward with injections of synthetic testosterone, and aggression returns.

The subtraction and replacement paradigm represents pretty damning proof that this hormone, with its synthesis and efficacy under genetic control, is involved in aggression. "Normal testosterone levels appear to be a prerequisite for normative levels of aggressive behavior" is the sort of catchy, hummable phrase the textbooks would use. That probably explains why you shouldn't mess with a bull moose during rutting season. But it's not why a lot of people want to understand this sliver of science. Does the action of testosterone tell us anything about *individual* differences in levels of aggression, anything about why some males—some human males—are exceptionally violent? Among an array of males, are the highest testosterone levels found in the most aggressive individuals?

Generate some extreme differences and that is precisely what you see. Castrate some of the well-paid study subjects, inject others with enough testosterone to quadruple the normal human levels, and the high-testosterone males are overwhelmingly likely to be the more aggressive ones. Obviously, extreme conditions don't tell us much about the real world, but studies of the normative variability in testosterone—in other words, seeing what everyone's natural levels are like without manipulating anything—also suggest that high levels of testosterone and high levels of aggression tend to go together. This would seem to seal the case that interindividual differences in levels of aggression among normal individuals are probably driven by differences in levels of testosterone. But that conclusion turns out to be wrong.

Here's why. Suppose you note a correlation between levels of aggression and levels of testosterone among normal males. It could be because *a)* testosterone elevates aggression; *b)* aggression elevates testosterone secretion; or *c)* neither causes the other. There's a huge bias to assume option *a*, while *b* is the answer. Study after study has shown that if you examine testosterone levels when males are first placed together in the social group, testosterone levels predict nothing about who is going to be aggressive. The subsequent behavioral differences drive the hormonal changes, rather than the other way around.

Because of a strong bias among certain scientists, it has taken forever to convince them of this point. Suppose you're studying what behavior and hormones have to do with each other. How do you study the behavioral part? You get yourself a notebook, a stopwatch, a pair of binoculars. How do you measure the hormones and analyze the genes that regulate them? You need some gazillion-dollar machines; you muck around with radiation and chemicals, wear a lab coat, maybe even goggles—the whole nine yards. Which toys would you rather get for Christmas? Which facet of science are you going to believe in more? The higher the technology, goes the formula, the more scientific the discipline. Hormones seem to many to be more substantive than behavior, so when a correlation occurs, it must be because hormones regulate behavior, not the other way around.

This is a classic case of what is often called physics envy, a disease that causes behavioral biologists to fear their discipline lacks the rigor of physiology, physiologists to wish for the techniques of biochemists, biochemists to covet the clarity of the answers revealed by molecular geneticists, all the way down until you get to the physicists who confer only with God. Recently, a zoologist friend

An adventurous soul long ago managed to lop off a surly bull's testicles, thus inventing behavioral endocrinology.

had obtained blood samples from the carnivores he studies and wanted some hormones in the samples tested in my lab. Although inexperienced with the technique, he offered to help in any way possible. I felt hesitant asking him to do anything tedious, but since he had offered, I tentatively said, "Well, if you don't mind some unspeakable drudgery, you could number about a thousand assay vials." And this scientist, whose superb work has graced the most prestigious science journals in the world, cheerfully answered, "That's okay. How often do I get to do real science, working with test tubes?"

Difficult though scientists with physics envy find it to believe, interindividual differences in testosterone levels don't predict subsequent differences in aggressive behavior among individuals. Similarly, fluctuations in testosterone levels within one individual over time don't predict subsequent changes in the levels of aggression in that one individual—get a hiccup in testosterone secretion one afternoon and that's not when the guy goes postal.

Look at our confusing state: normal levels of testosterone are a prerequisite for normal levels of aggression. Yet if one male's genetic makeup predisposes him to higher levels of testosterone than the next guy, he isn't necessarily going to be more aggressive. Like clockwork, that statement makes the students suddenly start coming to office hours in a panic, asking whether they missed something in their lecture notes.

Yes, it's going to be on the final, and it's one of the more subtle points in endocrinology—what's referred to as a hormone having a "permissive effect." Remove someone's testes and, as noted, the frequency of aggressive behavior is likely to plummet. Reinstate pre-castration levels of testosterone by injecting the hormone, and pre-castration levels of aggression typically return. Fair enough. Now, this time, castrate an individual and restore testosterone levels to only 20 percent of normal. Amazingly, normal pre-castration levels of aggression come back. Castrate and now introduce twice the testosterone levels from before castration, and the same level of aggressive behavior returns. You need some testosterone around for normal aggressive behavior. Zero levels after castration, and down it usually goes; quadruple levels (the sort of range generated in weight lifters abusing

anabolic steroids), and aggression typically increases. But anywhere from roughly 20 percent of normal to twice normal and it's all the same. The brain can't distinguish among this wide range of basically normal values.

If you knew a great deal about the genetic makeup of a bunch of males, enough to understand how much testosterone they secreted into their bloodstream, you still couldn't predict levels of aggression among those individuals. Nevertheless, the subtraction and reinstatement data seem to indicate that, in a broad sort of way, testosterone causes aggressive behavior. But that turns out not to be true either, and the implications of this are lost on most people the first 30 times they hear about it. Those implications are important, however—so important that it's worth saying 31 times.

Round up some male monkeys. Put them in a group together and give them plenty of time to sort out where they stand with each other—grudges, affiliative friendships. Give them enough time to form a dominance hierarchy, the sort of linear ranking in which number 3, for example, can pass his day throwing around his weight with numbers 4 and 5, ripping off their monkey chow, forcing them to relinquish the best spots to sit in, but numbers 1 and 2 still expect and receive from him the most obsequious brownnosing.

Hierarchy in place, it's time to do your experiment. Take that third-ranking monkey and give him some testosterone. None of this within-the-normal-range stuff. Inject a ton of it, way higher than what you normally see in rhesus monkeys, give him enough testosterone to grow antlers and a beard on every neuron in his brain. And, no surprise, when you check the behavioral data, he will probably be participating in more aggressive interactions than before.

So even though small fluctuations in the levels of the hormone don't seem to matter much, testosterone still causes aggression, right? Wrong. Check out number 3 more closely. Is he raining aggressive terror on everyone in the group, frothing with indiscriminate violence? Not at all. He's still judiciously kowtowing to numbers 1 and 2 but has become a total bastard to numbers 4 and 5. Testosterone isn't causing aggression, it's *exaggerating* the aggression that's already there.

Another example, just to show we're serious. There's a part of your brain that

probably has lots to do with aggression, a region called the amygdala. Sitting near it is the Grand Central Station of emotion-related activity in your brain, the hypothalamus. The amygdala communicates with the hypothalamus by way of a cable of neuronal connections called the stria terminalis. (No more jargon, I promise.) The amygdala influences aggression via that pathway, sending bursts of electrical excitation that ripple down the stria terminalis to the hypothalamus and put it in a pissy mood.

Once again, do your hormonal intervention: flood the area with testosterone. You can inject the hormone into the bloodstream, where it eventually makes its way to the amygdala. You can surgically microinject the stuff directly into the area. In a few years, you may even be able to construct animals with extra copies of the genes that direct testosterone synthesis, producing extra hormone that way. Six of one, half a dozen of the other. The key thing is what doesn't happen next. Does testosterone make waves of electrical excitation surge down the stria terminalis? Does it turn on that pathway? Not at all. If and only if the amygdala is already sending an excited volley down the stria terminalis, testosterone increases the rate of such activity by shortening the resting time between bouts. It's not turning on the pathway, it's increasing the volume of signaling if it is already turned on. It's not causing aggression, it's exaggerating the preexisting pattern of it, exaggerating the response to environmental triggers of aggression.

In every generation, it is the duty of behavioral biologists to try to teach this critical point, one that seems a maddening cliché once you get it. You take that hoary old dichotomy between nature and nurture, between intrinsic factors and extrinsic ones, between genes and environment, and regardless of which behavior and underlying biology you're studying, the dichotomy is a sham. No genes. No environment. Just the interaction between the two.

Do you want to know how important environment and experience are in understanding testosterone and aggression? Look back at how the effects of castration are discussed earlier. There were statements like "Remove the source of testosterone in species after species and levels of aggression typically plummet."

Not "Remove the source . . . and aggression always goes to zero." On the average it declines, but rarely to zero, and not at all in some individuals. And the more social experience an individual had being aggressive prior to castration, the more likely that behavior persists sans *cojones*. In the right context, social conditioning can more than make up for the complete absence of the hormone.

A case in point: the spotted hyena. These animals are fast becoming the darlings of endocrinologists, sociobiologists, gynecologists, and tabloid writers because of their wild sex reversal system. Females are more muscular and more aggressive than males, and are socially dominant to them, rare traits in the mammalian world. And get this: females secrete more of certain testosterone-related hormones than the males do, producing muscles, aggression, and masculinized private parts that make it supremely difficult to tell the sex of a hyena. So high androgen levels would seem, again, to cause aggression and social dominance. But that's not the whole answer.

High in the hills above the University of California at Berkeley is the world's largest colony of spotted hyenas, massive bone-crunching beasts who fight each other for the chance to have their ears scratched by Laurence Frank, the zoologist who brought them over as infants from Kenya. Various scientists are studying their sex reversal system. The female hyenas are bigger and more muscular than the males and have the same weirdo genitals and elevated androgen levels as their female cousins back in the savanna. Everything is just as it is in the wild—except the social system. As those hyenas grew up, there was a very significant delay in the time it took for the females to begin socially dominating the males, even though the females were stoked on androgens. They had to grow up without the established social system to learn from.

When people first realize that genes have a great deal to do with behavior—even subtle, complex, human behavior—they are often struck with an initial evangelical enthusiasm, placing a convert's faith in the genetic components of the story. This enthusiasm is typically reductive—because of physics envy, because reductionism is so impressive, because it would be so nice if there were a single gene (or hormone or neurotransmitter or part of the brain) responsible for everything. But even if you completely understood how genes regulate all the important physical factors involved in aggression—testosterone synthesis and secretion, the brain's testosterone receptors, the amygdala neurons and their levels of transmitters, the favorite color of the hypothalamus—you still wouldn't be able to predict levels of aggression accurately in a group of normal individuals.

This is no mere academic subject. We are a fine species with some potential, yet we are racked by sickening amounts of violence. Unless we are hermits, we feel the threat of it, often every day, and should our leaders push the button, we will all be lost in a final global violence. But as we try to understand this feature of our sociality, it is critical to remember the limits of the biology. Knowing the genome, the complete DNA sequence, of some suburban teenager is never going to tell us why that kid, in his after-school chess club, has developed a particularly aggressive style with his bishops. And it certainly isn't going to tell us much about the teenager in some inner city hellhole who has taken to mugging people. "Testosterone equals aggression" is inadequate for those who would offer a simple biological solution to the violent male. And "testosterone equals aggression" is certainly inadequate for those who would offer the simple excuse that boys will be boys. Violence is more complex than a single hormone, and it is supremely rare that any of our behaviors can be reduced to genetic destiny. This is science for the bleeding-heart liberal: the genetics of behavior is usually meaningless outside the context of the social factors and environment in which it occurs.

BY KAREN HOUPPERT

RISKY SEX

The new bedroom mistakes women are making

"I always use a condom," Susan, a 26-year-old California woman, declares. Without pausing for breath, she continues, "But there is that 10 percent of the time when I won't use one."

Always, except 10 percent of the time? "Well, with a stranger I would definitely use a condom," Susan explains. "But my rationale is different with someone I know well. Then I ask, 'When were you last tested for HIV, how well did you know the person you last had sex with, did you know her sexual history?'" If she gets the right answers, Susan says, "I think, I like this person. I trust him. He's not a sleaze." She might ask the guy to use a condom, but if he doesn't have one handy, she may very well have sex with him anyway.

Susan knows she's behaving unwisely. She grew up on the AIDS-conscious West Coast and attended the University of California at Santa Barbara, where freshman orientation included a video about safe sex and the infirmary dispensed free condoms. She knows all the facts about sex and sexually transmitted diseases (STDs). She knows she should use a condom every time she has intercourse. (And yeah, she should even use one for oral sex.) Like thousands of others, Susan knows when she's having risky sex; like thousands of others, she does it anyway.

The consequences can be disastrous. According to the Centers for Disease Control and Prevention (CDC), AIDS is the leading cause of death for 25- to 44-year-olds; health officials assume most of these people were infected in their teens and twenties. And AIDS is only one of numerous STDs now quietly thriving among young people. An estimated eight million Americans under the age of 25 contract STDs annually; in one major study, 25 percent of women who became sexually active in college acquired human papillomavirus (some strains of which are linked to cervical cancer) within one year.

Given these alarming statistics, health officials, psychologists and educators wonder why so many young people still don't use condoms. Women like Susan aren't uninformed. They've heard the rhetoric, they know the drill. What's going on in their minds?

"People don't behave logically when it comes to sex," says Brenda Chabon, Ph.D., a psychologist who works with young people at Montefiore Medical Center in New York City. She explains that health educators used to operate under the Health Belief Model, which says that if people understand they're at risk, they will change their behavior. But with sex, she says, "it just doesn't work that way." Sex, after all, is no purely physical act; it is mixed up with religion, power, fantasy, body image, self-esteem and other explosive issues.

For that reason, evaluating risk becomes an intensely subjective process. Whitney Wright, a safe-sex educator in New York City, has counseled everyone from homeless teens trading sex for drugs to bankers who think working at Morgan Stanley precludes becoming infected. In her experience, each person sets up a private, often arbitrary, risk level: "If I know him, it's OK;" "If he withdraws before ejaculation, it's OK;" "If it's only oral sex, it's OK."

To find out more about the newest bedroom mistakes people are making, *Glamour* went to health-behavior experts—and to young women and men themselves.

"I KNOW MY PARTNER"

Kim, a 27-year-old waitress, recently spent a few months working in Yellowstone National Park. It was summer, life was easy and the surroundings were beautifully unfamiliar. She and the other young employees hung out a lot together. In particular, there was this guy....

"It just sort of happened," Kim says, still trying to explain how she ended up on a long drive with a man she had only recently met, had mad, passionate sex and never used a condom. They did talk—briefly—about using one, but he hadn't come prepared and neither had she. Out in the middle of the woods, miles from a 7-Eleven, their only recourse would have been to forgo sex. Which seemed extreme, under the circumstances.

Kim worried about her recklessness afterward—but later that summer had unprotected sex with him again. And again. Though they had only recently met, she felt that she knew this man: He was from Minnesota, he was into nature, he was clean-cut and straightforward. For her, these were safety signs. "He seemed like a risk-free kind of person," she says. "Even though I know you can't tell by looking."

Luckily Kim went home at the end of the summer with nothing worse than a mild case of chlamydia—a common, easily cured STD. (Even luckier, the boyfriend she left behind and then rejoined back home never thought to ask how she'd acquired the chlamydia they both required treatment for.) She was upset to have contracted an STD—but realized that it could have been a deadlier one.

Kim may have made the most common mistake out there, say experts. While the twenty- to thirtysomething generation has internalized the message that casual sex (which they define as a one-night stand) can be risky unless a condom is used, they generally feel that sex with somebody they "know"—someone they've been dating or just someone they've talked to at length—is OK. They're familiar with the surgeon general's Know Your Partner campaign, but these days knowing your partner isn't enough. "People can have a lot of information about someone without having the right information," explains William Swann, Ph.D., a psychology professor at the University of Texas at Austin.

According to Swann, prospective lovers ask each other all kinds of questions but usually skip the key ones: How many partners do you have in one month? Have you had an STD? Have you had an HIV test? What were the results? The diligent few who do ask are quick to jump into bed once their questions are answered, which is unfortunate, since "they're far more confident about their ability to detect lies than they ought to be," says Swann. In fact, his subjects—hundreds of undergraduates over the years—can detect lies only about half the time. "They could flip a coin and be right just as often," Swann says. The main reason: Reassuring but irrelevant information—a person's political attitudes, taste in movies, hometown—throws off our decision-making.

In one study, Swann set up students in front of a video monitor. He told them there was a 50 percent chance that the woman on the tape had HIV. Then he ran the video. A pretty young woman talked for 60 seconds about her life—slumber parties in junior high, field hockey in college, work at a pet store. She said nothing about sex. "Just hearing her talk about all that normal stuff convinced people she was not HIV positive, when she was," Swann says, observing that in a mere 60 seconds students' perception of the likelihood she carried the AIDS virus dropped from 50 to 36 percent.

Other studies show that 96 percent of women and 92 percent of men lie about their past sexual history to current part-

ners. Says University of California at Los Angeles psychologist Mary-Jane Rotheram-Borus, "Ask yourself: Have you ever lied about how many partners you've had? Have you ever lied about whether you've always had safe sex? Have you ever lied about whether you really care for someone? Most people have."

"I've done it once—why not do it again?"

Jim, a 24-year-old Phoenix resident, has been with his girlfriend for about a year—and 90 percent of the time, he uses a condom when they have sex. "But every once in a while, it's not convenient," he says. "And once you do it without a condom, you think, Why not do it again?" Like Kim, who repeatedly had risky sex with her summer fling, Jim was inspired by one condomless encounter to have another. Still, he makes a clear distinction between a one-nighter and a relationship. He would certainly use a condom for the former; he *might* use one for the latter. "When you're in a long-term relationship, your guard slips," says Jim. "You think, This person couldn't hurt me."

That isn't true: Each time Jim had unprotected sex, his chances of catching an STD went up. Still, his thinking is typical, says Constance Pilkington, Ph.D., a psychology professor at the College of William and Mary in Williamsburg, Virginia, who studied 200 students at the college. "We found that people's feelings about the relationship affected whether or not they had safe sex," says Pilkington. Although most of her subjects and their lovers had never been tested for HIV, "people who loved their partners were less concerned about AIDS and more likely to have sex without a condom than those in a more superficial relationship."

"Love means never having to wear a condom"

If people think of a condom as a protective measure appropriate for the cautious early stages of a relationship, then suspending condom use often serves as a signal that the relationship is moving to a new level. In this late-nineties thinking, sex without a condom is like sex without emotional barriers—shorthand for "I trust you. This is something special."

This attitude displays wishful thinking about monogamy, says Rotheram-Borus. Many women, she believes, are still raised to think that the man they are sleeping with is the man they will marry is the man

they will be with for the rest of their lives. Condoms violate that myth by implying that a particular man is neither a woman's first lover nor her last—and that he too has had previous partners she must be protected from. Of course, "if you're young and in a relationship, there's a very good chance that this *won't* be the one for the rest of your life," notes Rotheram-Borus. Still, we like to believe we're more monogamous than we are; condoms tell us something about ourselves we'd rather not know.

"Traditionally men control condom use, and women have to be assertive about insisting that men use one," adds Rotheram-Borus. "The reason women often don't insist is their reluctance to admit that the relationship may not last."

"Sex is rebellious without a condom"

"About two years ago," says Lisa, a 25-year-old massage therapist in Los Angeles, "I went through a stage where I would sometimes sleep with guys and not use a condom." Here, Lisa laughs self-consciously and corrects herself. "Where I never used a condom."

At the time, Lisa was working for crummy wages and desperately missing the college social scene. It was hard to meet people, work went slowly, life sucked. "I was looking for love—or I don't know what—and going with the moment," she says. The "moment" brought five guys her way in a short time, and Lisa slept with all of them. She didn't use a condom once.

After each encounter, Lisa worried for several months, then got tested for HIV. Each time, her test came back negative. And each time, she would vow to be more careful. "Looking back, I see that I wanted the man to say, 'Yeah, you're beautiful, you're smart, you count,' " she says. "I also wanted to escape from my life." Lisa wanted to be transported out of her miserable self for a while, to live with glamorous recklessness. "Asking him to use a condom didn't fit in with that," she says.

Deborah, 32, an actor in Miami, has also been drawn to the rebellious aspects of sex. In her twenties, Deborah had a series of boyfriends. She never asked one to use a condom—but not because she was shy or reserved. Outgoing and chatty, she is known among her friends as frank in the extreme, one of those oh-my-god-what-have-you-done-to-your-hair types. Deborah was never reticent about her opinions. Except when it came to sex.

"I kept on having sex and never getting pregnant, so I thought I could keep doing that," she explains. "Partly, I just hated initiating that awkward conversation about condoms." Deborah, who is talking to me on the phone, pauses to listen to her boyfriend in the background. "He wants to know why," she says. She thinks about it, then explains how her Catholic upbringing complicates things. "For Catholics, there's something rebellious about having sex when you're not married," she says. Her unprotected encounters were titillating, an in-your-face affront both to conservative religious mores and, perhaps, more modern politically correct always-use-a-condom naysayers. Sex was appealing as a way to rebel, and, says Deborah, "there's nothing rebellious about stopping midway to put on a condom."

Deborah's thinking dovetails with our culture's celebration of sacrificial love. From *Romeo and Juliet* to *The Scarlet Letter* to *The English Patient*, our romantic history is full of self-sacrificing heroes (and even more heroines) who prove their love by taking risks. But there is a modern reality check on such dreamy idealization of love: At some point, the risk taker may get an STD. The challenge for health educators is to change people's behavior *before* a disease enlightens them.

Toward the end of Deborah's 10-year risky-sex spree she got genital warts. "These can be removed," the doctor told her. "But you can get all kinds of things that are not so easily treated. Debilitating, life-threatening diseases."

Today, Deborah says, "I use condoms all the time"—well, all the time except when she's having her period because then the threat of pregnancy, though not disease, is reduced. But listening to our conversation, Deborah's boyfriend corrects her. "You don't use condoms, I do," he says. "He's right," Deborah concedes. "Even now, if I were with someone who didn't insist on condoms, I'd probably still be having unprotected sex. It's stupid, I know, but there's a thrill in it."

Deborah's boyfriend disagrees. "I've worked as a mortician," he says. "I've seen what taking risks can do to people."

Karen Houppert is an award-winning writer for The Village Voice. *She is at work on a book about menstruation.*

1 9 9 6

A I D S

Crushing HIV

AFTER MANY FRUSTRATING years, AIDS researchers finally have reason to believe that the human immunodeficiency virus (HIV) can be controlled. Several studies reported in 1996 found that a combination of drugs could sharply curtail the amount of virus in the bloodstream—in many cases reducing it to undetectable levels. Since the virus count is the best predictor of how the disease will progress, it now seems that aggressive drug therapy may provide a powerful weapon against AIDS.

The recent successes depend on the addition of a new class of drugs, called protease inhibitors, to the anti-HIV arsenal. The older antiviral drugs—such as AZT and 3TC—block reverse transcriptase, an enzyme the virus needs to copy its genetic material into a host cell's DNA. Protease inhibitors, in contrast, block an enzyme that helps assemble the virus at a later stage in its life cycle. Because that protease enzyme is smaller and thus less prone to mutations that might make it drug-resistant, and because the protease inhibitors themselves are more readily absorbed into an HIV-infected cell, they may be more effective at shutting down viral replication.

David Ho, a virologist at the Aaron Diamond AIDS Research Center in New York City, is conducting several trials of drug combinations. Last summer, he reported results from a trial involving nine men who received three drugs— a protease inhibitor, AZT, and 3TC—within 90 days of being infected with HIV. At that stage of infection, Ho explains, the diversity of the virus is relatively low, thus limiting the possibility of drug-resistant mutants. Within a few months of treatment, HIV could not be detected in the men's blood. Even after a year of treatment no trace of it could be found.

"The virus has to mutate at many positions simultaneously if it is to resist the three drugs we're giving," says Ho. "And it finds that very difficult to do."

Even in much more advanced cases of infection, drug combinations that include a protease inhibitor have worked well. This past year, in a study conducted at four medical centers around the country, New York University's Roy Gulick and his colleagues gave three drugs to 97 patients who had already taken AZT, on average for over two years. These patients—a diverse mix of ages, races, and sexes—had virus levels averaging 41,000 copies per milliliter of blood. Yet after another year of treatment with AZT, now supplemented with 3TC and a protease inhibitor, some 80 percent of the patients showed no trace of virus at all. Meanwhile, their counts of CD4 T cells—the virus's main target—had risen dramatically. Equally promising results were reported in 1996 from a study of 1,090 patients with advanced AIDS: those who added a protease inhibitor to their drug regimen had a 50 percent lower mortality rate than those receiving a placebo.

Both Ho and Gulick plan to sample

A daily dose of these 14 pills can shut down HIV replication.

TOP: Courtesy InterScience; BOTTOM: map by Nigel Holmes

THE PANDEMIC CONTINUES

AIDS has killed more than 300,000 Americans, and some 750,000 are currently infected with HIV, the virus that causes AIDS. In the first years of the epidemic, deaths were concentrated among gay and bisexual men. But over the past ten years, the incidence of the disease has surged among women— from 6 percent of reported cases in 1985 to 19 percent in 1995. In about half these cases the virus was contracted through heterosexual sex. The other half were infected through intravenous drug use. The spread has been most dramatic among African-American women, who now make up more than half of American women with AIDS.

Despite this alarming trend, the rate of new HIV infections in the United States has declined from roughly 80,000 a year in the late 1980s to somewhere between 60,000 and 70,000 in 1995, largely because of programs that promote safe sex among gays. The epidemic appears to have begun stabilizing here, as it has in Europe and Australia. Elsewhere, though, the virus is still spreading rapidly. Since the epidemic's onset, there have been more than 27 million estimated cases of HIV infection worldwide and some 4 to 5 million deaths—and about 14 million of those cases have been in sub-Saharan Africa, where the rate of new infections is still rising. In Asia the disease is spreading as fast or faster. India, with a population of 950 million, has 3.5 million cases of HIV infection—the largest number of any Asian country.

Thus although recent drug trials in the United States offer hope for the HIV-infected, the disease is most prevalent in countries too poor to afford even the most basic medical treatment. Those countries need condoms and needle-exchange programs more

the lymph nodes of patients whose blood appears to be virus-free. If the lymph nodes show no signs of the virus, the researchers and the patient will face the difficult question of whether to stop drug treatment. Patients cannot be considered free of the disease until all virus-infected cells throughout the body die. How long that might take, says Ho, is not known. It is not yet clear, for instance, whether the new drug combinations can reach such areas as the brain, where the virus is tucked away.

Moreover, even if the drugs are as effective as they

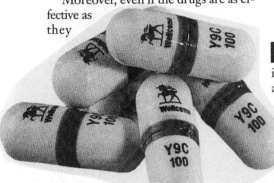

seem, several compelling problems remain. First, triple-drug therapy is so expensive—up to $15,000 or more a year—that it will probably remain unavailable to many uninsured patients in this country, let alone to patients in the poor countries of Africa and Asia that have been hard hit by AIDS. Second, despite the drugs' comparatively mild side effects, patients must have tremendous discipline to adhere to the treatment regimen—which ranges from 14 to 20 pills a day. Third, the possibility remains that HIV mutants will emerge that are resistant even to drug combinations.

Still, the prospects for treating HIV-infected patients are better than ever before. Just as combinations of drugs have worked against diseases like tuberculosis and cancer, triple-drug therapy may work for HIV, especially if treatment begins soon after infection. "It's like treating breast cancer," Ho speculates. "If you pick it up early, your chances of a complete remission are very high." Gulick is more cautious. "You hear a lot of talk these days about eradicating the virus from the body," he says. "If anyone had mentioned that idea two years ago, they would have been laughed out of the room. It is interesting to think we can even begin to imagine that approach. But until we're there, managing the disease as a chronic illness is pretty acceptable."

—*Sarah Richardson*

The Second Key

FOR A DECADE, AIDS researchers have known one thing about how the virus infects human immune cells: it binds to a receptor molecule called CD4 on the cell surface. But they've also known that CD4 is not enough. Even if an animal has been engineered to produce human CD4 on its immune cells, those cells cannot be infected with HIV. Last May, biochemist Ed Berger of the National Institutes of Health and his colleagues announced that they had finally succeeded—where many before them had failed—in identifying an elusive "coreceptor" that makes certain human cells peculiarly vulnerable to HIV. Their finding unleashed a storm of papers that not only help clarify our understanding of AIDS but also may lead to new treatments for the disease.

Berger's method was straightforward: he and his colleagues added hundreds of different genetic sequences, one by one, to nonhuman cells that had been engineered to express human CD4, until they finally found one genetic sequence that made the cells susceptible to HIV. That

sequence encoded the coreceptor, which Berger has dubbed fusin—and which is found along with CD4 on the surface of human T cells. One theory is that binding to CD4 brings the virus into the right position to interact with a nearby molecule of fusin. That interaction may change the shape of HIV's protein coat so that the virus can fuse with the cell membrane and funnel its genes into the cell.

Of course, that role cannot be fusin's original purpose in life—quite the opposite. Fusin, Berger's group found, belongs to a large family of cell-surface receptors whose purpose is to glom on to chemokines: molecular SOS signals with which immune cells rally themselves to the site of an infection. Within weeks of Berger's report, a spate of papers had appeared identifying at least four other chemokine receptors through which HIV can gain entry into a CD4-bearing cell. Why those receptors in particular? No one knows for sure. But chemokine receptors happen to be made of proteins that dive in and out of the cell membrane several times—which may make them ideal

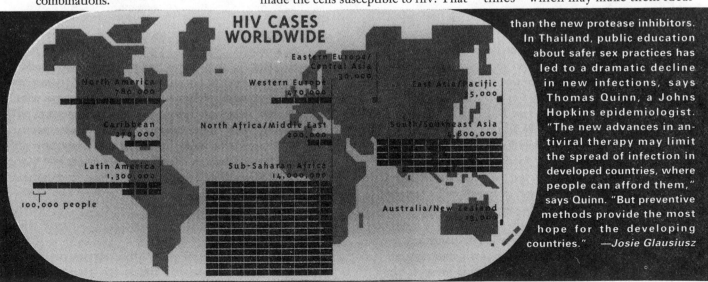

HIV CASES WORLDWIDE

North America 780,000

Caribbean 270,000

Latin America 1,300,000

Eastern Europe/Central Asia 30,000

Western Europe 470,000

North Africa/Middle East 200,000

Sub-Saharan Africa 14,000,000

East Asia/Pacific 55,000

South/Southeast Asia 4,800,000

Australia/New Zealand 13,000

100,000 people

than the new protease inhibitors. In Thailand, public education about safer sex practices has led to a dramatic decline in new infections, says Thomas Quinn, a Johns Hopkins epidemiologist. "The new advances in antiviral therapy may limit the spread of infection in developed countries, where people can afford them," says Quinn. "But preventive methods provide the most hope for the developing countries." —*Josie Glausiusz*

docking sites for a virus that must wallow in a cell's membrane in order to infect it.

In any case, the discovery that chemokine receptors are also HIV coreceptors helps us make sense of some earlier, puzzling findings. The gist of those findings was that some chemokines seem to inhibit the spread of virus in T cells. As a result of Berger's discovery, researchers now suspect that chemokines somehow shut the door on HIV, perhaps by occupying the coreceptor or by somehow reducing its availability in some other way.

Among the first cells that HIV typically invades are macrophages, the scavenger cells that patrol body tissues looking for infection. Macrophages don't carry fusin. On them the virus exploits a different chemokine receptor, called CKR-5, which was identified this past year by Dan Littman of the Howard Hughes Medical Institute at New York University and his colleagues. Littman speculates that the virus must first infect macrophages, even though T cells are its ultimate host, because only infected macrophages can "activate" T cells, turning on their internal

protein factories—which HIV needs to churn out more HIV. Whether or not that is true, the virus seems to have the ability to switch its focus from one coreceptor to another, from CKR-5 to fusin, as the infection progresses.

That might make HIV sound more invincibly cunning than ever. But it also suggests a new weakness that researchers may be able to exploit. Three other studies published in 1996 found that people with defective CKR-5 receptors are resistant to HIV infection. Moreover, the de-

fect doesn't seem to harm their health in other ways. With the right small-molecule drug that would bind to one of its nooks or crannies, it might be possible to disable the receptor—and thus erect a barrier to the progress of HIV infection.

And with the recognition of the importance of chemokine receptors, AIDS researchers may have broken through a barrier of their own. "I've never seen anything like this," says Berger, whose paper last May started it all. "We opened up the floodgates." —*Sarah Richardson*

AN ANCIENT IMMUNITY This past year will be remembered as a watershed year for AIDS research. Among the breakthroughs was the finding, in August, that a mutation in the CKR-5 gene, which encodes the receptor that the virus uses as a doorway into a cell, provided resistance to HIV infection. Then, in September, the surprising extent of that resistance was documented by population geneticist Stephen O'Brien and his

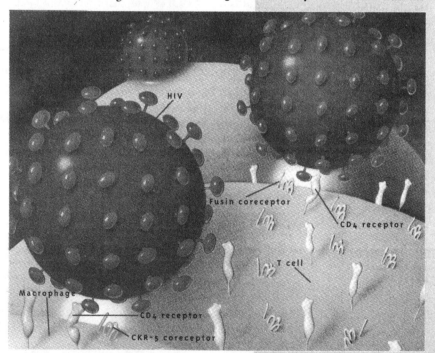

HIV needs more than the CD4 receptor to slip into immune cells. When it enters the body, the virus uses CD4 and CKR-5 receptors to invade scavenging cells called macrophages. But as the disease progresses, HIV switches and uses CD4 and fusin receptors to infect T cells—the virus's ultimate host.

colleagues at the National Cancer Institute, who studied 1,955 people at high risk for contracting the virus.

Roughly 1 percent of the study group carried two copies of the mutated CKR-5 gene, says O'Brien—and they had all resisted infection despite multiple exposures to HIV. A much larger percentage—about 14 percent—

carried one mutated CKR-5 gene. Although these people could and did become infected with HIV, the progression from asymptomatic infection to AIDS was likely to take two to three years longer in them than in a person with two normal copies of CKR-5.

The differences in vulnerability have to do with the number of available doorways into an immune cell, O'Brien explains. People with one mutated CKR-5 gene have half as many doorways for HIV as people with two normal genes, so the virus spreads more slowly in them. People with mutations in both copies of the gene are completely lacking in the doorways that HIV prefers, so the virus can't infect enough cells to establish itself in the body.

Surprisingly, Caucasians were nearly ten times as likely to carry the beneficial mutation as African Americans. Roughly 20 percent of the Caucasians in the study group carried one copy of the gene—making it more common, O'Brien notes, than red hair. O'Brien suspects that it cropped up in the Caucasian lineage after the common ancestor of Africans and Caucasians migrated out of Africa around 150,000 to 200,000 years ago. But a random mutation, he adds, wouldn't have risen to such a high frequency in the population unless it had also provided some benefit long before the current AIDS epidemic. That benefit, O'Brien suspects, may have been protection against some ancient scourge. "An AIDS epidemic before historic times might have wiped out large numbers of Caucasians," he says. "Or the cause might have been some other rather highly pathogenic microbe that also used the CKR-5 receptor as an entry point." —*Sarah Richardson*

Are Women the Weaker Sex?

They live longer than men but suffer more from chronic, debilitating illnesses

Winifred Conkling

Winifred Conkling writes on health and consumer issues and is a regular contributor to AMERICAN HEALTH.

Women and men are not created equal. As the most obvious example, Mother Nature favors her own sex when it comes to longevity, with women living about seven years—or 10%—longer than men.

Still, men actually get a head start in the battle of the sexes, since male embryos outnumber female embryos by 115 to 100. Higher rates of miscarriage and stillbirths of males reduce this advantage, so they in fact outnumber females by only 105 to 100 at birth. A higher death rate among infant boys during the first six months of life erodes the male edge even further.

By about age 30, women have caught up with men numerically, and they then leave men in the dust, with three women alive for every man by age 85.

But here's the paradox: While women live longer than men, they're generally sicker. Men tend to die from rapidly fatal health problems such as heart attacks, accidents, suicides and homicides. Women, on the other hand, tend to develop lingering illnesses that often inflict years of discomfort—not to mention higher medical bills.

Women spend twice as much money on health care as men do. They also consult doctors more frequently, take more drugs, spend more days in hospitals and have more operations. They also take more sick time off from work. Why? The chief causes seem to be genes, hormones and interactions of the two.

The chronic illnesses common in women tend to be inherited. Female hormones, particularly estrogen, added to that genetic susceptibility seem to tip the balance—a woman who inherits a defective gene develops the illness, while a brother with the same gene remains healthy.

Estrogen also seems to protect women against some illnesses. Most notably, estrogen helps keep heart disease at bay until well into menopause, which may explain why women live longer than men. "There's a saying, 'Diamonds aren't a girl's best friend—estrogen is,'" says immunologist Denise Faustman, director of the immunobiology labs at Massachusetts General Hospital in Boston. "Estrogen is probably the best drug out there for preventing heart disease, but it may be the worst when it comes to certain types of autoimmune disease."

Autoimmune diseases. Evidence that genes interact with estrogen to cause illness seems especially persuasive when it comes to autoimmune diseases, a category encompassing some 80 distinct health problems. In all of them, the immune system misfires to attack the body's own tissues and organs as if they were foreign invaders.

Examples include rheumatoid arthritis, multiple sclerosis, scleroderma, and thyroid disorders such as Graves' disease and Hashimoto's thyroiditis. (Some experts also include migraine headaches in the list because they, like autoimmune disorders, tend to cluster in individuals and in families, and because migraines often accompany autoimmune problems.)

Autoimmune diseases usually affect both sexes, but women develop them much more often. On average, three of four people with autoimmune disease are women, though the female/male ratio varies from disease to disease (see table, "Women, Men and Illness").

"Nobody knows why these diseases affect women more than men, but we do know there is a fundamental problem with the immune system of women," says Dr. Robert Lahita, chief of rheumatology at St. Luke's–Roosevelt Hospital in New York City. He and other experts believe estrogen makes a woman's immune system so sensitive that it attacks the body's own tissues as well as genuine invaders. "Estrogen appears to rev up women's immune systems periodically," says Lahita.

Supporting the estrogen-trigger theory is the way some autoimmune diseases ebb and flow along with levels of the hormone. When estrogen surges at puberty, for example, the migraine headache rate for females surpasses the rate for males; it continues increasing into a woman's 30s and 40s and then drops suddenly when estrogen levels fall at menopause.

With other autoimmune diseases, the estrogen connection isn't so obvious. Graves' disease, for example, usually shows up after menopause, when estrogen levels fall. Rheumatoid arthritis is doubly contradictory: Rates increase steadily over time, becoming highest in the seventh or eighth decade, well after estrogen levels have plummeted, but the disease often goes into temporary remission during pregnancy, when estrogen levels rise.

"Sex hormones definitely are very important, but they don't tell the entire story," says Dr. J. Lee Nelson, a rheumatologist at the University of Washington in Seattle. "If sex hormones caused autoimmune disease, you'd assume that taking postmenopausal estrogen would make the situation worse, and it doesn't." A person's genetic makeup, it now appears, also plays a role.

"The tendency to develop these diseases runs in families, but not necessarily the specific diseases themselves," notes Dr. Frank Arnett, a rheumatologist at the University of Texas Health Science Center in Houston. "One family member may have lupus, while another has rheumatoid arthritis or thyroid disease."

Arnett says several genes seem to be responsible for causing any one autoimmune disease. Studies of families with a history of these diseases suggest why men are less susceptible. "Compared with women, it looks as if men have to inherit more genes—from both parents—to develop an autoimmune disease," says Arnett.

Depression. Women are more likely than men to suffer from major depression and experience sadness, panic disorders and seasonal affective disorder. Could this be true merely because women are more willing to seek professional help than men? Not according to Dr. Myrna Weissman, a depression researcher at Columbia University's New York State Psychiatric Institute who has studied the prevalence of depression in 10 countries. In every culture studied, she says, women have at least twice men's rate of depression. In the U.S., one out of eight women will experience at least one episode of clinical depression in her lifetime, compared with one in sixteen men. "We know it's a real phenomenon, and it's a very consistent finding across cultures," Weissman says. The explanation is thought to lie in the different ways men's and women's brains function.

Who Should

When 38-year-old Margi Mannix Creamer's hacking chest cold got worse recently, she went to a doctor she hadn't seen in more than 20 years. Creamer never thought to call the obstetrician/gynecologist she'd seen since reaching adulthood. She assumed he knew nothing about colds. Not that the Sandy Spring, Md., journalist wouldn't prefer one-stop health care. "If I could get my Pap smear and prescriptions for my cold at the same time," she says, "it would be really convenient."

What type of doctors *are* best qualified to provide the health care that Creamer and many other women want? Ob/gyn's, family practitioners and internists are all vying for the job, thanks to the rapid growth of managed care.

To control costs, managed-care plans such as HMO's employ primary-care physicians as "gatekeepers" who refer patients to specialists only when necessary. In most plans, ob/gyn's are considered specialists to be seen only by referral.

When Jenny Doane, 48, of Baldwinsville, N.Y., switched jobs two years ago, she found that her new health plan prevented her from seeing an ob/gyn without a referral from her gatekeeper. Doane, whose mother died of ovarian cancer, discussed her unusually heavy menstrual bleeding with an internist at her HMO, but he didn't examine her. Instead he sent her home with a video about hormone replacement therapy and a sample package of estrogen tablets.

"The heck with this," Doane recalls thinking. "I'll pay full price and go back to my old ob/gyn." During an exam, her ob/gyn discovered "ovarian cysts as big as softballs," says Doane, who subsequently had a hysterectomy.

Now a New York State law guarantees access to ob/gyn's for all women in managed-care plans, regardless of whether they have a previous gynecological condition. The law allows women at least two ob/gyn visits a year without a referral from an internist or a family physician.

In the past two years, three of the four states with the highest proportion of residents in HMO's—California (38%), Maryland (36%) and Oregon (38%)—have also made it easier for women to obtain the services of an ob/gyn. All told, 13 states have now passed laws or resolutions allowing women greater access to ob/gyn's (see table at right).

But choosing an ob/gyn as a primary-care physician doesn't guarantee good medical care. In California, one HMO has reversed its policy of letting ob/gyn's provide primary care out of concern over quality. Even some ob/gyn's say their colleagues are stretching their stethoscopes too far by calling themselves primary-care doctors.

"Most ob/gyn's are not particularly well trained in primary care and not particularly focused on it," says Dr. Elizabeth Buechler, director of ob/gyn for the health centers division of the Harvard Pilgrim Health Plan, a Massachusetts HMO. "I don't think they're doing a great service to women, since they often provide only primary reproductive care."

Dr. Mark Glasser, chief of ob/gyn at the Kaiser Permanente Medical Center in San Rafael, Calif., admits he

Care for Women?   By Rita Rubin

State Actions on Women's Health Care

	Calif.	Conn.	Del.	Fla.	Ga.	Md.	Miss.	N.Y.	N.C.	Oreg.	Utah	Va.	Wash.
In some circumstances, women no longer need prior authorization from a gatekeeper to see an ob/gyn.		•				•		•	•	•	•		•
Women's health exams can be performed by ob/gyn's, even if they're not designated as primary-care providers.		•				•		•	•	•	•		•
All women's health care providers (including ob/gyn's and midwives) can do health exams, even if they're not designated as primary-care providers.		•						•²	•	•			•
Women have access to ob/gyn's for pregnancy care and other specified conditions.		•						•	•	•			•
Women have access to all women's health care providers for pregnancy care and other specified conditions.		•							•	•			•
Ob/gyn's can be designated as primary-care providers if they meet specified conditions.	•	•¹	•				•						•³
Nonphysician women's health care providers can be primary-care providers under specified conditions.										•			
The law applies to all general health insurance organizations and/or managed-care plans.	•	•	•				•				•		•
The law applies only to HMO's.								•				•	
Legislatures passed resolutions pertaining to women's health care providers.			•		•							•	

(1) Connecticut says insurance plans "may," not "shall," designate ob/gyn's as primary-care providers. (2) Nonphysician providers must work with an ob/gyn. The law applies to all "obstetrician/gynecologist services." (3) The law does not formally designate ob/gyn's as primary-care providers, but the state medical association defines ob/gyn's as such, and the law gives women wide access.

TABLE RESEARCHED BY JIM FISCUS

doesn't have time to read journals outside his specialty. He routinely tests patients' cholesterol levels, takes their blood pressure and assesses certain other body functions, and he's happy to refill a prescription for a patient's regular medication. But he lets internists adjust the dose if necessary. Glasser says he doesn't understand ob/gyn's who want to be primary-care doctors. "You are being paid to be female reproductive surgeons," he tells colleagues. "That's what you did a four-year residency for."

In the past, residents in ob/gyn devoted one year to general medicine if they wished. Starting last January, they must also complete a four-month rotation in internal medicine or family practice, one month in emergency medicine and at least one month in geriatric medicine.

Some experts insist that the best practitioner for women is neither an ob/gyn nor a generalist. Instead, they say, what's needed is an entirely new class of physicians who specialize in women's health.

"The system we have doesn't work," argues San Francisco psychiatrist Karen Johnson, cofounder of the Women's Health Specialty Project, which is dedicated to creating a primary-care residency program in women's health. Dr. Johnson's appeal has won support from such organizations as American Medical Women's Association and the Ms. Foundation. But opponents say a women's health specialty would ghettoize women's health care.

"*All* physicians ought to be trained to deal with women's health issues," says Dr. Sally Guttmacher, chairwoman-elect of the Public Health Association of New York City. "Physicians should all be referring women for mammograms and doing manual breast exams. If you create a specialty for women's health, you're letting all other doctors off the hook when it comes to caring for women."

For now, women who'd like one doctor to take care of all their health needs should examine their priorities. Healthy, premenopausal women may find an ob/gyn most satisfactory. Postmenopausal women, especially those with a chronic condition such as heart disease, may want a family practitioner or an internist. In either case, having a doctor with cross training in a different specialty is a real plus. ●

Rita Rubin examined women's health issues as a media fellow with the Kaiser Family Foundation (not affiliated with Kaiser-Permanente).

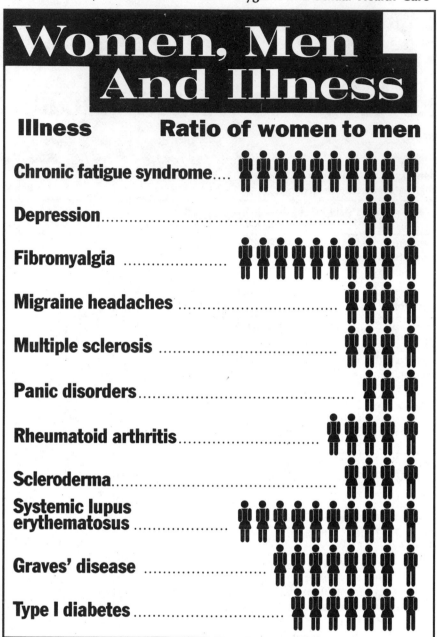

Women, Men And Illness

Illness	Ratio of women to men
Chronic fatigue syndrome	
Depression	
Fibromyalgia	
Migraine headaches	
Multiple sclerosis	
Panic disorders	
Rheumatoid arthritis	
Scleroderma	
Systemic lupus erythematosus	
Graves' disease	
Type I diabetes	

Psychiatrist Mark George of the Medical University of South Carolina in Charleston has used positron-emission tomography (PET) scans to look at how blood flows in the brain when a person is blue. Before the test, subjects are asked to recall a sad event and to rate their feelings on a sadness scale. The scans showed that men and women reporting the same level of sadness had radically different levels of brain activity.

"When we looked at the blood flow changes, the women had much more profound activity in the front of the brain—about eight times more blood flow to the area than in men," says George. This is the brain region affected during episodes of clinical depression. George speculates that intense activation of this area over time sets the stage for clinical depression. Interestingly, similar PET scan studies involving anger, anxiety and happiness failed to find significant gender differences in brain activity.

Of course, the PET studies assume the sexes perceive sadness equally—that a man rating his sadness as a "9," for example, feels as anguished as a woman reporting the same value. But that may not be the case. "If it's true that women are more in touch with their feelings," says Dr. Joan Zilbach, a psychoanalyst in Brookline, Mass., "then a woman describing herself as 'very sad' may be affected much more deeply than a 'very sad' man. So it's not surprising that you'd see a difference in blood flow to the brain."

Clearly, men and women process emotions differently. "Women tell you they feel sad, but men tell you they have a bellyache," says Zilbach.

The way girls are raised could also make them more vulnerable to emotional problems. Dr. Diane Ruble, a psychologist at New York University, contends that girls, who are usually more closely watched and protected than boys, are less likely to develop independence, and with it, self-esteem. She also notes that even before puberty, girls are somewhat more vulnerable to a negative self-image that can lead to depression, suggesting that hormonal changes alone cannot account for the gender disparity.

**ystery illnesses**. Women are especially prone to two controversial conditions, fibromyalgia and chronic fatigue syndrome (CFS). There is strong disagreement over whether they're physical disorders (caused by viruses or glitches in the immune system) or are psychological in origin.

Fibromyalgia is a condition involving chronic muscle and joint pain. Other symptoms include sleep disturbances, depression, anxiety, headaches and bowel problems. The main symptom of CFS is prolonged, debilitating exhaustion. As defined by the Centers for Disease Control and Prevention, the illness may also include aching muscles and joints, headaches, sore throat, sleep disturbances and painful lymph nodes. Both conditions together affect 3 million to 6 million Americans and afflict up to nine women for every man.

"Fibromyalgia and CFS are probably sister illnesses, or they may be overlapping variations of the same illness," says Dr. Jack Waxman, director of rheumatology training at the Ochsner Clinic and Foundation Hospital in New Orleans. "There is no known cause for them, but they probably result from the body's abnormal response to stress."

Under stress, the brain produces hormones, which can be measured in the spinal fluid. Studies have shown that fibromyalgia patients have three times the normal level of these stress-related substances. "This chemical imbalance," says Waxman, "appears to cause their symptoms."

Since both illnesses seem to be stress related, they are dismissed by some physicians as psychosomatic—modern equivalents of 19th century hysteria. "Patients want to think their illness is entirely a physical problem, and some doctors want to think it's all in their minds," says Waxman. "But this is an artificial distinction, since the mind and body obviously interact. These diseases are not all in women's heads. They're also in women's spinal fluid and brain chemicals."

Women may be more susceptible than men to CFS and fibromyalgia simply because they're under more stress. According to CFS researcher Dr. Peter Manu, an internist at the Albert Einstein College of Medicine in New York City, "Women with one of these illnesses is often under tremendous stress to fulfill what she sees as her obligations to her family, her community and her employer."

"What we don't know about women's health is appalling," says Phyllis Greenberger, executive director of the Society for the Advancement of Women's Health Research. "There is clearly a need for more research into why women come down with chronic illnesses and what can be done about it."

Horizontal Fitness

HOW TO KEEP YOUR SEX DRIVE HUMMING

David Hochman

I ONCE MET a rugby player from Edinburgh who insisted that the secret to a superior sex life was a daily regimen of brewer's-yeast milkshakes, saline nasal washes, and afternoon fixes of Macallan's single-malt scotch. I thought he was feeding me a load of haggis until he showed me pictures of his wife—and their seven kids.

Instinct tells me this particular gent (he went about six-foot-four, 240 pounds) could knock back kerosene cocktails all day and still be the randiest man in all of Scotland. Think how wonderful it would be, though, if there were a sure-fire formula for being a sure-fire lover.

As of yet, sad to report, no such elixir exists. But that's not to say you can't soup up your sexual fitness. Exercising regularly, eating a diet high in protein and fiber and low in fat, quitting smoking, drinking in moderation, and maintaining a positive mental outlook not only can make you live longer, look better, and feel more self-confident but can also help you have a richer, more satisfying sex life. "Enjoying sex and having a capacity to perform well is undoubtedly linked to a person's well-being and physical health," says Dr. John Bancroft, the director of the famed Kinsey Institute for sexual research. How do you whip yourself into peak sexual condition? Try taking this class in truly *physical* ed.

SWEAT REWARDS

When it comes to exercise, the bottom line is that people who work out regularly have better sex lives and remain sexually active longer than those who don't. The research is rock-solid. In 1990, physicians and psychologists at the University of California at San Diego followed 78 sedentary men through a nine-month exercise regimen (nothing fancy, just jogging, stationary bicycling, and some light calisthenics) and asked them to keep detailed journals of their sexual activity. The results? The exercisers experienced an average of 20 percent more deep kissing, 26 percent more orgasms, a 50 percent increase in masturbation (to once every 10 days), and a 30 percent increase in intercourse (to three times a week) over what they had before they started working out. For two of the study's participants, the regimen apparently worked too well: They had extramarital affairs.

If that's not enough to get you to a gym, consider the findings of Phillip Whitten, Ph.D., a behavioral scientist at Bentley College in Waltham, Massachusetts. Whitten examined the sex lives of 160 competitive swimmers between the ages of 40 and 80. Almost all of these superfit adult athletes reported having sex lives more like those of people 20 years younger. Even those in their 60s were doing the deed an average of 6.7 times a month.

"Working out is simply great for sex," says Linda De Villers, Ph.D., an adjunct psychology professor at Pepperdine University in Malibu, California. A few years back, De Villers found that 40 percent of the 8,000 women she polled experienced an increase in their sexual arousal after they began a steady exercise program, and nearly 90 percent said they felt more "sexually confident." Among the physiological effects exercise has on sex: Brain-wave activity changes, making you feel more energized and mentally focused; body temperature rises, replicating one of the main sensations associated with arousal; and you experience a feeling of well-being that can linger for hours. "Probably the best thing to do is to exercise, take a quick shower, and hop in the sack while you're still hot," De Villers advises.

Just because a little exercise is good, though, don't think a lot will turn you into Wilt Chamberlain. Studies have shown that continuous, exhausting exercise causes testosterone and libido levels to wither. How much is too much? "Forty miles or more of running a week, and you're bound to have a decreased capacity for sex," says Bancroft. "Moderation is vital."

There is one exercise you can't overdo: flexing your pubococcygeus (PC) muscles. Strengthening the PCs, the muscles you use to stop your urine stream, can stave off premature ejaculation and build stronger erections. Flex your PCs anywhere—at work, sitting in traffic, or while watching TV. "Do at least 10 in a row when you do them," says Dr. E. Douglas Whitehead, an associate clinical professor of urology at Mount Sinai School of Medicine in New York City.

INCREDIBLE EDIBLES

The heart isn't the only organ that gets clogged arteries. Arterial blockage in the penis is a leading cause of impotence, affecting millions of men. (Because the arteries of the penis

From *Men's Journal*, August 1996, pp. 87-89. © 1996 by Men's Journal Company, L.P. Reprinted by permission.

tend to clog earlier than the arteries of the heart, impotence due to artery damage can be an early sign of heart trouble.) What can you do to keep your "other" arteries clean? The same thing heart patients do: Eat a low-fat, low-cholesterol diet.

Dr. Morton Walker, the author of *Sexual Nutrition*, outlines what he calls "a sex menu." For breakfast he recommends poached eggs (protein strengthens penile tissue) and fresh-squeezed orange juice (which contains ascorbic acid, an anti-clogging agent). For lunch have tuna (rich in protein as well as essential fatty acids and fish oils, which also have an anti-clogging effect). Finish your midday meal with papaya (it contains the artery-cleaning mineral bromelain). Snack on Brazil nuts between meals (they're high in zinc, which is needed for the synthesis of dihydroxytestosterone, the active enzyme of testosterone). For dinner have chicken almondine (both chicken and almonds are loaded with phosphorus, which plays a part in the formation of nucleoproteins, responsible for cell division and reproduction).

Into aphrodisiacs? Bad news. "There's no such thing as an aphrodisiac with scientific value," says George Armelagos, Ph.D., an anthropologist at Emory University in Atlanta who's studied the lust-upping potential of everything from rhino horn to camel hump. (In 1989 the Food and Drug Administration officially banned the sale of "any product that bears labeling claims that it will arouse or increase sexual desire or that it will improve sexual performance.") The good news? If you *believe* that eating oysters or exotic herbs will put you in the mood, they probably will. "The brain is the only organ affected by these sex aids," Armelagos says. As for vitamin E, which earned a reputation as an aphrodisiac after studies showed that the testicles of rats started to atrophy after they were deprived of the substance, Armelagos says, "It only [works] if you already have a vitamin E deficiency."

THE VICE SQUAD

Anyone who's ever had a drink or two knows that the people around you suddenly start looking remarkably better after you start imbibing (this is known as a "disinhibitive effect" in scientific terms, "beer goggles" in common parlance). Studies show that alcohol also increases genital blood flow in men and women.

A strange thing happens, though, by the third drink: Desire is still there, but performance is impaired. "Very quickly, alcohol switches from being a sexual boon to a sexual boondoggle," says Arnold Washton, Ph.D., the executive director of New York City's Washton Institute, a drug-treatment center. After more than three drinks, most people take longer to become aroused and reach orgasm; they also derive less pleasure from sex. The long-term effects of alcohol are even more frightening: Alcoholics tend to have a diminished sex drive and an increased incidence of impotence.

Smoking may be even worse for your love life. A team of urologists at Queen's University in Kingston, Ontario, found that 81 percent of the 200 impotent men examined in a 1987 study were smokers or former smokers (smoking reduces penile blood flow, the researchers believe). In addition, lighting up has been shown to significantly reduce the number and the liveliness of sperm. In fact, it's one of many environmental factors that some researchers believe have contributed to a dramatic decline in sperm counts in the past half-century (despite that drop, most men have more than enough swimmers to be fertile). Among the other culprits: plastics, chlorine, pesticides. Researchers believe the body mistakes these substances for the female hormone estrogen (they aren't sure why) and, in turn, produces less sperm. Another sperm zapper is too much heat. To maintain a healthy sperm count, experts recommend that you take cool showers and avoid staying too long in hot baths.

HEAD GAMES

Depression is one of the most common, and least recognized, causes of a diminished sex drive. In a study of 1,700 middle-aged men conducted in 1989 by the New England Research Institute in Watertown, Massachusetts, nearly 90 percent of severely depressed men reported moderate or complete impotence, and 60 percent of those who were moderately depressed experienced erectile difficulties. Other research has found that depressed men have fewer, and softer, nocturnal erections. Compounding the problem, men often overlook depression as a cause of sexual problems. If you suspect you're depressed, Whitehead says, get professional help. Talk to your doctor, a psychologist, or a psychiatrist.

Certain drugs prescribed for prolonged or serious depression, such as Prozac and Zoloft, can sap the libido and cause ejaculatory problems, but others, such as trazodone, can actually improve your sex drive. Other common medications with unwanted sexual side effects, Tagamet, the popular ulcer medication, and many antihypertensives, including Apresoline.

PRACTICE, PRACTICE, PRACTICE

Perhaps the best way to stay sexually healthy is simply to have sex. "Nothing keeps you in shape for lovemaking like lovemaking," Whitehead says. If possible, ejaculate at least twice a week to maintain a steady flow of oxygenated blood in the penis, he advises. Without that regular blood flow, penile tissue begins to atrophy and harden, and eventually will fail. "Guys who have a lot of sex, or those who masturbate frequently, are the guys who keep functioning sexually well into old age," he adds. Now that's an exercise regimen that should be easy to follow.

T E L E V I S I O N

ROLL OVER, WARD CLEAVER

And tell Ozzie Nelson the news.
Ellen DeGeneres is poised to become TV's
first openly gay star. Is America ready or not?

By BRUCE HANDY LOS ANGELES

DIFFERENT MEDIA HAVE DIFFERENT thresholds for scandal. Controversy in the movies might mean making a film that glorifies one of the nation's most repugnant pornographers. Controversy in literature might mean writing a memoir about the affair you had with your father when you were in your 20s. In television, which functions not just as a business and debased art form but also as an increasingly fractured nation's de facto mirror of itself, the threshold is much lower. Controversy could mean starring in a sitcom as a gently scatter-brained former bookstore owner who, after years of adult floundering, reluctantly comes to a realization about her homosexuality and begins to take a few hesitant baby steps out of the closet and toward getting a life.

"I hate that term "in the closet," says Ellen DeGeneres, the aforementioned sitcom star whose all-pants wardrobe and sometimes awkward chemistry with male ingenues was provoking curiosity from fans and reporters long before her sexuality become a minor national obsession. "Until recently I hated the word lesbian too," she continues. "I've said it enough now that it doesn't bother me. But lesbian sounded like somebody with some kind of disease. I didn't like that, so I used the word gay more often."

What she hasn't been able to bring herself to do, until now, is use the word gay along with "I am" in public. Indeed, for a lot of men and women whose livelihood depends on the goodwill of millions, those may be the three scariest words in the English language. "I always thought I could keep my personal life separate from my professional life," says DeGeneres while sitting in a patio at her home in Beverly Hills. "In every interview I ever did"—she's squinting, too polite to interrupt this one even though the sun is clearly in her eyes—"everyone tried to trap me into saying I was gay. And I learned every way to dodge that. Or if they just blatantly asked me, I would say I don't talk about my personal life. I mean, I really tried to figure out every way to avoid answering that question for as long as I could."

That became a lot harder last September when the news leaked, unintentionally by all accounts, that DeGeneres wanted to have the character she plays on *Ellen,* her three-year-old ABC sitcom, discover that she—the character, that is—is a lesbian. For DeGeneres, 39, the decision was the culmination of a long process of struggling with feelings about her own sexuality, her fears about being rejected for it, her wish to lead a more honest and open life in public, her weariness at the effort it took her not to. For the public,

the news was a sensation: a gay lead on TV—that would be a first, and to those who attach importance to these sorts of things, either a long time coming or another way station on the road to moral abandon.

Or maybe it was just something to gossip about. In a series of TV interviews last fall, previously scheduled to promote a new CD but suddenly subjected to intense scrutiny because of the coming-out rumors, DeGeneres joked awkwardly that she was Lebanese, or that the real news was that a character named Les Bian would be joining *Ellen's* cast. She even kidded her own teasing reticence on an episode of *The Larry Sanders Show* that had her hopping into bed for man-woman sex with the fictional male talk-show host.

Finally, after things dragged on all winter, ABC announced last month that the character of Ellen Morgan would indeed be coming out in a special one-hour episode on the last day of April, just in time for sweeps. That resolved, DeGeneres, who had felt constrained from speaking frankly about the issue while her sitcom's fate was still in the balance, is coming out too. "For me," she says, "this has been the most freeing experience because people can't hurt me anymore. I don't have to worry about somebody saying something about me, or a reporter

NOT ALWAYS READY FOR PRIME TIME

Ellen is far from the first TV series to take on a controversial social issue. Remember when:

1953 *I Love Lucy*

Even though the stars, real-life husband and wife, were actually expecting a baby, the word pregnant wasn't permitted on the show. But millions tuned in the night Lucy gave birth to Little Ricky

1968 *Star Trek*

Despite the network's reservations, Captain Kirk and Lieut. Uhura went where no couple had gone before when they embraced for television's first interracial kiss

1972 *Maude*

She had always been outspoken, but her decision to have an abortion was viewed as brave by some, an outrage by others

1989 *thirtysomething*

ABC lost over $1 million when uneasy sponsors backed away from an episode that showed two gay men talking in bed

1991 *Murphy Brown*

Her choice to become a single mother set off a debate over family values, with Vice President Dan Quayle leading the opposition

---

trying to find out information. Literally, as soon as I made this decision, I lost weight. My skin has cleared up. I don't have anything to be scared of which I think outweighs whatever else happens in my career."

In a sense, the burden lifted from DeGeneres' shoulders has landed on those of her bosses at ABC and Touchstone Television, which co-produces *Ellen* (both, of course, are part of the Walt Disney Co.). Dealing with controversy isn't usually a TV executive's strongest suit. It's not that there aren't already gay characters on television. There are—so many, in fact (22 as of February, according to the *Advocate,* a national gay-and-

lesbian magazine, from the lovelorn Smithers on *The Simpsons* to the lovelorn Matt on *Melrose Place*), that one of *Ellen's* producers offers the half-joking observation that homosexuals "have become the new stock character, like the African-American pal at the workplace."

But all those characters are either peripheral or part of an ensemble. Like Mary Richards before her, Ellen Morgan functions as her show's center, around whom the rest of the cast revolves—structurally, Ellen Morgan *is* Mary Richards, except she likes girls. She provides the window into the show's comedic world; she is the character we are asked to identify with, the person to whom we are asked to give tacit approval. That's why, in a country that still has a lot of conflicts about homosexuality, this formerly innocuous, intermittently funny series is now pushing buttons in a way that other shows with gay characters haven't. It's also why, after a telephone threat, the soundstage on the neat and tidy Disney lot in Burbank where *Ellen* is filmed had to be cleared before the final segment of the coming-out episode was shot and bomb-sniffing dogs brought in.

All this comes at a time when television is subject to greater scrutiny than ever before—dating back, at least, to then Vice President Dan Quayle's famous 1992 speech in which he lambasted the character Murphy Brown for choosing to have a child out of wedlock. One can endlessly debate the question of whether television influences society or reflects it: Does Ellen Morgan's coming out in what is still our massest medium legitimize homosexuality, or does the sponsorship of a bottom-line business like ABC merely reflect its acceptance by a significant portion of the population? Clearly, the answer is both, that TV and culture play off each other in ways that are hard to codify. Any attempt to reduce these complex reverberations to a black-or-white issue is, well, the kind of thing you'd expect from television.

Ironically, this ongoing obsession with TV's responsibility comes at a time when the networks' hold on the viewing public continues to erode—just this past February the networks' share of the total viewing audience dropped 4.6% from a year ago, continuing a two-decades-long decline. But whatever *Ellen's* fate with the Nielsens, television's treatment of sexuality is likely to continue becoming increasingly frank, vulgar or immoral, depending on one's vantage point and what, of course, one is viewing (*Chicago Hope? Married . . . With Children?* A made-for-TV movie starring Tori Spelling as a hooker?) The medium—and America—has patently come a long way from the 1952–53 season, when the cast of *I love Lucy* couldn't utter the word pregnant during Little Ricky's gestation period, or 1965 when, a year after network TV got its first double marital bed on *Bewitched,* Barbara

Eden was forbidden by NBC to show her belly button on *I Dream of Jeannie.*

It would be a mistake, however, to think of TV history as one long, uninterrupted drift toward untrammeled license. Moral values are, of course, relative. *Party of Five* features yards of premarital sex, yet is also a warmer celebration of family bonds than, say, *Leave It to Beaver* or *The Donna Reed Show.* Today there are new taboos. "Nobody's going to do abortion on a sitcom today, but Maude did it back in 1972," says Bruce Helford, co-creator and executive producer of *The Drew Carey Show.* He's referring to the famous episodes of *Maude* in which Bea Arthur's title character not only considered having an abortion, as a number of TV characters have in years since, but actually went out and got one. "Abortion," Helford believes, "is way too hot a subject now. Stuff that shows like *All in the Family* did—I don't think they'd let you get away with the kind of show with humor about racism, like the episode where Archie Bunker met Sammy Davis Jr. We've really gone backward in a big way." Marta Kauffman, co-creator and executive producer of *Friends,* complains that her series wasn't allowed to show an actual condom, whereas just a few seasons earlier, *Seinfeld* was. "Things have changed over the past few years," she grumbles. "You couldn't do the masturbation episode of *Seinfeld* today."

In the big *Ellen* episode—filmed over two consecutive Fridays last month amid an atmosphere that seemed half party, half support group—an old college friend (male) comes on to Ellen, who slowly realizes that she is attracted to the friend's female colleague, played by Laura Dern, a close friend of DeGeneres' in real life (a description that should not be read into). Oprah Winfrey, in a surprisingly droll and low-key performance, plays Ellen's therapist. A whole flock of other celebrities—also friends of DeGeneres', including Demi Moore, Melissa Etheridge, k.d. lang and Billy Bob Thornton—showed their support by doing cameos on the episode.

Both ABC and Touchstone seem to be genuinely pleased with the results. "We're very proud. We think Ellen and the show's staff have executed it beautifully," says Jamie Tarses, president of ABC Entertainment. At the same time, she adds, "obviously this is an experiment. We're not sociologists. We don't know how this is going to be received."

Well, they could have wagered a few easy guesses. The news that Ellen Morgan would come out brought predictable applause from the Gay & Lesbian Alliance Against Defamation, which is building a national "Come Out with Ellen" day around the episode; and predictable denunciations from the Rev. Jerry Falwell, who referred to the star in gentlemanly fashion as "Ellen DeGenerate," and from the Rev. Donald E. Wildmon, whose American Family Association has issued barely veiled threats to boycott *Ellen's* advertisers. A stalwart ABC says it nevertheless expects that *Ellen* will be fully sponsored, although two occasional advertisers on *Ellen*, J.C. Penney and Chrysler, have announced they won't continue to sponsor the show. This can't have made ABC happy. But even for controversial shows there are usually enough advertisers to go around if the ratings promise to be high enough, which controversy often ensures. The network remains optimistic.

In less vested precincts of Hollywood, there seems to be little consensus about how the show will do. "What you'll find is that *Ellen* is going to take a hit on this," says Dick Wolf, creator of *Law & Order*. "If it was my show I probably wouldn't have done it. This is one specific area that a large percentage of the population is still very uncomfortable with." Bruce Helford, the *Drew Carey* producer, is more bullish: "I think there will be a big spike in the ratings. But if it's just one big thing and then they go back to the same show, and she's a lesbian, but the same old things happen to her, the boost won't last."

He is getting at something that has long plagued *Ellen*, which sometimes feels like Seinfeld after a game of telephone. Although the show debuted three years ago in the Nielsens top five as *These Friends of Mine*, the sitcom has since stumbled through a number of cast, staff and time-slot changes, never quite jelling creatively, even by DeGeneres' estimation, and settling into the ratings' upper midrange. A major problem has been the indistinct character of Ellen Morgan, who seems to drift wackily through each show without ever offering much in the way of believable motivation, even in the elastic sense that usually applies to sitcoms. For a while she owned a bookstore, but the profession seemed more an arbitrary choice to inject "workplace humor." After the second season she stopped dating—some writers say because DeGeneres was uncomfortable with overtly heterosexual story lines, although she says she simply wasn't interested in doing a show that focused on relationships. As it happens, the code working title of the coming-out script, *The Puppy Episode*, is an in-joke reference to one of the lamer attempts to juice up the show: an executive's suggestion—DeGeneres won't say whose—that the show's creative problems might be solved if Ellen Morgan got a puppy.

Was Ellen Morgan really gay all along, before not only the character knew it but DeGeneres and the writers as well? According to Dava Savel, one of *Ellen's* three executive producers, sparks often flew between DeGeneres and female guests. She cites in particular an episode with Janeane Garafalo. "There wasn't supposed to be a lesbian thing at all, but afterward we were watching the tape and we were like, 'Whoa!' "

DeGeneres is certainly not averse to the idea that the new plot twist is organic rather

IS COMING OUT GOING TOO FAR?

Camille Paglia, author
Sexual Personae; Vamps & Tramps

"As an open lesbian, I say that the entertainment industry has been exploiting the artistic talents of gay people throughout the 20th century without ever giving them their due. [But] the objections of conservative Christian ministers who believe in the Bible are well founded. People on the left have got to accept that it is not simply bigotry that causes believing Christians to object to this kind of element in popular culture."

Jacquelyn Mitchard, author
The Deep End of the Ocean

"Though they don't say this on *Sesame Street*, a lesbian is a person in your neighborhood. And if television is a mirror as well as a window, then that's how it is."

Lori Lucas, car-repair-shop manager
TIME's Oct. 14, 1996, cover subject

"If she has a relationship on the air where she might actually kiss another woman, I think that would make me uncomfortable. But you know what else makes me uncomfortable? Seeing Jimmy Smits' butt on *NYPD Blue*!"

Randall Murphree, editor
American Family Association Journal

"TV is one of our culture's greatest teachers, but just how—and what—does prime time teach? Any careful observer of human nature knows that what we immerse ourselves in, we become. A culture that immerses itself in casual, illicit sex will become a culture adrift in a sea of moral irresponsibility. Parents should stay on the alert—the flood is still building!"

Mary Pipher, psychologist; *Reviving Ophelia; The Shelter of Each Other*

"I think it's good to have conversations in this country about gender issues, or race, or *whatever* is controversial. So when television can do that in a way that is not polarizing—that is healing—I'm all for it. People have a tremendous fascination with TV people, because they are the people we have in common. They are the connecting tissue in our culture that allows us to talk to one another."

William Kristol, editor and publisher
Weekly Standard

"There is so much that Hollywood already does that is bad for kids that this is just a drop in the ocean. What is most annoying is the false courageousness of it. All they are going to get are applause and approbation. A really courageous act would be if she were to come out as a Republican or a pro-life Christian. I'll be happy if *Touched by an Angel* continues to defeat *Ellen* in the ratings."

Wendy Wasserstein, playwright
The Heidi Chronicles

"When I was growing up and watching television, there was Marjorie Lord in a shirtwaist and Donna Reed and all of those women who didn't seem remotely like my mother and other people. I think what's good about Ellen coming out is that it shows another sort of person you can be on television."

Marshall Herskovitz, TV producer
thirtysomething; Relativity

"There are always kids watching television, and I'm a parent. What do I want to protect my children from? What do I think the most dangerous stuff on television is? As far as I'm concerned, the two most dangerous influences are commercials and the news, more so than anything you'll ever see on a prime-time show. You have to put controversy in a context; things are controversial because people fear them."

than desperate: "It made sense the character was gay—not that I ever started with that intention." At ABC and Disney, the idea of Ellen Morgan's coming out had been discussed off and on as a possible fix for the show almost since its inception. So executives were receptive, if cautious, when De-Generes and the show's producers first approached them last summer about the possibility. "It's not a no-brainer," understates Tarses, but tentative permission was granted for the show to go ahead, pending final approval of the script. Regrettably, at least from DeGeneres' and her staff's vantage point, the dragged-out decision process left them twisting in the wind.

Among other problems, a source says, there was also a feeling at Disney—perhaps because of an overzealous reading of management's mood—that the *Ellen* decision might best be delayed until after last February's Disney stockholders' meeting so that chairman Michael Eisner would be spared having to defend that as well as his salary and Mike Ovitz's lavish payout. "When Disney or ABC were worried about boycotts or this or that, I kept saying to everybody, 'I'm the one who's going to get the biggest boycott,'" says DeGeneres. "'You can cancel the show, you can go and make another one. It's not going to hurt you. *I'm* the product here.'"

HER SHOW'S NEW DIRECTION WILL be groundbreaking not only for having a gay lead character, but for having a gay lead character who is not yet entirely comfortable with her sexuality—a departure from the normal run of things in the '90s, when gay characters on TV tend to be proud, assertive and more or less uplifting. It's surely not happenstance that *Melrose Place's* Matt is the only character on the show with any kind of grace or nobility, nor that a pair of secondary lesbian characters on *Friends* have the most stable relationship on the show, as do, for that matter, a secondary pair of gay male characters on *Ellen*. Ellen Morgan, on the other hand, ends her coming-out episode sitting awkwardly in a lesbian coffeehouse, unsure of how to comport herself in this new environment and with this new knowledge of herself. It's actually kind of poignant. The character is also denied an affirming liplock with her female love interest—a former taboo that was long ago shattered by *L.A. Law, Roseanne* and, earlier this season, *Relativity* (men kissing men, on the other hand, remains, for now, a no-no).

When asked about kissing women on TV, DeGeneres is adamant: "It was the last thing I wanted to do. I don't want people to watch me kiss somebody. That's not what this is about. Ellen Morgan is scared to death. She just found out she's gay. She doesn't know how to kiss a girl yet. When you realize you're gay, it's like being in grade school. It's your first kiss—that's a nervous thing, you know? That's what's so exciting about this, to be able to show the whole process of coming out for the first time." She's right—much of the episode mines a rich new comic vein for the series. And in this case, DeGeneres' desire for truthfulness—and for keeping her show's focus off dating, gay or straight ("Mary Richards didn't date that much," she points out)—fits well with Touchstone's and ABC's that the show proceed cautiously. "*Ellen* won't become the lesbian dating show" is the party line one hears again and again.

"Ellen Morgan is still in a very heterosexual situation," insists Dava Savel. "Almost all her friends are heterosexuals. If one of the other characters has a guy that they're interested in, she's the first to say, 'Omigod, he's hot.' It's just not going to be an option for Ellen to date him." Not that lesbians shouldn't appreciate male beauty, but this does smack a bit of the we're-doing-it-but-we're-not-doing-it attitude with which television often ends up approaching taboos, which might best be exemplified by the first interracial kiss on TV between *Star Trek's* Captain Kirk and Lieut. Uhura. Back then, in 1968, the couple was forced by alien telepathy to smooch against their will.

In *Ellen's* last two episodes of the season, she will come out to her parents and then to her new boss at the bookstore. She will suffer some rejection. Next season—assuming that ABC wants to renew the show and DeGeneres wants to return, which she says she might not—is uncharted territory. It would be hyperbole to say television will never be the same. But clearly this has been a landmark for DeGeneres. "I was thinking," she says, "what's the thing anyone could ask me now or say about me? And it's like nothing, really. I mean, not even Howard Stern can hurt me now." In 1997, that's power.

—With reporting by Elizabeth L. Bland and William Tynan/New York and Jeffrey Ressner/Los Angeles

Bisexuality

is the wild card of our erotic life. Now it's coming out in the open—in pop culture, in cyberspace and on campus. But can you really have it both ways?

John Leland

Steven and Lori are what you might call the marrying type. They met on the first day of freshman orientation at the University of Chicago in 1988. By Thanksgiving, she was taking him home to meet her family; the following year they got engaged. This May they celebrated their first wedding anniversary.

In their one-bedroom apartment in Hyde Park, a collegiate affair down to the cinderblock bookshelves, Steven and Lori, now both 24, have developed an almost telepathic relationship. If anyone tells one of them anything, they joke, the other knows about it immediately. But during their freshman year, Steven says, he used to go off on his own every so often. "I think I told you I was going to a Democratic Socialist meeting," he recalls to Lori. He was really going to a campus gay and lesbian support group. Steven had come to college with a "practically nonexistent" romantic life, but a clear attraction to both men and women. After one of the group meetings, he decided to come clean to Lori.

STEVEN: [I said] Lori, I have something to tell you.

LORI: At which point, I thought he had cancer.

STEVEN: And I told her, and her response was "Oh, is that all?"

LORI: Yeah, it's not like cancer, after all. After that big buildup, it's like, gee, that's not a big deal.

When the couple got married at city hall last year, perhaps the most relieved person in the Midwest was Lori's mother. "Now she thinks I'm going to behave,"

Teresa and Ronnell

Ronnell Caprice Hunt and Theresa Hernandez have a large, active circle of bi friends. But they don't think they can be open with their families. "You're raised so that you don't want to disappoint people," says Caprice, 25, a dancer from Stockton, Calif., who hasn't told any relatives. Hernandez, 23, a student at San Francisco State, has told only a few people, although she's known she's been bi her whole life. Her orientation carries an extra stigma in the Latino community, she says: "People judge you."

says Lori. She says this with a playful smirk. In the years before their marriage—during their engagement—Lori had a serious relationship with another woman, and Steven had one with another man. Their marriage now is a home invention that they describe as "body-fluid monogamous." In conversation, they discuss condoms as matter-of-factly as the weather. Lori has an ongoing sexual relationship with another man and is looking for another woman; Steven has a friendship with a man that is sometimes sexual. Lori says, "At the time that I was coming out I was more interested in men, and now I'm more interested in women." Steven is "much more interested" in men right now. He still has sex with his wife, but he now identifies himself as gay, though he also calls himself a "once and future bisexual."

Bisexuality is the hidden wild card of our erotic culture. It is what disappears when we divide desire into gay and straight, just as millions of Americans of various ethnic origin disappear when we discuss race in terms of black and white.

Stephen and Linda

Stephen Getman and Linda Kamenetsky look just like the couple next door—and that's the problem. Steph, a self-described "gender radical," and Linda are both bisexual and work hard to establish that identity. He sometimes wears dresses or makeup to a party; she'll slip on a tuxedo. Sometimes they paint their fingernails together. "There is no doubt I'm a man, but I would like to see the bounds of what's appropriate for that gender expanded," Steph says. "I picture Stephen under the car changing the brake pads with a lace top on," says Linda. Both Steph, 30, and Linda, 47, have been married, as well as in serious gay relationships. They've been together for three years and, while committed to each other, "we're open to incorporating a third person," says Steph, who works for a gay, lesbian and bi Roman Catholic advocacy group in Washington. "Sexuality is fluid. There is no such thing as normal," he says.

Now, in scattered pockets, bisexuality is starting to become more visible. Bisexual characters have popped up in TV series like "Roseanne" and "Melrose Place" and in films like "Three of Hearts" and "Threesome." Two decades after Mick Jagger and David Bowie flaunted their androgynous personas, pop stars like Michael Stipe, Courtney Love and Sophie B. Hawkins and model Rachel Williams have discovered anew that there's more to life than when a man loves a woman. As Stipe told NEWSWEEK, promoting R.E.M.'s latest album, "I've always been sexually ambiguous in terms of my proclivities; I think labels are for food." MTV and fashion advertising, pumping out fetishized images of men and women, have created a climate that Harvard professor Marjorie Garber, author of the provocative new book "Vice Versa: Bisexuality and the Eroticism of Everyday Life," calls "virtual bisexuality": the only way to watch these naked torsos, male and female alike, is erotically. Many college students, particularly women, talk about a new sexual "fluidity" on campus. And most significantly, the Internet has emerged as a safe harbor where users can play fluidly with gender, both their own and that of their virtual partners. As Garber puts it, "We are in a bisexual moment."

In the splintered multiculturalism of the 1990s, an independent bisexual movement is starting to claim its own identity. The Bisexual Resource Guide lists 1,400 groups spread throughout the United States and abroad, including Bi Women of Color, Bi Adult Children of Alcoholics, Bi Star Trekkies. There are bi cable shows, bi web sites, bi newsletters and magazines. "We are taught we have to be one thing," says Howard University divinity professor Elias Farajajé-Jones. "Now people are finding out that they don't have to choose one thing or another. That doesn't mean they are confused."

The bridge: Freud called bisexuality a universal "disposition"; he believed that we all have male and female sides, each heterosexually attracted to people of the opposite gender, but that most of us repress one side. For him, it was exclusive *heterosexuality* that was "a problem that needs elucidating" (unfortunately, he never got around to it). Alfred Kinsey, in his famous 1948 report, mapped human sexuality on a scale of zero to 6, with zero representing exclusively heterosexual behavior and 6 exclusively homosexual behavior; bisexuality

Pamela and Amelia

Amelia Victoria Mederos grew up in Miami. In the Latin culture there, says this Cuban-American, the "five-cent definition" of bisexuality was that "you're dating more than one person at a time, of each sex." She didn't qualify. Mederos was married to a man in her 20s; after divorcing, she moved in with lesbian Pamela Streetz. Only later, says Mederos, 48, a civil-rights advocate in Massachusetts, did her bisexuality come into "focus." Though the revelation momentarily rattled her relationship with Streetz, the couple agreed to keep their vows of monogamy.

was the bridge that held the poles together. The anthropologist Margaret Mead urged in 1975 that we "come to terms with the well-documented, normal human capacity to love members of both sexes." And in 1995, "Adam," a bisexual teen in Oakland, Calif., says bisexuality is no guarantee of a date on a Saturday night; "A bisexual," he says, "doesn't have any more sex than the captain of the football team."

After a brief vogue during the sexual revolution—"Bisexual Chic: Anyone Goes," chortled NEWSWEEK in 1974—it moved back underground in the 1980s, pushed by fears of AIDS and by gay identity politics. Nobody knows how many bisexuals there are in the country, or just how bisexuality should be defined. Its existence alone makes many people uncomfortable; it suggests that all sexual identity might be subject to change or expansion, and that we may not ever really be able to fulfill our partners or be fulfilled ourselves. "I'll put it this way," says Faune, a bi New York grad student who asked to be identified by his online handle. "You're attracted to only one sex and you don't feel there's anything missing. To me that would be hell."

In a culture organized, however precariously, around monogamy, bisexuality lurks as a rupture in the social structure, conjuring fears of promiscuity, secret lives and instability. It can make the knotty issues of human relationships— jealousy, fidelity, finances, parental roles, custody—even more complex. And with these uncertainties comes an increased

threat of AIDS. Failed monogamy is already a principal source of pain in this country; bisexuality suggests that non-monogamy, or "polyamory," is an accepted part of life. Not for nothing does one bisexual journal call itself, with mock derision, Anything That Moves. In practice promiscuity is not an article of faith for all bisexuals; it's an option. Many bis are monogamous for all or parts of their lives. The sociologist Paula Rust, in the upcoming book "Bisexuality: The Psychology and Politics of an Invisible Minority," explains the paradox this way: "Imagine concluding that a person who finds both blue and brown eyes attractive would require two lovers, one with each eye color, instead of concluding that this person would be happy with *either* a blue-eyed or a brown-eyed lover."

Mostly, though, we'd rather not think about bisexuality. When Rolling Stone publisher Jann Wenner left his wife this spring for another man, bisexuality was the possibility missing from most accounts. Bisexuality has been written out of our literature: early publishers simply rewrote the genders of male love objects in Plato's "Symposium" and some of Shakespeare's sonnets; more often schools just teach around them. Bisexuality even disappears from many sex surveys, which count people with any same-sex behavior as homosexual. And yet it has had a tremendous impact on our culture. Many of the men who have taught us to be men—Cary Grant, James Dean—and the women who've taught us to be women—Billie Holiday, Marlene Dietrich—enjoyed sex with both men and women.

The bisexual blip of the '70s was an offshoot of the sexual revolution; it was straight, with a twist. By contrast, the current bisexual moment rises from the gay and feminist movements. For a generation that came of age during the gay-rights movement, same-sex relationships or experiments no longer carry the stigma they once did. More and more of us—at work, at school, in our families and in our entertainments—move comfortably between gay and straight worlds. "Those of us who are younger," says Rebecca Kaplan, 24, a psychology major at MIT, "owe a great deal to gays, lesbians and bisexuals who came before us. Because of them I was able to come out as a bisexual and not hate myself." Feminism has also made romantic attachments between two women—either provisional or lasting—more acceptable, even privileged. As president of the National Organization for Women, Patricia Ireland sets a quiet example: she has both a husband and a female companion. Nearly every college or university in the country, and some high schools, now have gay and lesbian student centers; sex with one's own gender, for anyone who's curious, is now a visible and protected part of campus culture. Queer studies and gender studies are now a part of the national curriculum. A popular T shirt, spotted recently in a Connecticut high school, puts it this way: DON'T ASSUME I'M STRAIGHT. As one 17-year-old bi says, "It's not us-versus-them anymore. There's just more and more of us."

Tim Höring, 21, a sophomore at City College in San Francisco, describes himself as "typical of bisexual youth. We just refuse to label ourselves as any of the five food groups . . . [We] revel in the fuzziness, in the blurred images." Working-class, Roman Catholic, son of a retired New York narcotics cop, Höring had his first sexual fantasies about Wonder Woman and the Bionic Woman. Then in his teens he admitted to himself, in a series of difficult steps, that he was also attracted to men. He came out to a few friends in high school; at his graduation, when his name was called, the last six rows in the auditorium mischievously yelled out, "the bisexual" (this news came as a surprise to his parents). For the most part he has been in monogamous relationships, usually with men—though now he is dating two gay men and

Tim and Ellen

Like more and more couples, Tim and Ellen found each other on the Internet. He posted a coffee recipe; she—jokingly—proposed marriage. They met two years ago, and "by the end of the day, we were head over heels," says Ellen, 30, a computer analyst at the University of Chicago. But marriage scared them. Ellen, who dated women after college, had been married to a bi man. Tim, 24, who started seeing men only during his friendship with Ellen, feared commitment would change their relationship. But practicality won: they wed to get health insurance. For now, they're monogamous, and, Ellen says, "This marriage is going to last for life."

a bisexual woman. "I never wanted a white picket fence," he says, "but I do want someone I can settle down with and raise my Benneton kids." His partner may be a man or a woman. "I don't feel forced to choose," he says. "I don't have to make any tough choices."

Softening tensions: For many bisexuals, it hasn't been that easy. "When I came out in '88, says Melissa Merry, 31, an energetic Chicagoan who calls herself Mel, "I was told by people from [local lesbian] support groups not to come out as bisexual or I'd be asked to leave." Many gays and lesbians, she says, dismissed bisexuals as fence sitters, unwilling to give up a "phase" they themselves had outgrown. As a college student in Michigan, Merry remembers, she went to a singles-heavy bar one night. "And I saw this woman across the room and I thought, 'She is just so attractive.' I thought, 'Where did that come from?' I was involved with a guy, we were going to get married, and then all of a sudden that didn't make sense anymore." Now Merry works in two organizations for bis, but says tensions between bis and gays have softened. After years of resistance, gay and lesbian organizations have started to add bisexuality to their banners. As for the lesbian groups that shunned her, Merry says, "I can't thing of any . . . that I can't go to now."

Many bis, though, still feel rejected on two fronts: by straights for being too gay, and by gays for not being gay enough. During the late '80s, bisexual men—especially married men who stepped out with other men—were painted as stealth assassins bringing AIDS to their unsuspecting wives. As Cosmopolitan warned in 1989, "If a man's eyes follow other men, be very cautious." This fear has cooled somewhat, particularly among younger women—both because of the availability of condoms, and because AIDS never swept through the heterosexual population, except around IV drug use. Of women who contract AIDS sexually, the portion who get it from bisexual males remains at 10 to 20 percent; 80 to 90 percent get it from drug users, Centers for Disease Control and Prevention estimates. Still, for many women this is reason enough to worry. The bisexual response: it is unprotected sex, not bisexuality, that transmits AIDS.

Luis, 36, has felt pressures from both gays and straights. A marine biologist by training, Luis now runs a Miami prescription-drug service for patients with HIV. For the last 5¹/₂ years, he has been in-

volved with a bi woman; recently, he invited a gay man into their relationship and home. Luis is HIV-positive; his partners are not. "My first lover and first relationship was with a [gay] man, Juan," says Luis. "I learned a lot from him, but there was this other part of me that needed to be expressed. Juan would tell me, 'You're just trying to conform and go back into the closet.' I didn't mind being called gay, but that's not all of who I am. I'm as queer as they come and as straight as they come. I'm 200 percent." Luis remembers once telling a man he's slept with that he also had sex with a woman. "He got up in the middle of the meal and walked out," Luis says. The prejudice is no more palatable when it comes from straights. Shopping at a northwest Miami mall with his male lover recently, Luis found himself assaulted with anti-gay slurs. "How did the guy know about us?" asks Luis, who does not dress outrageously. "We don't have any stickers on the car."

These dual pressures push some to lead bifurcated lives. William Wedin, a psychologist and director of the Bisexual Information and Counseling Service, says that most of the bisexuals he sees would rather remain in the closet. "Sometimes they will lead separate lives where they are known as gay to one group of friends and seen as straight by another group of people. Sometimes they will go to two doctors: one who deals with medical problems, another who deals with sexually transmitted diseases. They will create separate worlds."

Amid these fears and prejudices, scholars and researchers are looking for ways to rethink bisexuality: how to make sense of the millions of Americans, maybe tens of millions, who over the course of their lifetimes have sex with both men and women. Many, even most, don't call themselves bisexual. According to sex researcher Martin Weinberg of Indiana University, the majority of men who engage in sex with both men and women label themselves "heterosexual." Conversely, Paula Rust, in a 1992 survey of women who identified themselves as lesbians, found that two thirds of them said they were attracted to men, and 90 percent had been in sexual relationships with men. Further, most bisexuals are not attracted equally to men and women. Where do you draw the line? Should fantasy and desire count, even if they aren't acted upon? And what about married people who later come to recognize themselves as gay? "I don't have a definition [of bisexuality]," says John O. G.

Elias

Like many who came of age during the birth of the gay-pride movement, Elias Farajajé-Jones once considered being called bi an "insult," even though he's slept with men and women since he was 16. "I'm proud to say I'm a recovering bi-phobe," he says. Once he got over that hurdle, he re-evaluated his whole life. He even redefined his racial heritage, which includes Native American and African-American ancestors. "The large number of multiracial people in the bi movement is a powerful parallel," says Farajajé-Jones, 42, a divinity professor at Howard University who sports four tattoos and multiple body piercings. "We are taught we have to be one thing. Now people are finding they don't have to choose." Farajajé-Jones, who has a 2-month-old baby with his bi partner, Katherin, is determined that his child, Issa-Ajamu, will know no gender barriers. With help from a fillable, strap-on tube, both parents will breast-feed. And when people ask if the child—who has both ears pierced—is a boy or girl, Farajajé-Jones responds: "Ask the baby."

Billy, lead author of the 1991 study "The Sexual Behavior of Men in the United States," "because I'm not sure there is any one standard definition." The number of Americans who have sex with both men and women concurrently is very small. According to the University of Chicago's massive 1992 "Sex in America" study, about .7 percent of American men, and .3 percent of American women report having had both male and female sexual partners in the last 12 months. Most of the self-identified bisexuals interviewed for this article would not qualify under these terms.

Erotic patterns: In practice, bisexuality has come to describe an incredibly broad range of erotic patterns: some monogamous, some polyamorous, some fleeting and some wholly fantastic. Indigo Som, 28, a paper artist currently in a monogamous relationship with another woman, considers the word bisexual far too vague to describe her life. "My sexual orientation," she says, "is toward creative people of color who can cook."

So who are bi, and how did they get that way? Are they really different from everybody else? "Some people say everyone has the biological potential for bisexuality, but that's untestable," says Weinberg, who led one of the few major studies of bisexuals (published last year as "Dual Attraction: Understanding Bisexuality"). "The answer is, we don't know." Weinberg conceives of bisexuality as often being an "add-on"—we commonly develop one orientation first, usually straight, and then "add-on" an attraction to the other gender. "Learning bisexuality," he writes, is a matter of "failing to unlearn the desirable aspects of one's own gender."

J. Michael Bailey, a sociologist at Northwestern University, says bisexuality is in the genes. In a study of sexual orientation in nearly 5,000 Australian twins, he found that identical twins were more likely both to have bisexual feelings than fraternal twins, suggesting bisexuality might have a genetic basis. "I conceptualize bisexuality this way," he says: "if somebody has enough of the relevant genetic factors, they'll be homosexual. If they don't have enough, they'll be bisexual." His data are still preliminary and have not been subjected to peer scrutiny.

At bottom, though, bisexuality simply does not reduce neatly. There are no bisexual acts nor bisexual desires, only bisexual histories. Bisexuality is less a root than a construction—different in each individual—of passions and actions we are accustomed to calling heterosexual or homosexual. In its ambiguities, it calls into question the certainties of both gay and straight identities. Pushed far enough, it absorbs both.

Matthew Ehrlich, 25, argues that his own desire has nothing to do with gender. Ehrlich, managing editor of VH1 Online in New York, said he was attracted to both men and women once he "started smooching at age 14." He came

A Secret History

We've drawn many of our feminine and masculine ideals from our public figures—from dashing men like Gary Grant or James Dean and alluring women like Marlene Dietrich or model Rachel Williams. They're the archetypes we copy in the mirror; they teach us how to get the boy or girl. In real life, many knew how to get both.

out as gay at Williams College, he says, because he saw a lot of abusive heterosexual relationships around him; for the last five years he has identified himself as bi though he prefers the term queer. "There are some times that I want a certain kind of hair at the back of someone's neck, a look in their eyes, the way they hold their mouth, but it's not necessarily limited to one gender," he says. "It's often much stronger that I want to run my hands through short hair at the back of the neck than that it's a man or woman's hair." Ehrlich says some of his partners don't understand this, which leads to problems of trust or jealousy. "[They'll say], 'How can you be sure you desire me when I'm only one gender?' " he says. But this is not the point. "I don't desire a gender, I desire a person."

Many orientations: This remains the unresolved paradox of bisexuality: that in its most individuated moments, it is most indistinguishable from homosexuality or heterosexuality. Desire is desire. John Cheever, who described the breadth of his passions in his journals, deemed bisexuality a pitifully narrow way to look at human attraction. "To interrogate oneself tirelessly on one's sexual drives," he wrote, "seems to me self-destructive. One can be aroused, for example, by the sight of a holly leaf, an apple tree, or a male cardinal bird on a spring morning." As Garber argues, we all have manifold orientations: to green eyes, say, or to money or power. But deep down we remain defiantly attracted to individuals.

In San Francisco recently, Tim Höring was telling his friends about how he changed his approach to picking up boys.

He used to say, "Are you queer?" then he switched to, "Do you like boys?" Now his favorite line is "Do you like me?" As he sees it, "I've gone from the political to the historical attraction to the very personal. All that really matters is if they like me." This is the new bisexual moment in a nutshell: hard fought, hard thought, and distinctly individual. It is a thorny narrative, fraught with questions of identity and belonging. And in the end, it is really about the simple, mysterious pull between warm human bodies when the lights go out.

With STEVE RHODES *in Chicago,* PETER KATEL *in Miami,* CLAUDIA KALB *and* MARC PEYSER *in New York,* NADINE JOSEPH *in San Francisco,* MARTHA BRANT *in Washington and bureau reports*

PORTRAIT OF A
NEW MAN

Susan Stryker
SPECIAL TO *UTNE READER*

PHOTOGRAPHY BY
Loren Cameron

The mystery of gender through the eyes of a photographer who has crossed the divide

The desire to change sex is not an illness, although it is classified as such by the psychotherapeutic professions. Neither is it a perversion, a form of mutilation, or the wrong answer to a poorly framed question of personal identity. It is a form of communication, a way to manifest to others a deeply felt sense of identity that is otherwise unintelligible. It is about becoming real.

I met Loren Cameron, whose self-portraits you see here, outside the Moscone Convention Center in San Francisco in the spring of 1993, during a protest rally at the annual meeting of the American Psychiatric Association. I was a member of Transgender Nation, a militant transsexual rights group. I had begun the transition from male to female about two years earlier, just about the time I finished my Ph.D. in American history at the University of California, Berkeley. I was determined to use the privilege of my education to help change the way that transsexual people are treated.

Loren had made the transition from female to male in the late '80s, a decade after moving to San Francisco from rural Arkansas. He was at the protest looking for other transsexuals to photograph. After a series of low-paying jobs, he'd finally found his niche, taking portraits of people who had made or were making the journey he had made. "It struck me forcibly that [beginning as a photographer] was quite a bit like the experience of transitioning from female to male," he has written. "I felt like people would recognize immediately that I wasn't 'really' a man, and it took a while to build up my confidence that, yes, I really was. I became a photographer the same way I became a man—by just taking my act to the streets and doing it and learning to pass in the process." Now he splits his time between the art world—where his reputation is growing rapidly—and working just enough at other jobs to make ends meet. (The first book-length

collection of his work, *Body Alchemy*, is due out from Cleis Press in November.)

Of course, transsexuals looking for a camera to stand in front of can usually find one; we're popular sideshow

"All of the men I've looked to as role models have been body-builders and athletes. They seem like gods to me in their huge and beautiful bodies. I envy them. I want to be like them. They look so virile and invincible. I know deeply that being a man and having strength isn't all about my maximum bench press, but it doesn't seem to matter. All I can say is that as my muscles grow, being five foot three doesn't seem quite so small. Sometimes I wonder if I'll ever feel big enough. I wonder if I'll ever feel safe in this body."—Loren Cameron

From *Utne Reader*, July/August 1996, pp. 76-79. © 1996 by Susan Stryker. Reprinted by permission.

attractions in the fin de siècle cultural circus. Photographers as famous as Diane Arbus and Nan Goldin launched their careers by shooting us. But most nontranssexual photographers don't seem to really see us—rather, they use us to investigate their own discomfort with what they make us represent. Cameron is the first imagemaker to bring a sophisticated insider's eye to the subject. What he

"I learned a lot about hard work from my father. He taught me how to mend fences and haul hay, and sometimes we worked right into the night if rain was coming. As I get older it gets easier to understand and appreciate him for who he was, to forgive and forget our differences. The last time I saw him he told me that he thought I had a lot of guts to move to California with only a duffel bag and a hundred bucks in my pocket. I think if he could see me now he would be proud to call me his son."

sees is truly "something else"—not the sterotypical view of dejected social outcasts lurking in the dim hallways of derelict hotels, but a redemptive vision of transsexual people leading remarkable (though often quite commonplace) lives.

The missing ingredient in most representations of transsexuals, Cameron contends, is "the sense of satisfaction we feel about ourselves and our body changes. I want to show that we're not ashamed, that we're expressing pride in being who we are." If anybody wonders what pride there is to find in being transsexual, Cameron has a ready answer: "It takes a lot of guts to acknowledge how uncomfortable you are before transition, and to willfully accept the challenge of re-creating yourself."

That's a level of responsibility for one's own life most people never have to confront, he says. And given

the stigma that surrounds the entire process, it's a wonder anyone even attempts—let alone ever accomplishes—the arduous journey from one gender to another.

Why, then, *do* we go through with it?

Imagine a scenario in which you've been locked in a dark room with only a telephone. It rings constantly. You always answer it, longing to connect with something beyond the solitude of the space you inhabit. It's always a wrong number. You begin to talk with the people who call, for the simple reason that the conversation offers companionship, a link to something outside yourself. Over time you develop real relationships with the callers. Perhaps you even fall in love with a few of the voices. You want to tell everyone that you are not the person they think you are, but you are afraid they will hang up and leave you utterly alone if they realize after all this time that you are not the person they have been trying to call.

The body itself, transsexuals eventually discover, is what causes the perpetual "wrong numbers." Changing our bodies is how we get out of our Twilight Zone predicament. Transsexuality is thus about breaking out of psychological isolation, correcting a case of mistaken identity, and bringing a personal sense of self into meaningful interaction with others.

It also serves, in Cameron's words, "to set one's self in motion, and to survive an impossibly difficult space. It's an in-between space, outside duality. It's like standing in a neutral zone, where you can see and hear the opposing sides lobbing grenades of misunderstanding at each other. You can see the fictions of separation, this idea of distinct genders that everybody manufacturers, just like we manufacture fictions of race and class. The transsexual space feels sacred, a space where many things that are hidden become clear." Expressing the courage his transsexual subjects have shown in undertaking this project is what Cameron strives for in his work.

And courage is needed. As the fate of Brandon Teena shows, the act of transgressing gender norms can get you killed in this country. (Teena chose to live as a man in a small Nebraska town, and after being exposed as biologically female, he was brutally beaten, gang raped, and eventually murdered. His case is one of many.) Only a handful of cities and one state, Minnesota, now have laws to help protect the rights of transgendered people.

Despite all this, the thing that Cameron most wants people to understand about transsexuality when they look at his photographs is "the joy of the experience. That's the bottom line. It's not about failing. I didn't fail to be a woman. I just decided to have another experience."

Susan Stryker is currently working on Trans: Changing Sex and Other Ecstatic Passages Into Postmodernity, *forthcoming from Oxford University Press.*

Interpersonal Relationships

Establishing Sexual Relationships (Articles 20–22)
Responsible Quality Sexual Relationships (Articles 23–26)

Most people are familiar with the term "sexual relationship." It denotes an important dimension of sexuality—interpersonal sexuality, or sexual interactions occurring between two (and sometimes more) individuals. This unit focuses attention on these types of relationships.

No woman is an island. No man is an island. Interpersonal contact forms the basis for self-esteem and meaningful living. Conversely, isolation results in loneliness and depression for most human beings. People seek and cultivate friendships for the warmth, affection, supportiveness, and sense of trust and loyalty that such relationships can provide.

Long-term friendships may develop into intimate relationships. The qualifying word in the previous sentence is "may." Today many people, single as well as married, yearn for close or intimate interpersonal relationships but fail to find them. Discovering how and where to find potential friends, partners, lovers, and soul mates is reported to be more difficult today than in times past. Fear of rejection causes some to avoid interpersonal relationships, others to present a false front or illusory self that they think is more acceptable or socially desirable. This sets the stage for a game of intimacy that is counterproductive to genuine intimacy. For others a major dilemma may exist—the problem of balancing closeness with the preservation of individual identity in a manner that satisfies the need for both personal and interpersonal growth and integrity. In either case, partners in a relationship should be advised that the development of interpersonal awareness (the mutual recognition and knowledge of others as they really are) rests upon trust and self-disclosure—letting the other person know who you really are and how you truly feel. In American society this has never been easy, and today some fear it may be more difficult than ever.

These considerations in regard to interpersonal relationships apply equally well to achieving meaningful and satisfying sexual relationships. Three basic ingredients lay the foundation for quality sexual interaction: self-awareness, understanding and acceptance of the partner's needs and desires, and mutual efforts to accommodate both partners' needs and desires. Without these, misunderstandings may arise, bringing anxiety, frustration, dissatisfaction, and/or resentment into the relationship. There may also be a heightened risk of contracting AIDS or another STD (sexually transmitted disease), experiencing an unplanned pregnancy, or experiencing sexual dysfunction by one or both partners. On the other hand, experience and research show that ongoing attention to these three ingredients by intimate partners contributes not only to sexual responsibility, but also to true emotional and sexual intimacy and a longer and happier life.

As might already be apparent, there is much more to quality sexual relationships than our popular culture recognizes. Such relationships are not established by means of sexual techniques or beautiful/handsome features. Rather, it is the quality of the interaction that makes sex a celebration of our sexuality. A person-oriented (as opposed to genitally oriented) sexual awareness, coupled with a whole-body/mind sexuality and an open, relaxed, even playful, attitude toward exploration make for equality in sexuality.

The subsection *Establishing Sexual Relationships* opens with an article that addresses the real starting point of intimate relationship potential: how people feel about themselves and their bodies. This follow-up to an earlier body image survey contains some troubling findings. The next two articles tackle gender issues and behaviors that have the potential to increase attraction, kindle romance, lead to exciting relationships, or undermine all of these.

In the subsection, *Responsible Quality Sexual Relationships,* the examination of sexual and intimate relationships continues through a blending of articles based on research, experience, and advice-giving. It includes wisdom that is helpful for maintaining intimacy in all relationships, while it also covers several potentially disastrous crises that relationships can face. A thought-provoking challenge to our often complex and contradicting cultural beliefs about sex is in "Celibate Passion: The Hidden Rewards of Quitting Sex." These articles provide a backdrop of perspectives and experiences that can assist all in considering, comparing, and improving their own interpersonal and/or sexual relationships.

Looking Ahead: Challenge Questions

What do you feel about your body? How often do you check your appearance in the mirror? How often do you wonder what you look like when you are engaging in intimate or sexual behavior? What impact do you feel these behaviors have on you and your relationships?

What do you see as the greatest barriers to attaining satisfying intimate relationships? Are some people destined to fail at establishing and/or maintaining them? Explain who and why.

What makes male-female intimacy difficult to achieve? Have you learned any lessons about yourself and the opposite sex "the hard way"?

What do you think about flirting and guides like "The Rules" and "The Code"? Are they manipulative retreats to the adversarial roles of the past that prevent equality and spiritual connectedness or a welcome return to romance, the art of courtship, and a needed retreat from boundless sexual freedom?

Do we as a society focus too little or too much on sexual mechanics—sexual parts and acts? List at least six adjectives you find synonymous with *great* sex.

If you had to lose one of your senses *for sex only*, which would it be and why? Is this the same sense you would choose to do without if it were all-encompassing? Why or why not?

Why does intimacy seem more difficult to achieve in the 1990s than in previous generations? If you had a time machine, would you prefer to go back in time, forward in time, or stay where you are as you search for intimacy? Explain your reasons.

If you and your partner were to have different levels of sexual desire/need for sexual intimacy (you want sex more than your partner does or your partner wants sex more than you do, for example), which would be more difficult for you to deal with and why?

The 1997 Body Image Survey Results

BY DAVID M. GARNER, PH.D.

For the past three decades, women and, increasingly, men have been preoccupied with how they look. But the intense scrutiny hasn't necessarily helped us see ourselves any more clearly. While as individuals we are growing heavier, our body preferences are growing thinner. And thinness is depicted everywhere as crucial to personal happiness. Despite the concerns of feminists and other observers, body image issues seem to be only growing in importance.

When most people think of body image, they think about aspects of physical appearance, attractiveness, and beauty. But body image is so much more. It's our mental representation of ourselves; it's what allows us to contemplate ourselves. Body image isn't simply influenced by feelings, and it actively influences much of our behavior, self-esteem, and psychopathology. Our body perceptions, feelings, and beliefs govern our life plan—who we meet, who we marry, the nature of our interactions, our day-to-day comfort level. Indeed, our body is our personal billboard, providing others with first—and sometimes only—impressions.

With that in mind, Psychology Today decided it was time for another detailed reading of the state of body image. The landmark PT national surveys of 1972 and 1985 are among the most widely cited on the subject. We wanted to try and understand the growing gulf between actual and preferred shapes—and to develop the very revealing picture that can be seen only by tracking changes over time. We asked David Garner, Ph.D., to bring his vast expertise to our project. Garner, the director of the Toledo Center for Eating Disorders, is also an adjunct professor of psychology at Bowling Green State University and of women's studies at the University of Toledo. He has been researching and treating eating disorders for 20 years, heading one of the earliest studies linking them to changes in cultural expectations for thinness. From measurements of *Playboy* centerfold models and Miss America contestants, he documented that these "model women" had become significantly thinner from 1959 to 1979 and that advertising for weight-loss diets had grown correspondingly. A follow-up study showed the trend continuing through the late 1980s.

Garner, along with Cincinnati psychotherapist Ann Kearney Cooke, Ph.D., and editor at large Hara Estroff Marano, crafted five pages worth of questions and in our March/April 1996 issue we asked you how you see, feel, and are influenced by your bodies. The response was phenomenal: about 4,500 people returned questionnaires from every state, not to mention Europe, Israel, Puerto Rico, Pakistan, Saudi Arabia, South Africa, New Zealand, Peru, Australia, Japan, and China. Ten months after the questionnaire hit the newsstands, responses are still coming in. Many of you supplemented your surveys with pages pouring out heart and soul. And though you could reply with complete anonymity, a whopping two-thirds chose to include names, addresses, and phone numbers. Some of you even included pictures!

Our statistical analyses were conducted on the first 4,000 responses—3,452 women and 548 men (86 percent women, 14 percent men)—a much wider gender split than in our readership as a whole, which is 70 percent women and 30 percent men. (See "Who Responded to the Survey," below.) The predominantly female response clearly says something about

Who Responded to the Survey

Some of your vital statistics:

	WOMEN	MEN
Total number	3,452	548
Average age	32	35
Actual weight	140	180
Desired weight	125	175
Height	5'5"	5'11"
Caucasian	87%	82%
College grad +	62%	54%
Income: $50,000 +	39%	38%
Heterosexual	93%	79%
Bisexual	4%	8%
Health problems	36%	30%

How You Describe Yourselves

What you have to say about yourselves:

	% WOMEN	% MEN
Relationship-oriented	74	63
Career-oriented	62	56
Happy person	69	66
Spiritually-oriented	66	53
Feminist	55	20
Traditional in values	44	43
Athletic	33	45
Pro-choice	73	64
Politically conservative	21	28
Strong belief in astrology	16	14

Reprinted with permission from *Psychology Today*, January/February 1997, pp. 30-36, 38-40, 42-44, 75, 76, 78, 84. © 1997 by Sussex Publishers, Inc.

A Very Revealing Picture: Psychology Today's 1997 Body Image Survey Findings

Many of our survey results astounded even us veteran observers of the body wars. Among the most important findings:

• Body image is more complex than previous research suggests. It's influenced by many factors, including interpersonal factors, individual factors such as mood, and physical factors like body weight. Cultural pressures also play their part. Which factors are most important vary from person to person.

• Body dissatisfaction is soaring among both women and men—increasing at a faster rate than ever before. This is the great paradox of body preoccupation—instead of insight, it seems to breed only discontent. But a revolution in the way women see themselves—or, more accurately, *want* to see themselves—may be brewing.

• How important is it for people to be the weight they want? Fifteen percent of women and 11 percent of men say they would sacrifice more than five years of their lives to be the weight they want. Twenty-four percent of women and 17 percent of men say they would give up more than three years.

• Among young women ages 13 to 19, a whopping 62 percent say they are dissatisfied with their weight. And it gets a bit worse with age: Sixty-seven percent of women over age 30 also say they are unhappy with how much they weigh.

• While body hatred tends to stay at about the same level as women age, today's young women may be more vulnerable to self-disparagement as they get older. They are being initiated into feelings of body dissatisfaction at a tender age, and this early programming may be difficult to undo.

• Body dissatisfaction afflicts those women who describe themselves as feminists (32 percent) as well as those who say they are more traditional (49 percent). Nevertheless, feminist beliefs seem to confer some behavioral protection: Feminists say they are less willing to use drastic measures like vomiting to control their weight.

• Physical factors, such as gaining weight, are the most common cause of negative feelings about the body. Nevertheless, relationships also have an impact. If your mate doesn't think you look great, you're likely to feel devastated.

• Pregnancy is increasingly being seen not as a normal body function but as an encumbrance to body image. And some women say they are choosing not to have children for this reason.

• More than 75 percent of women surveyed say that menstruation, another normal body function, causes them to have negative feelings about their bodies.

• Bad moods wreak havoc on women's feelings about their bodies. Women get caught in a vicious spiral: emotional distress causes body loathing; disgust with their body causes emotional distress.

• Teasing during childhood or adolescence has an indelible effect on women's feelings about their bodies. Women say that the negative fallout can last for decades—no matter what shape they're currently in.

• What's a quick way to feel good about your body? Good sex. The survey found that in general, good sexual experiences breed high levels of body satisfaction.

• Sexual abuse is an important contributor to body dissatisfaction—but only women who have been sexually abused think so. Other women don't grasp the damage abuse can do to feelings about the body. The experience of sexual abuse seems to create a divide that mirrors the general cultural debate over the validity of allegations of sexual abuse.

• What's the most reliable way to develop positive feelings about your body—to say nothing of boosting your health? Respondents say it's exercising—just for the pleasure of it.

• Curiously, most people say that when it comes to weight control, exercising does not boost body satisfaction. Only women who are very heavy disagree.

• It's no longer possible to deny the fact that images of models in the media have a terrible effect on the way women see themselves. Women who have eating disorders are most influenced by fashion models.

• A model backlash has already begun. Although images of fashion models are intended to inspire identification and emulation, more than three out of ten women say they make them feel angry and resentful. They make more than four out of ten women feel insecure. Women say they are dying to see models that are more representative of the natural range of body types.

the stake women have in this topic. Participants were primarily Caucasian, college-educated, in their early to mid thirties, middle-income, and heterosexual. Women who responded range in age from 13 to 90 and weigh between 77 and 365 pounds (89 women weigh 100 pounds or less; 82 women weigh more than 250 pounds). Men range in age from 14 to 82 and weigh between 115 and 350 pounds. You describe yourselves as relationship-oriented, pro-choice, intellectual, politically liberal, and spiritual. At the top of your worry list are financial matters and romantic relationships. A significant segment described health problems that vary from relatively minor ailments to cancer and AIDS.

Appearing to Be Dissatisfied

The 1997 Psychology Today Body Image Survey shows there's more discontent with the shape of our bodies than ever before. Okay, there are some things we like about our appearance: height, hair, face, feet, and the size of our sex organs generate the most approval. In the span between face and feet, our primary sex organs are a small oasis of favor amidst a wasteland of waist land. Apparently there's little pressure to change the things that we can't see or change. Of course, these areas tend not to be repositories for the accumulation of fat, that object of abhorrence. In contrast, the negative focus remains on our visible attributes, the ones that display fat—the ones that can presumably be controlled or corrected with enough self-discipline.

Fifty-six percent of women say they are dissatisfied with their overall appearance. Their self-disparagement is specifically directed toward their abdomens (71 percent), body weight (66 percent), hips (60 percent), and muscle tone (58 percent). Men show escalating dissatisfaction with their abdomens (63 percent), weight (52 percent), muscle tone (45 percent), overall appearance (43 percent), and chest (38 percent).

What Shaped Your Body Image When You Were Young?

Some of the facts that figure into body image:

	% WOMEN	% MEN
PHYSICAL		
My personal feelings about weight	58	35
INTERPERSONAL		
Being teased by others	44	35
My mother's attitude about my body	31	13
My father's attitude about my body	23	11
Positive sexual experiences	26	28
Sexual abuse	18	7
CULTURAL		
Movie or TV celebrities	23	13
Fashion magazine models	22	6
Sports figures	7	16

Extreme Weight Control

To control my weight during the past year, once a week or more:

	% WOMEN	% MEN	EATING DISORDER*	NO EATING DISORDER
Induced vomiting	6	1	23	1.5
Abused laxatives	6	3	17	3
Took diuretics	5	4	10	4
Used diet pills	12	6	20	9

*Women identifying themselves as having a diagnosed or undiagnosed eating disorder.

Weight dissatisfaction means one thing to men and something entirely different to women. The overwhelming majority of women—89 percent—want to lose weight. How much? The average woman's weight is 140 pounds; the preferred weight is 125 pounds. Only 3 percent of the women who say they are dissatisfied with their bodies want to gain weight; 8 percent want to stay the same. By contrast, 22 percent of the men who say they are dissatisfied with their bodies want to *gain* weight. (See "Men and Body Image.")

The survey also shows a correlation between body dissatisfaction and body weight—those who are more dissatisfied tend to be heavier. In fact, the average weight of the most dissatisfied women is about 180 pounds; the least dissatisfied weigh in at 128 pounds. Both groups have an average ideal weight that's lower than their actual weight; however, in the former group it's fifty pounds away from reality, compared with three pounds for the least dissatisfied.

How important is it for people to be the weight they want? We put the question in stark terms and asked, "How many years of your life would you trade to achieve your weight goals?" The findings are astounding: Fifteen percent of women and 11 percent of men say they'd sacrifice more than five years of their lives; 24 percent of women and 17 percent of men say they would give up more than three years. These answers make us regret not testing the extremes and offering 10- and 20-year options. Still, we can confidently conclude that a significant minority of you believe life is worth living only if you are thin.

A rather drastic measure of weight control is cigarette smoking. Statistics reveal that smoking is on the rise among young women. Robert Klesges, Ph.D., and colleagues at the University of Memphis have repeatedly shown that smoking is used by many women for weight control. While we didn't specifically ask whether you smoke, we did ask whether you smoke to control your weight. About 50 percent of women and 30 percent of men say they puff away to control the pounds.

Body dissatisfaction has very different implications for people depending upon how heavy they are. Among those well above normal weight, body dissatisfaction is a painful expression of despair, but understandable given the cultural stigma of being fat. However, an equivalent amount of self-loathing on the part of thin people suggests a different type of problem—distortion on top of dissatisfaction. Thin

The Weight of Influence: Factors Fostering Positive Body Image

What's instrumental in making you feel good about your body?

	% WOMEN	% MEN
PHYSICAL		
Exercising regularly	64	62
Losing weight	62	39
Feeling thin	53	24
Accepting my body the way it is	50	36
Wearing flattering clothes	46	21
INTERPERSONAL		
Compliments on my appearance	48	44
Love from another person	43	44
Positive sexual experiences	40	41
Good relationships	33	34
EMOTIONAL		
Confidence in my abilities	39	38
Feeling effective as a person	39	36
Meditating	11	9

women distort reality by seeing themselves as fat. Today this type of distortion is rampant and has become the norm. It explains why so many women are susceptible to eating disorders, where the pursuit of thinness is driven by faulty perceptions rather than reality. One hundred and fifty-nine women in our sample are extremely underweight—and 40 percent of them still want to lose weight. Many have eating disorders, to be described later.

Age and Body Image

A number of national studies have shown that body weight is increasing among American adults. Moreover, epidemiologic studies find that body weight increases with age. For both men and women it tends to increase during the first five decades of life, then decline on the way to our inevitable destiny. Although the pattern of gradual weight gain during adulthood recently sparked a public health frenzy, leading to such programs as C. Everett Koop's Shape Up America, an analysis of 13 major studies of weight change by Reuben Andres, M.D., of the Gerontology Research Center in Baltimore, Maryland, found that people who put on some pounds during adulthood survive longer than those who maintain or even lose weight.

Our findings confirm that body weight usually increases with age. On average, both men and women tend to put on five to ten pounds per decade, a trend that stops between the ages of 50 and 59. Weight declines slightly after age 60.

Since satisfaction with our appearance is so closely tied to how much we weigh, particularly for women, it's logical to assume that our self-disparagement would gradually increase over a lifetime. But that's not what we found. The youngest

women, ages 13 to 19, are both the thinnest and the most satisfied with their appearance, however 54 percent of them are still dissatisfied. The number barely increases to 57 percent among women ages 20 to 29. And it remains at around this level, even though women gained five to ten pounds each succeeding decade.

We can't say for sure how these young women will feel as they get older; a survey, of course, taps different women at each age, not the same women over time. Nevertheless, the magnitude of self-hatred among young women is astonishing. Despite being at a weight that most women envy, they are still plagued by feelings of inadequacy. The good news is that even though women gain weight with age, they don't become more dissatisfied as they get older. In fact, there's some evidence that as they age they gain insight and appreciation of their bodies' abilities.

Induction into our culture's weight concerns is happening for women at younger ages. Girls today not only have more weight concerns when they're young, they also lack buffers to protect their psyches. Kids don't know themselves well and have not yet developed many competencies to draw on. It's easier for them to look outside themselves to discover who they are—and find themselves lacking. While we may not be able to draw conclusions about them based on the experiences of older women, we can only hope that over time they develop the insight of this 55-year-old woman from Pennsylvania: "From age 15 to 25, I was very concerned about my body image and went on many diets. As I matured, I realized that personality and morals are more important than how you look and stopped beating myself up and accepted my body. Now I don't worry about my weight but I do eat healthfully and exercise moderately."

In contrast to women, only 41 percent of young men ages 13 to 19 say they are dissatisfied with their appearance. The fig-

The Weight of Influence: Factors Fostering Negative Body Image

What's instrumental in making you feel bad about your body?

	% WOMEN	% MEN
PHYSICAL		
Gaining weight	66	37
Not exercising regularly	44	36
Looking at my stomach in the mirror	44	33
Looking at my face in the mirror	16	15
A certain time in my menstrual cycle	29	—
INTERPERSONAL		
My partner's opinion of my appearance	40	29
Being around someone critical	32	19
Someone rejecting me	26	24
Relationships not going well	24	21
Negative sexual experiences	20	16
EMOTIONAL		
Not feeling confident	22	18
Being in a bad mood	15	9

ures stay about the same for men ages 20 to 29 (38 percent), then spike to 48 percent among 30- to 39-year-olds. They decline again for the 40 to 49 age group (43 percent) and increase for men ages 50 to 59 (48 percent). Again, in contrast to women, a significant proportion of dissatisfied men want to *add* body mass, not lose it. But the critical point is that men as a group are more satisfied with their appearance, although the number who are tormented about their weight and shape appears to be growing.

The Locus of Focus

Because we were interested in discovering what was most instrumental in creating positive and negative feelings about your bodies, we asked how your body image is influenced by certain aspects of physical appearance: gaining weight, feeling thin, looking at your face in the mirror, looking at your stomach in the mirror. Exercise was also included, because we use it to change our body weight and shape.

We assumed focusing on features like the face and the stomach—the latter the bearer of fat and of children—would produce highly-charged feelings, both good and bad. However, we were specifically interested in trying to understand the relative impact of different physical features on body feelings—the locus of focus. We also wanted to measure how physical aspects of appearance stack up against interpersonal factors, such as being rejected, receiving compliments, being teased, and sexual experiences, as well as emotional components, like feeling effective as a person and over-all happiness.

When it comes to what causes negative feelings, gaining weight is at the top of the list for everyone: two-thirds of women and about a third of men say it's a very important cause of their disapproval of their bodies. And the stomach, not the face, is the prevailing locus of disapproval for both men and women. Looking at your stomach in the mirror is an extreme downer for 44 percent of women and 33 percent of men—compared to the face, which was a downer for 16 percent of women and 15 percent of men.

Women are hit with a very specific source of body antipathy: more than 75 percent say that "a certain time in the menstrual cycle" is an important cause of negative feelings about their bodies. And a fear of fatness may be perverting women's attitudes toward pregnancy and childbearing. About a third of women say that, for them, pregnancy itself is an important source of negative body feelings.

If these feelings are strong enough, it's only reasonable to assume that they may affect some women's decisions to have kids. As one 25-year-old Maryland woman offers: "I love children and would love to have one more—but only if I didn't have to gain the weight." A 43-year-old woman from Georgia proselytizes against pregnancy: "I tell every young girl that if they like the way their body looks, don't get pregnant. It messes up a woman's body."

While interpersonal factors are the cause of negative feel-

ings about the body for fewer people, they are highly influential for a significant minority. Forty percent of women and 29 percent of men say their partner's opinion about their appearance is very important to their body image. About a quarter of all respondents say the same goes for someone rejecting them. Thus there's a major connection between the way we feel about our body and the way we perceive others feel about it. One 54-year-old New York woman says: "Since my partner sees me as beautiful, I feel beautiful." This interpersonal connection seems to take root early, as a 17-year-old woman from New York explains: "My partner's feelings about me and my looks mean everything to me. If my mate had an unfavorable opinion, that would be devastating."

What impact does our mood have on our feelings about our body? The survey, as well as other research, suggests a potentially deadly two-way self-perpetuating process. When we feel bad about anything, our body satisfaction plummets, and when we hate our body, our mood takes a dive. A 39-year-old Connecticut woman captures the vicious cycle: "When I'm in a bad mood about anything, I get more critical of my body. When I am more critical of my body, I lose confidence in my abilities." A 35-year-old woman from Pennsylvania illustrates the process: "When I am in a bad mood about something else, my focus often goes right to my body weight and I either feel fat or I obsess about food."

The connection between mood and body is critical; it suggests that body dissatisfaction is not a static entity but rather is governed, at least in part, by our general emotional state. When we feel bad about something else, our bodies get dragged down in the negative tide.

Among the many aspects of body image we looked at was the role of certain life orientations. For example, we compared women who call themselves feminists with those who view themselves more traditionally. There are no differences between

Do Fashion Models Influence How You Feel About Your Appearance?

What's the media's impact on how we see ourselves?

	% WOMEN	Extremely Satisfied Women	Extremely Dissatisfied Women	%MEN
I ALWAYS OR VERY OFTEN:				
Compare myself to models in magazines	27	17	43	12
Carefully study the shapes of models	28	18	47	19
VERY THIN OR MUSCULAR MODELS MAKE ME:				
Feel insecure about my weight	29	12	67	15
Want to lose weight	30	13	67	18
Feel angry or resentful	22	9	45	8

the groups in average body weight. But 32 percent of feminists, compared with 49 percent of traditional women, are strongly dissatisfied with their overall appearance. When asked more specifically about their weight, 24 percent of feminists and 40 percent of traditional women are extremely dissatisfied. The differences translate directly into behavior—twice as many traditionally oriented women vomit to control their weight as women claiming to be feminists. It appears that feminist beliefs confer some behavioral protection.

When we asked what leads to positive feelings about your bodies, the results generally mirrored the findings about negative feelings, but there are some interesting differences. Weight-related factors tended to top the list of sources of positive feelings, paralleling the results for negative feelings. Exercise generated the greatest source of positive feelings. But moderate exercise, we found, goes a long way. People who exercise a lot do not seem to feel any better than those who exercise moderately.

And while both men and women identify a few circumstances that could crash their feelings about their bodies, you point out more factors that bolster it. About twice as many people judge sexual experiences as a source of good feelings rather than bad. For both sexes, interpersonal and emotional factors more often serve to reinforce, not punish. This is encouraging news; it implies that there are many avenues for us to improve our feelings about our bodies.

When we asked what shaped your body image during childhood and adolescence, most women and a significant minority of men reiterate the cultural theme that thinness is the key to happiness. But interpersonal factors also weigh heavily on most of us during development, and women rank them more important than men.

For many, teasing during childhood or adolescence had a crushing affect on body image. So much so that the extent of the damage can't be captured by a questionnaire. The narratives paint a graphic picture of the pain. As one 59-year-old Illinois man recounts: "Being teased when I was a child made me feel bad about my body for years and years." A 37-year-old woman from Ohio admits: "No matter how thin I become, I always feel like the fat kid everyone made fun of." An 18-year-old Iowa woman says: "The memories absolutely haunt me and make me feel like something is wrong with me."

By far, however, the dominant factor that regulates our feelings about our appearance is our body weight—actual body weight as well as attitudes about it. The weight of this influence is staggering compared to other factors. Body weight alone accounts for 60 percent of our overall satisfaction with our appearance; all other physical features combined add only 10 percent more to our level of satisfaction. This suggests a simple solution—just change your weight and happy times will follow. Unfortunately, it's not that simple.

Exercise: The New Holy Grail?

Virtually everyone surveyed says they exercised during the past year—97 percent of both sexes. And exercise gets high marks when it comes to breeding positive body feelings (by a narrow margin for women, a substantial majority for men). Seventy-six percent of women and 86 percent of men report exercising at least two hours a week; 20 percent of women and 27 percent of men exercise five or more times a week for at least 30 minutes. There's a modest relationship between the amount of time spent exercising and satisfaction with appearance, and this is stronger for men than women.

On the surface, it appears that exercise is an uncomplicated remedy for achieving harmony with our bodies. But a closer look at our findings tempers this conclusion. More than 60 percent of women and 40 percent of men indicate that at least half of their workout time is spent exercising to control their weight. And for a significant proportion of both sexes—18 percent of women, 12 percent of men—all exercise is aimed at weight control.

But all that exercise is not leading to body satisfaction, since 88 percent of these women and 79 percent of these men say they are dissatisfied with their appearance. By contrast, among those who exercise for weight control less than 25 percent of the time, only a third are dissatisfied with their appearance. For many women, exercise is simply one more weapon in the weight-control war, a practice that mutes its ability to boost body satisfaction.

However, heavier women say the more they exercise, the bigger the boost to body satisfaction. Among women who weigh more than average, 30 percent of those who exercise more than five times a week are satisfied, compared to 20 percent who exercise less than once a week.

Whether or not exercise is effective as a method of weight control, it does tend to make us feel better about our appearance. It also improves both health and mood.

Sex and Body Image

Sexual experiences affect our body image, and our body image affects our sexual liaisons. You describe this reciprocal relationship poignantly. Body image affects sexual experiences: "The less attractive I feel, the less I desire sex," says a 31-year-old woman from Louisiana. "If at all possible I avoid sex; however, if it should happen, I am unwilling to let go. I have the feeling I may be vulgar to my partner."

The Big Bad Body

The dissatisfaction we feel toward our bodies has not only risen since 1972, the rate at which it's rising is accelerating:

	1972 Survey %		1985 Survey %		1997 Survey %	
	WOMEN	MEN	WOMEN	MEN	WOMEN	MEN
Overall appearance	25	15	38	34	56	43
Weight	48	35	55	41	66	52
Height	13	13	17	20	16	16
Muscle tone	30	25	45	32	57	45
Breasts/chest	26	18	32	28	34	38
Abdomen	50	36	57	50	71	63
Hips or upper thighs	49	12	50	21	61	29

Sexual experiences affect body image: "A bad sexual experience makes me feel embarrassed about my body," admits a 19-year-old Texas woman. Sexual abuse amplifies this self-abasement: "Having been sexually assaulted brought a lot of body hatred, and a desire to not have a body," a 24-year-old woman from Illinois says.

As has been the case for so many other variables in the 1997 Survey, weight gets in the middle of the picture. One 20-year-old Missouri woman states: "I try to lose weight for boyfriends. When I am fat, I know that no one wants to be with me. I feel like unless I have a good body, no decent guy wants me!"

The connection between sexual experiences and body image is affirmed in our overall findings. More than a third of all men (40 percent) and women (36 percent) say that unpleasant sexual experiences are moderately to very important in causing negative feelings of their body. But an even greater percentage—70 percent of men and 67 percent of women—feel that good sexual experiences contribute to satisfactory feelings about their bodies. Few believe they are irrelevant (6 percent of men and 7 percent of women).

Twenty-three percent of women consider sexual abuse moderately to very important in having shaped their body image in childhood or adolescence. That's twice the number of men—10 percent—who think so, perhaps reflecting the difference in rates of abuse between men and women. But the vast majority of men (85 percent) and women (74 percent) declare that it's almost or completely irrelevant, no doubt indicating their lack of personal experience.

The personal accounts of some respondents leave no doubt as to the devastating effects of sexual abuse. An 18-year-old woman says: "As a young child, I was sexually abused by my father. I grew up feeling as though there was something inherently dirty and evil about my body." Abuse is clearly a dominant factor in body image for members of both sexes, but it's not ubiquitous, unlike such factors as teasing by others (73 percent of women and 57 of percent men) and personal feelings about weight (79 percent of women and 56 percent of men).

Intriguingly, those who are dissatisfied with their bodies are much more inclined to view negative sexual experiences as important than those who are body-satisfied. Only 15 percent of women who are extremely satisfied with their bodies say that negative sexual experiences are very important in determining their body image (42 percent say that negative sexual experiences are completely irrelevant). In contrast, 41 percent of body-dissatisfied women regard negative sexual experiences as very important (only 16 percent say they are completely irrelevant). The same is true for men.

Sexual and physical abuse are important contributors to body dissatisfaction—but again primarily it's women who have been sexually abused who think so. Sexual abuse is judged very important by 30 percent of women who are extremely body-dissatisfied, versus 13 percent of the extremely body-satisfied group. Women who feel good about their bodies and have not been victims of abuse just don't grasp the damage abuse can do to feelings about the body.

Men and Body Image

In general, men say they are more satisfied with their bodies than women. And weight plays a less important role in shaping their feelings about their bodies. A little over 12 percent of the men who responded to our survey say they're gay. In general, gay men are more concerned about their weight and have more eating concerns.

	% ALL MEN	% GAY MEN	% WOMEN
I am extremely or somewhat satisfied with my body	57	44	44
Gaining weight is very important in making me feel bad about my body	37	46	66
Feeling thin goes a long way toward making me feel good about my body	24	34	53
Do you ever diet?	58	70	84
Have you ever been diagnosed with an eating disorder?	3	9	14
Do you think you have an eating disorder but haven't been treated?	5	17	14
DO YOU USE:			
Diet pills	5	12	10
Laxatives	2	6	4
Diuretics	3	8	4
Vomiting	1	3	4

EXTREME WEIGHT CONTROL

Eating disorders occur when a person's intense preoccupation with their "fatness" leads them to extreme measures to control their weight. Considerable research indicates that anorexia and bulimia are outgrowths of a negative body image and, further, that today's epidemic increase in eating disorders is related to the intense pressure put on women to conform to ultraslender role models of feminine beauty.

A remarkable 84 percent of women and 58 percent of men report having dieted to lose weight. A sizable proportion of respondents say they have resorted to extreme and dangerous weight-control methods in the last year: 445 women (13 percent) and 22 men (4 percent) say they induce vomiting; more than a third of each of these groups vomit once a week or more. Fourteen percent of women (480) and 3 percent of men (16) say they have actually been diagnosed with eating disorders. Among the very underweight women in our survey, 31 percent (49) indicate they have been diagnosed with an eating disorder. And 11.5 percent of women and 2 percent of men say they have an eating disorder but have never received treatment, although the type of eating disorder was not specified.

Vomiting was more common among those who say they have been diagnosed (23 percent), less common among those who identify themselves as having untreated eating disorders (11 percent). Perhaps most surprising is that 1.5 percent of women (38) vomit for weight control and don't feel they have an eating disorder!

Laxative abuse for weight control is common among those diagnosed with eating disorders (17 percent) and those self-identified (9 percent). It is also reported by 3 percent of women (72) who don't feel they have eating disorders.

Vomiting and laxative abuse seem to be increasingly accepted as "normal" methods of weight control. And eating disorders themselves have become the object of envy, gaining celebrity status with each new high-profile victim. There's even evidence that eating disorders acquire a positive patina with media exposure—even it it's negative—and that actually helps spread them by social contagion. This was driven home by a patient I recently saw. When told she really didn't meet the diagnostic criteria for an eating disorder, she burst into tears. "I tried so hard to get an eating disorder, to be like [a high profile gymnast]," she lamented, "but I guess I can't even get this right."

Not surprisingly, one of the keys to helping people overcome eating disorders is fostering the development of a positive body image. Unfortunately, this means swimming against the cultural stream, as it's extremely hard to avoid ubiquitous thin-is-beautiful messages. Studies of prime-time television indicate that programs are dominated by people with thin body types and thinness is consistently associated with favorable personality traits. But one of the most interesting aspects of the psychology of appearance is that not everyone succumbs to the same pressures.

MEDIATING SELF-PERCEPTION

The media play an important role as a cultural gatekeeper, framing standards of beauty for all of us by the models they choose. Many observers, including eating-disorder specialists, have encouraged producers and editors to widen the range of beauty standards by including models more representative of real women. But often they respond by saying that more diversity will weaken sales; recently *Vogue* magazine acknowledged the outrage toward gaunt fashion models—but denied there's any evidence linking images of models to eating disorders.

The 1997 Body Image Survey gathered direct information on this issue and more generally on the media's impact on self-perception. The results are nothing short of fascinating. Forty-three percent of women report that "very thin or muscular models" make them feel insecure about their weight. This is true for only 28 percent of men. Just under half of women (48 percent) indicate very thin models make them want to lose weight to look like them; 34 percent of men agree. Though drawn to and driven by the image of fashion models, 34 percent of women declare they are angry and resentful at these presumed paragons of beauty, as are 15 percent of men.

The impact of the media, however, is somewhat selective, affecting most strongly those who are dissatisfied with their shape, and who are generally heavier and farther away from the cultural ideal. Women who are extremely satisfied with their weight compare themselves to and study the shapes of models less than half as often as women who are body-dissatisfied.

Even more striking, 76 percent of the women who are dissatisfied with their bodies say that very thin or muscular models make them feel insecure about their weight very often or always (versus 12 percent of body-satisfied women). Sixty-seven percent also say models make them want to lose weight (versus 13 percent of body-satisfied women), and 45 percent say models make them angry or resentful (versus 9 percent of body-satisfied women).

Similarly, those who say they've been diagnosed with an eating disorder report being highly influenced by fashion models. Forty-three percent compare themselves to models in magazines; 45 percent scrutinize the shapes of models. Forty-nine percent say very thin models make them feel insecure about themselves, and 48 percent say they "make me want to lose weight to be like them."

Clearly, body satisfaction, a rather rare commodity, confers relative immunity to media influence. But the existence of a large number of women who are drawn to media imagery but resent the unreality of those images is cause for concern. It suggests they are experiencing an uncomfortable level of entrapment. We wonder how long it will take for their resentment to be unleashed full force on the fashion industry and/or the media—and in what form.

Women and, to a lesser degree, men are not only affected by images in the media, they also want to see themselves represented differently. They're clamoring for

Altering Your Image: Strategies from the Trenches

One of the major goals of the 1997 Body Image Survey was to learn more about how people have remade their image. Though we anticipated receiving a few brief suggestions, we were inundated with your personal accounts of change. We have summarized your suggestions but kept your words. Try and discover what factors play a role in your struggle with your body. And be deliberate about creating a lifestyle that increases your chances for ending the war with your body.

1. Develop criteria for self-esteem that go beyond appearance. One way to make appearance less important is to develop other benchmarks for self-evaluation. A 51-year-old woman from California summarizes the approach: "By achieving in other areas, balancing successes and failures, searching where positives are possible." A 53-year-old Washington man says, "focusing on succeeding at work, participating in sports, and friendships have helped me overcome my negative body feelings."

2. Cultivate the ability to appreciate your body, especially how it functions. One middle-aged woman writes: "I have often wanted to write an article called 'I Have a Beautiful Body.' No, I don't look like Jane Fonda. I look like a normal 46-year-old woman who has had three children. But my body is beautiful because of all it does for me. I have two eyes that can see, a large nose for smelling, a large mouth for eating and smiling, two hands that can hold and hug, two breasts that have nursed three sons, an abdomen that was home to three babies, two legs that can walk everywhere I want to go, and two feet to take me there."

"I have extremely red hair and as a child I hated it because it was so different," says a 20-year-old woman from California. "I have come to realize that my hair is a beautiful and exotic part of me. Now I cherish it."

3. Engage in behavior that makes you feel good about yourself. "When I have negative thoughts and feelings about my physical appearance, I try to behave in ways that will turn them around, like exercise and buying a piece of clothing that enhances my appearance," says a 30-year-old Missouri woman.

"Although Rubenesque at age 54, I currently model nude for a local university art school, meditate daily to focus inward, and enjoy dancing, swimming, archery, art, and my writing projects," says a Georgia woman.

4. Reduce your exposure to noxious images. "I stopped buying fashion magazines completely when I was about 24," says a 30-year-old woman from Michigan. "Comparing myself to the models had a very strong and negative impact."

"One of the things that helped me become more accepting of my body was the realization that it was okay to be female," says a 67-year-old woman from Ohio. "It sounds hokey, but watching old movies starring Sophia Loren and Ava Gardner helped. These women had shoulders, and breasts, and hips, and are some of the sexiest women I have ever seen."

5. Exercise for strength, fitness, and health, not just weight control. "When I was able to stop focusing on how my body looked and began experiencing what it could help me accomplish—climbing, swimming, cycling, surviving in the wilderness—it made me feel extremely satisfied," says a 28-year-old woman from Louisiana.

"About a year ago I started walking every day for about an hour," says a 22-year-old woman from New York. "Because I was walking I felt so good. I also lost 10 pounds, but that didn't matter. My attitude changed because I cared about my health."

6. Seek out others who respect and care about your body; teach them how to talk about and touch your body. "The most recent experience that has helped has been a lover," says a 67-year-old Ohio woman. "He makes me glad to be in this body with this shape and these dimensions."

7. Get out of abusive relationships. "If my partner didn't like my appearance, he would no longer be my partner," says a 31-year-old woman from Alabama. "I eliminate the negative."

8. Identify and change habitual negative thoughts about your body. "I constructed a tape of positive self-talk with personal goals and feelings I want to achieve," says a 25-year-old Washington woman. "When I have a bad attitude about my body, I pop in my tape. It really helps improve my self-image."

"When I look in the mirror at my body I always try to say nice things rather than cringe," continues the wise-beyond-her-years 25-year-old.

9. Decode more complicated thoughts about the body. Are negative thoughts and feelings about your body distracting you from other issues that are really bothering you? A 60-year-old woman writes: "A factor that has helped me come to terms with my body was recognizing that much of my relationship problems had more to do with shyness and lack of social skills than physical appearance. Once I worked on my people skills, I found that I worried less about my appearance."

10. If you can't get over your bad body image, consider seeking professional help. "I was bulimic for 12 years," says a 36-year-old woman from Oregon. "My recovery was based on individual counseling, support from friends, and a hell of a lot of hard work on my part."

11. Control what you can, forget about what you can't. "As far as negativity about my physical appearance," says a 33-year-old woman from Michigan, "I've had one simple rule: work on improving what you can realistically change, and don't spend time worrying about the rest."

change and willing to put their money on their predilections. The overwhelming majority of all respondents—93 percent of women, 89 percent of men—want models in magazines to represent the natural range of body shapes; 82 percent of women assert they are willing to buy magazines containing heavier models, as do 53 percent of men, even though most still believe that clothes look better on thin models.

One 30-year-old woman captures the feeling: "The media portray an image of the perfect woman that is unattainable for somewhere between 98 to 99 percent of the female population. How are we supposed to live up to that standard that is shoved in our faces constantly—I hate it."

THE SHAPE OF THINGS TO COME

More than ever before, women are dissatisfied with their weight and are fighting it with relentless dieting and exercise. Thinness has become the preeminent yardstick for success or failure, a constant against which every woman can be measured, a gauge that has slowly permeated the male mentality. Yet the actual body weight of women in the U.S. has increased over the last 30 years, and consumer pressure for weight-loss products is surging.

Research shows that dieting to lose weight and fear of fatness are now common in girls as young as nine years old—and escalate dramatically during adolescence, particularly among those at the heavier end of the spectrum. The risk of developing an eating disorder is eight times higher in dieting 15-year-old girls than in nondieting 15-year-old girls.

The 1997 Body Image Survey results and cumulative clinical experience suggest there is merit to becoming comfortable with yourself even if you don't conform to current cultural body-size ideals. Some people are naturally fatter, just as others are naturally thinner. Despite a $50 billion-a-year diet industry, conventional treatments for obesity are an abysmal failure. Traditional dietary and behavioral treatments may have an effect in the short term, but they do not produce lasting and clinically significant amounts of weight loss. They are no match for the genetic and biological factors that regulate body weight. They certainly reinforce the myth that weight loss is the preferred route to improve self-esteem. Perhaps the wisest course is to get plenty of exercise—and accept yourself the way you are rather than try to mold yourself into a narrowly defined and arbitrary ideal, no matter how widely pictured it is.

Preoccupation with body image is undoubtedly not good for our mental health, but it also seems to be a metaphor for something larger in the culture—if we could only figure out what. Over a decade ago, the late social critic Christopher Lasch argued that our culture of mass consumption encourages narcissism, a new kind of self-consciousness or vanity through which people have learned to judge themselves not merely *against* others but *through* others' eyes. The "image" projected by possessions, physical attractiveness, clothes, and "personality" replace experience, skills, and character as gauges of personal identity, health, and happiness. We are thrown into a chronic state of unease, perfect prey for an array of commercial "solutions."

Psychiatrists and psychologists have also weighed in on the meaning of body image issues. At the 1996 meeting of the American Psychological Association, Yale psychiatrist Alan Feingold, M.D., received an award for detailing differences in body-image pressures on men and women. Dr. Feingold contends that pressure on women to look good is not only growing but reflects intensified competition for dwindling resources; after all, looks confer a kind of status to women. Others point to role conflicts for women; power issues; a mother-daughter generational rift; and the possibility that in a world of rapidly shifting realities, we seize on the body as an island of certainty—numbers on a scale represent quantifiable accomplishment. Perhaps it's all of these; the body is a big screen on which we now project all of our anxieties.

A Woman's Guide to Flirting

Don't laugh. Courtship pro Susan Rabin swears you'll try her methods someday

JEANNE MARIE LASKAS

SLIGHTLY OPENED MOUTH

TYPE III GLANCE

THE WHISPER

THE TWO-GRIP HANDSHAKE

THE NECK PRESENTATION

THE LIPSTICK APPLICATION

THE HAIR CARESS

Men and women sit attentively on folding chairs in a St. Louis bookstore, belting out the mantra "It's okay to flirt."

"I don't hear you. . . ," says Susan Rabin, the leader of the group.

"It's okay to flirt," they repeat, 200 strong, ranging in age from about 16 to 70. "It's okay to flirt."

Looking on, another few hundred line up in the cookbook section of the store. The turnout for this flirting mini-seminar, part of Rabin's book tour, is so large she'll have to do it twice tonight.

Rabin is the director of the School of Flirting in New York City, which has recently expanded to St. Louis, San Francisco, and Portland, Oregon. Participants pay $20 to listen to Rabin's flirting secrets, learn the flirting handshake (grip, then cover the grip with the other hand), practice the flirting posture (spine flexible and relaxed, arms free to gesture), and receive a diploma.

Why this interest, you ask? Because flirting, at least according to Rabin, is back. Because single people—divorced, never married, never even had a date—aren't sure how to do it. Because ours may very well be the most mixed-up, overanalyzed, misunderstood era of dating in courtship history.

Witness last year's publishing phenomenon *The Rules: Time-Tested Secrets for Capturing the Heart of Mr. Right.* The retro guide ("Rule number five: Don't call him, and rarely return his calls") encourages women to practice the fine art of manipulating a man to the altar. Inevitably, the male response followed: *The Code,* a book promising "time-tested secrets for getting what you want from women—without marrying them!"

Adding to the already crowded self-help and relationships section in bookstores is Rabin's far less combative guide, *101 Ways to Flirt: How to Get More Dates and Meet Your Mate.*

Rabin, a former sex education coordinator for the New York City board of education, believes that flirting is an essential ingredient in courtship and that it's recently gotten a bad rap, partly in reaction to the general sensitivity to sexual harassment and partly because dating got too serious. "My mission is to restore the ancient art of flirting," she says to the bookstore crowd. "Look at old movies—those people were wonderful flirts. Watch Scarlett O'Hara at Twelve Oaks when she had nine men around her, all wanting to bring her some food. Why don't people flirt like that anymore? Why do we think of flirting as manipulative or deceitful or bad? It's not! It's a game! And it's a win-win game because you're making the other person feel good."

But there's a difference between a game you play just for fun and a game you play with a goal in mind. Flirting, Rabin says, falls in the latter category: You flirt to attract a mate. To be a successful flirt, however, is to flirt without such weighty concerns.

"Women, you are not out there to get a ring on your finger," says Rabin. "And men, you are not out there to hop into bed. You are all out there to form a relationship." To do that, you must communicate. Flirting, she says, is the first step.

Scientists would agree. (Yes, there are scientists who study this.) According to academics and other serious types who research human courtship, we're all incurable flirts, programmed to perform a mating dance when the time is right.

Monica Moore, an associate professor in the department of behavioral and social sciences at Webster University in St. Louis, has seen this. For more than a decade Moore has been watching people flirt in the same way bird-watchers watch birds. Her research eventually led her to catalog 52 behaviors women unconsciously use to attract a potential mate.

There is, for instance, the Type I glance ("the room-encompassing glance"), the Type II glance ("the short, darting glance), and the Type III glance ("the gaze fixate"). There's the eyebrow flash, the neck presentation, the pout, the whisper, the giggle, the hair caress, and the lipstick application.

Women do these things in public. Moore saw them. And men like watching these things. Moore saw that, too. "Women initiate courtship with these sexual signals," she says, "and set the pace of courtship."

She also discovered that it was not necessarily the so-called fashion-model types who were approached by the most men. "People think physical attractiveness is the number one thing in the mating game," says Moore. "But it isn't. It makes more sense that a man would approach a high-signaling but less attractive woman, because he doesn't want to be shot down."

The message for women seeking dates is clear: Put away your makeup, your killer heels, your *Rules* and other dating tools—and get out there and practice your neck presentation.

Or some such flirting signal. Rabin has studied all 52 and lists them on a handout. She teaches men (who make up two-thirds of her students) how to recognize the signals, how to know when someone is giving them the green light. She tells them not to act on a single cue—"It's like RSVPing to a party before you're invited"—and to wait for a cluster of messages. She teaches women how to signal and when. For instance, you don't jump right into a gaze fixate without progressing through Type I and Type II glances.

At the bookstore, she assigns an exercise: Turn to your neighbor, and stare. The place erupts with nervous giggles.

"How do you like being stared at?" asks Rabin. "As a matter of fact, in the animal kingdom it's an aggressive act. It's the way you kill your prey. And we don't want to do that in flirting."

Instead, Rabin instructs, take a cue from babies: "Peekaboo, I see you. Then look away. You're playing a game. Flirting is all about eye contact and how you respectfully play with the eyes.

"And men, when you finally get up the nerve to talk to a woman, don't be the sunshine of your own life, okay? Avoid 'I' statements. Try a 'you' statement."

Listening, says Rabin, is a powerful flirting skill, but a smile is even more potent. The perfect smile is one with a slightly opened mouth, indicating an openness to others.

"You can have sex on your mind, but keep it off your lips. And no whining. No criticism, no politics, no opinions . . ."

One thing even the best flirts have to prepare for is rejection. It's inevitable. "But you can't be a mind reader," Rabin says. "You have no idea why someone rejects you. Maybe you remind him of his mother. Try not to take it personally."

Finally Rabin sends the crowd off on a "flirting safari."

"Go browse through the area that has books you want to read. That's where you'll find people with your interests."

Two hundred people mill about, heads down, embarrassed. But soon, it becomes audible: a hello, comments about the weather, a low giggle, a loud guffaw.

"The sound of flirting," says Rabin. "Isn't it beautiful?"

exclusive

men
FOR
SALE

➤ *We challenged 3 advertising agencies to create a campaign to make men more appealing*

BY CARYS BOWEN-JONES

1 Selling their sex drive

SAATCHI & SAATCHI, NY: The Saatchi team—five women led by creative director Meg Rogers —agreed that they'd been saddled with a flawed product and considered ways to improve it. "We thought, well, we could attach a vacuum to his foot to make him more appealing, but that's not very realistic," Rogers recalls. So they decided to concentrate on the product's redeeming features.

The team brainstormed for men's possible selling points. "We came up with dozens: they're cute, they take the tops off pickle jars, they keep your feet warm at night, etc. But we kept coming back to the same thing— they will do anything for sex," says Rogers. Worried that her team had failed to come to grips with the true nature of the product, Rogers assembled a focus group made up of men in the agency. "We asked them what they thought women should like about them as a gender. Number Two on their list was, 'We'll kill bugs for you.' Number One? 'We'll do anything for sex.'"

"Suddenly the light switched on," says Rogers. "'Yes!' we thought, 'men will do anything for sex.' How many times have we had our apartments moved or our cars

fixed by men? It's because men love women, and because they love sexuality, that women have a certain power.'"

They'd cracked it. Suddenly this product, with its boundless sex drive, looked like something they could sell. They wrote a creative brief, just as they would for a bar of soap or a box of corn flakes. And the message was the same as for cereal or soap: "When used correctly, men can improve the quality of your life."

The next step was to create a piece of advertising. "We'd been saying things like 'guys help you move' and 'guys carry your bags,'" says Rogers. "That pointed to an innate quality in men that says, 'If I lift heavy objects for you, I may get sex.'"

And so the image of a naked man hoisting a crimson sofa was born. "This approach is meant to be a bit flirtatious—teasing back, if you will," says Rogers. "Women have become so used to being portrayed as sex objects, and here the tables are turned. It's humorous because that's how you have to look at the relationship between men and women. You have to laugh at it. It's an age-old, very comedic dance between the sexes."

MEN®

Because you can't train your cat to do this.

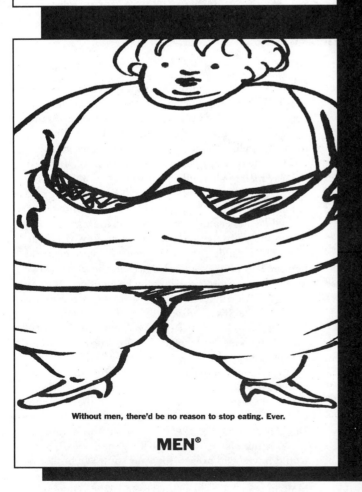

Without men, there'd be no reason to stop eating. Ever.

MEN®

2 Imagine life without men

MAD DOGS & ENGLISHMEN, NY: Mad Dogs art director Carol Holsinger liked the idea of an ad that would buff up the image of the contemporary male. "I thought, 'Men get a bad rap. Maybe they're really not that awful,'" she says. Copywriter Deacon Webster felt the same: "Men seem to be the battered item of the day. Everybody's taking potshots at them." But when they began casting around for men's marketable features, they were hard pressed to find any. It was difficult, Holsinger confesses.

They toyed with promoting the masculine talent for "fixing stuff." They noodled with his sex appeal. But most of the qualities they listed didn't seem likely to persuade consumers to try the product. "A lot of the things we were coming up with were negative—men eat up all the beef jerky, drink a lot of beer, and make more money than women," he explains.

Holsinger, who teaches an advertising course at the School of Visual Arts in New York, decided to throw open the brief to her students and see if they could think of something nice to say. They could. One student, David Polle, depicted a woman appraising her reflection in a mirror and asking her husband, "Do I look fat?" "No, darling," replies her husband, more loyal and obedient than any pet could ever be. "Men. Because you can't train your cat to do this," ran the tag line. Holsinger liked it. "It's a classic exchange between a man and a woman. I think women believe men like really skinny women. But women actually judge themselves a lot more harshly than men do. I think this ad makes men look good."

Webster, meanwhile, came up with what he calls the "oversized lady" ad. Like Holsinger, he believes that the pressure to be thin comes more from women themselves than from men. "The ad is obviously a joke," says Webster. "Women say, 'Oh, life without men would be a lot better because we could eat all we want.'" That, argues Webster, is patently not true: In a man-free world, a lot of women would continue to diet and exercise as furiously as ever. Webster hopes that women will laugh at the ad's sarcasm while reflecting on its message—that men aren't always guilty of bullying women into diet and exercise. And when they laugh, they will like men better and will say to themselves, "Oh, those guys aren't so bad after all."

> Woman,
>
> I know you sometimes have doubts about me. About my feelings for you. I know you sometimes think the very qualities that make me a man, make me a pig. I'm not soft and sensitive like you. I'm self absorbed. I'm callous. I'm a slob. I'm afraid to cry. I forget what I promised. I act like a child. I flirt when I shouldn't. I take you for granted. So I thought I should tell you my feelings so you'd know why I love you and that might remind you why you love me. We are two halves of an amazing creature. I love how we fit together so perfectly despite our very different proportions and angles. I love the feeling of your small delicate hand in my big clumsy paw. I love the way you know just when I need a hug. I love how you forgive me. I love how you can coax out the small boy hiding behind my macho exterior. I love how you make me feel strong and protective. I love being your best friend. I love being your opposite. I love how you make me a better human being. I love you woman. I love being your other half.
>
> Love, Man.

3

A love letter to women

DEUTSCH, INC., NY "One of the first things we did was try to figure out what the hell was the matter with men," says art director Chris Van Oosterhout. With his creative partner, copywriter David Graham, he came up with a litany of masculine failings: Self-absorption. Childishness. Flirting. Fear of crying. The two produced some ads which promised guys could change—then dumped them. A New, Improved Man, they decided, was not what women really wanted. "We made up our minds that there isn't an awful lot wrong with men. Women are already pretty satisfied with them—otherwise there wouldn't be relationships," says Graham. "The vast majority of women love the vast majority of men. It would be artificial to try and reinvent Man and put bells and whistles on him and say, 'Now do you like him?' "

"Yeah, we've got some bad habits," agrees Van Oosterhout, "but there's nothing really wrong with us. After beating our heads against the wall trying to think of how we could improve men, we began to think that women love men for what they are, including some of the stupid, awkward things. We decided that you don't really have to sell a man to a woman. What you do is find the piece of Man that women really love, and reveal it."

So what is this "piece of Man" which makes him so appealing? Graham explains: "Our argument is that whatever physical characteristics a man has, whatever race he is, whatever background he comes from, at his core he has a love of women and a desire to express that love. We think that's what women find appealing in a man—his willingness to confess, to say, 'I love you.' "

This, the pair insist, is Man's true nature. "It shows the way men really think about women, not the stereotypical 'big breasts and nice ass.' That might be said among men, but it's bull—," says Van Oosterhout.

So their ad became a love letter—an intimate piece of communication from Man to Woman in which Man unveils his feelings without his friends there to snigger at him. He not only owns up to his vices and declares his love for Woman, he also explains why he loves her. It is, he argues, because they are two complementary halves of a perfect whole. It's because of their differences that they get along so well. "In this letter you get the sensitivity of Man," says Van Oosterhout. "It's his true self, without the guy thing, without the social veneer," adds Graham.

"I think women make men much better, and I think men make women better. It's a symbiotic relationship," says Van Oosterhout. "A lot of what's in the ad comes from the way I feel about my girlfriend and the way David feels about his wife. It's personal and it's universal. We could have done a wacky, gimmicky ad, but it would have been hollow for your soul. We hope this one makes you feel you're genuinely being sold on Man, instead of him being sold to you with a coupon."

'It' Doesn't Just Happen

A lifetime prescription for sizzling sex

by Clifford L. Penner and Joyce J. Penner

DO YOU REMEMBER the anticipation of going on a date with your future spouse and how desperately you desired one another? And how the sexual tension seemed to mount as you moved toward marriage? Today you may be wondering, "Where's our energy and desire for sex now?"

After 20 years as sex therapists, we're convinced that good sex in marriage doesn't "just happen." Couples who keep the sexual spark glowing through the changing stages of marriage are those who are deliberate about their sexual relationship.

Early Years

Setting the Stage

Vibrant married sex depends in part on getting off to a good start. Newlyweds must compare and work through their conflicting expectations. The most common surprises couples face are differences regarding how often they have sex and who initiates it. If couples discuss and negotiate their differences, they can avoid a good deal of frustration and confusion.

A few possible solutions to differences in desire are: compromise on frequency; the husband brings his wife pleasure with or without release, even if he doesn't feel the need himself; the two can cuddle while the husband or wife bring him release; increase the amount of nonerotic cuddling; or enjoying sexual intimacy with-

out intercourse or orgasm.

Surprisingly, couples often think they are arguing about frequency when the real issue relates to who initiates sex. In therapy, when we ask spouses how often each of them initiates sex, a common response is that the husband initiates sex 90 percent of the time and the wife 10 percent. And yet when we ask the same couple how often they each desire sex, he answers three to four times a week, and she says two to three times a week. Frequency isn't the issue, so what's going on?

Men and women differ in how they initiate sex. The wife, for example, might snuggle with her husband and give him a few kisses. If he takes her overture one step further, he seems like the one who is initiating sex since he has become more direct. Over time, this pattern leads a couple to believe the husband is always the pursuer and the wife is never the initiator. Better communication and reversal of roles can help break this negative pattern, as was the case with Jim and Jenny.

From *Marriage Partnership* magazine, Summer 1997, pp. 16-18. © 1997 by *Marriage Partnership* magazine, Christianity Today, Inc. Reprinted by permission.

Jim feared that if he left it up to Jenny, they would never have sex. However, he was surprised to learn that she actually enjoyed preparing for and initiating time with him once she gave herself permission to overtly express her desire and he gave her the space to do so.

For some couples, expectations aren't the problem area. Instead, they must work through past sexual experiences that have a way of creeping into their relationship and destroying the joy of new discoveries and unique experiences, as Tony and Beverly learned.

Naturally shy, Tony didn't date much in college. The few relationships he did have involved limited physical contact because of his Christian values. Then he met Beverly. She was everything he wanted in a wife—except she wasn't a virgin. Knowing that Beverly had been sexually active with several serious boyfriends left Tony caught between his attraction to her and his desire to enter marriage as a virgin and marry a virgin.

The intensity of his dismay over Beverly's past didn't hit Tony until a month after he proposed to her. After they married, he continually let her know how disgusted he was with her. He asked detailed questions about her previous boyfriends, then used that information to shame her. Their sex life continued to deteriorate, and finally they sought help.

The first step we recommended was for both Tony and Beverly to experience God's forgiveness. We helped Tony realize that Beverly's actions were not an intentional violation of him as her current husband. He needed to acknowledge that she had been spiritually washed clean before God and could now be considered his virginal bride.

Next, he had to stop asking questions about his wife's past and then learn to distract his mind from any mental images of her previous involvements. We further recommended that they temporarily stop having intercourse and learn to delight in each other by working through a step-by-step retraining program. This process would eventually lead them to re-consummate their marriage based on a foundation of mutual trust and desire.

Finally, many couples have difficulty transferring their premarital passion into their marriages because they have false assumptions about married sex. Jamie had been raised in a warm, nurturing home, but much of her knowledge about sex came from movies and television—especially daytime soap operas. Curtis, on the other hand, had grown up seeing playful flirting and open physical affection between his father and stepmother. Jamie was devastated when Curtis would come up behind her and start fondling her. She was convinced that a satisfying and delightful sex life should be like what is portrayed on the

"soaps." She envisioned the powerful pull of desire and the wooing of a new or "illicit" sexual relationship. Her tears of disappointment left Curtis befuddled, and eventually his frustration over not being able to please her led to outbursts of anger.

To develop a mutually satisfying and delightful love life, couples have to make the shift from the newness of passion to the intimacy of deeply sharing themselves with each other for the joy of companionship and the pleasure of each other's bodies. Jamie needed to counter her myth that passion just happens with the knowledge that she and Curtis were responsible for making great sex happen.

The Middle Years
Making Time, Finding Energy
During marriage's middle years, you may feel as though you are merely surviving sexually. The demands of life use up your energy, and your primary desire is often for sleep, not sex.

Jerry and Elaine, married for 13 years, know firsthand that with three kids, two careers and other commitments, finding the time and energy for sex is a challenge. However, another issue complicates their love life. Jerry clings to the false assumption that Elaine should be available to him sexually whenever he desires. The reality is that marriage is a license to freedom without demand; not a license to possess and control a spouse.

Couples who keep the sexual spark glowing are those who are deliberate about their sexual relationship.

Couples in the second stage of marriage will find their sex life stymied if they continue to believe certain myths about sex. For instance, if Jerry believes that sex has to be spontaneous to be wonderful, he and Elaine won't be having a whole lot of sex. And when they do have sex, it will come at the end of the day when they are both fatigued—something neither of them would prefer.

Another common myth is that spouses must wait for sexual desire before they initiate lovemaking. If they follow that principle, couples can expect to do a lot of waiting and not much acting. Activities and jobs are not the only distractions. At this stage, the privacy necessary for sexual freedom must be protected. For the sexual relationship to survive the challenges of these middle years, private, uninterrupted time for the two of you must be planned into your schedule.

You must keep the pilot light of your sexual relationship lit—even if you don't have the time and energy to turn the flames up as high as you used to. But how do you do that?

• *Keep kissing, passionately, every day.* Kissing is the barometer of the state of your sexual relationship.

• *Keep open by sharing every day.* Also, plan regular times to talk about sex. Talk about what you like and don't like. Share your dreams and desires. Negotiate your differences. Don't give up.

• *Keep committed to sex, in spite of all the distractions.* Your marriage and sexual relationship must continue to be high priorities. Be cautious of commitments that rob you of time for one another.

• *Keep physically fit.* Rather than watch TV, take a walk together or go bicycle riding. In fact, the best thing you can do for your sex life is to put the TV in the garage!

• *Keep well-groomed.* Maintaining proper care of your body and practicing good hygiene show that you care about and respect your spouse.

• *Keep your sexual feelings turned toward home.* Fantasize being with each other. If sexual feelings are triggered in response to someone other than your mate, immediately put your spouse in the picture and bring the spark home!

• *Keep scheduled.* Just as you need to schedule quality time with your family or individual time with a child, you need to schedule time for your sexual relationship.

• *Keep sex positive.* Your sexual times will be most satisfying if they are free of demand and anxiety and full of care, warmth, physical pleasure and fun.

• *Keep learning about your own body and your mate's body.* Read books on sexual enhancement out loud together. Experiment with new ideas.

• *Keep coming up with surprises to keep sex from becoming boring.* Leave a love note on your spouse's pillow, light a candle, buy new sheets or change your position in bed.

The Later Years
Saving the Best for Last

With children out on their own, personal distractions reduced and work pressures lessened, marriage's later years can be the most delightful, relaxed years of a couples' sexual life. When our last child left for college three years ago, she wondered if we'd get bored. Far from it! We can spontaneously have a candlelight dinner by the fireplace and make love anytime, anywhere. We're once again enjoying the freedom we had in the early years of our marriage, a freedom that we gladly relinquished during the 26 years we had children at home.

> Past sexual experiences have a way of creeping into a marriage and destroying the joy of new discoveries.

In a society that worships youth and disregards the elderly, it is not uncommon to encounter the attitude that sexual activity among the "older set" is suspect or strange. Since sex is so highly connected with the virility of youth, it is no wonder that some people assume sexuality disappears as the skin wrinkles and the hair turns gray. But couples who remain sexually active to the end are likely to be healthier and happier as well as more agile and virile. In fact, the oldest couple we've ever counseled was an 85-year-old man and his 84-year-old wife. They just needed a few sessions for some "mid-course" adaptation!

Certain physical changes are to be expected as the body ages, and those changes naturally affect sexual functioning. However, knowing what to expect can eliminate some of the stress you may experience as you adjust to the changes.

The production of estrogen and progesterone decrease when a woman reaches menopause. Physical and emotional symptoms accompany the hormonal changes. Hot flashes, general aches and pains and weight gain are common. Emotional reactions such as depression, anxiety or erratic mood swings can affect the sexual relationship. The physical changes that most affect sex are a thinning of the vaginal wall, a lessening of vaginal lubrication and a sluggishness of the vaginal muscle. Hormonal replacement therapy, a vaginal lubricant, regular exercise, exercise of the vaginal muscle and good nutrition with a vitamin-mineral supplement can increase a woman's sense of well-being and sexual pleasure.

Men must also adapt to the changes that come as a result of lower testosterone levels. A husband may experience less urgent, and possibly less frequent, sexual desire. He will likely require direct penile stimulation to get aroused rather than responding to visual stimulation. His erections may not be as firm as they once were, but will still be sufficient for entry. He may not need to ejaculate with each experience, and his ejaculations will be less intense. But neither of these changes should detract from his satisfaction.

At any stage of life, an illness or accident may interfere with typical sexual patterns, but this is more likely true with aging. Touch and the intimacy of closeness are even more important when dealing with physical limitations. Pleasure does not need to stop; it may only need to change. New positions, such as lying side by side, may actually add a new spark. Sex in the morning or after a nap when both of you are well rested may be better.

There is something beautiful about two people enjoying physical intimacy in their fading years just as they did in their blooming years. Older couples can do most anything the young can do—it just may take them longer.

A married life of greater love, passion and intimacy begins with a husband who adores and affirms his wife, and a wife who invites her husband to share in all her sexual intensity. And that can only happen when couples commit time and energy to creating a rewarding, healthy sex life—from the honeymoon night right through to their golden years.

Clinical psychologist Clifford Penner, Ph.D., and Joyce Penner, a clinical nurse specialist, practice in Pasadena, California. They are co-authors of Getting Your Sex Life Off to a Great Start (Word), Restoring the Pleasure (Word) *and* Men and Sex (Thomas Nelson).

better
sex
in three days

Can a long-married couple find new ways to spice up their lovelife? What we learned may surprise—and delight—you. By Dianne Hales.

A stint at Canyon Ranch, in Tucson, one of the country's top spas. A romantic getaway with Bob, my beloved husband of almost twenty years. An entire workshop devoted to couples and sexuality. My first question: "How could I say no?" My second: "How could I get my husband to say yes?"

So I fudged. "You'll love Canyon Ranch," I assured Bob. I talked up the food, the facilities, the fun. As for the seminar's subject—"Sex: Body and Soul"—I spoke vaguely about intimacy and "couples' stuff"—issues that were right up his alley as a psychiatrist. When a friend asked when I planned to fill Bob in on the details, I replied, "On the plane." At that point of no return, Bob rolled his eyes heavenward and surrendered to his fate.

Warming Up

At the first session of the three-day workshop, thirty-six of us settled warily onto floor cushions in a large circle. With the exception of some cuddly newlyweds, the group was mainly middle-aged couples. As I surveyed the room, I couldn't help wondering: What were such ordinary-seeming married people doing at a sexuality seminar?

We soon found out. Lana Holstein, M.D., director of women's health at Canyon Ranch, who was conducting the seminar with her husband, David Taylor, M.D., a family physician, divided us into pairs. We were to ask each other two questions: What were their intentions in coming to the workshop? And what were their greatest fears?

Most of the women, with children growing or grown, felt ready to focus on an aspect of their busy lives they'd long neglected. "Sex is like driving: You can get where you want to go in a Geo or a Mercedes," said one woman. "I'm ready to move up." The men were dubious. A surgeon worried about wasting his valuable time. Several businessmen feared they'd anger their wives by walking out before the workshop's end. (None did.) Almost everyone, female and male, admitted to being embarrassed.

No need to worry about awkward revelations or demonstrations, Lana reassured the group. But there would be techniques to master. The first was a lesson in something most of us had been doing for decades: kissing. As instructed, each of us gave our spouses a cursory buss. It looked and felt awkward, like a bunch of overage players trying a reluctant round of spin the bottle.

Then, while closing our eyes and breathing slowly, we each sat back and focused on the sensations in our own lips, moving them in and out, around and about. After several minutes, we repeated lip-to-lip contact. Suddenly, the atmosphere seemed somehow cozier. And the experience was indeed better. A kiss, it turns out, doesn't always have to be just a kiss.

Homework during the workshop, we learned, would involve various ways for "honoring" and pleasing each other—supposedly without actually having intercourse until the final day (although the sex police weren't checking). The first night's assignment: practice kissing. Bob and I aced it.

Sexual Healing

As you might expect at a sexuality workshop, there was intense breath-

 From *Ladies' Home Journal*, August 1997, pp. 90, 94-96. © 1997 by Dianne Hales. Reprinted by permission.

Five Sexy Strategies

Want to put some sizzle in your life? Follow these tips from the Canyon Ranch workshop:

- Give each other "love zingers" every day. Communicate quick, positive statements of love and affection.
- Practice the Golden Rule. "When it comes to sex, do to your partner what you'd like done to you," suggests Lana Holstein, M.D. It may be the best way of inspiring your mate to try something new.
- Create a special space for sex. "If you want sex to be more meaningful, you have to think about [your surroundings]," notes Lana. Move the TV out of the bedroom and bring in flowers and candles.
- Develop a ritual for sexual intimacy. Find a way to connect—through touch, talking or looking into each other's eyes—before making love.
- Become mutual explorers. The most positive way for a couple to enhance their sexual relationship is with an attitude of shared adventure. That way, says Lana, "Both partners go forward together."

ing—but of the deep, not the heavy, variety.

We played "push hands," a tai chi technique in which partners take turns guiding each other's movements. We alternated inhaling and exhaling, looking into each other's eyes and synchronizing our breaths. Individually and in pairs, we focused on the rhythmic beating of our hearts and the flow of energy through our bodies.

What did any of this have to do with sex? A lot, said Lana. "By getting in tune with each other's heart rate and breathing, you make love with your whole being."

When the couples broke into small discussion groups, we realized that each of us usually focused on only one or two dimensions of sex. As one man put it, "Guys just want to get it on; we're almost entirely biological." The women, on the other hand, tried to explain why romantic symbols—flowers, music, gifts—still matter, even after all these years, as signs of enduring commitment.

Most of us had never used New Age terms, like "authentic," for sex. As Lana explained, this simply means opening up and revealing one's true self. "You're not making love to some object of desire or a fantasy, but to a real person whom you know and cherish," she said.

"You're able to let down some of your fears, to be accepted for who you are." Most of us, happily, had been there, done that and like it.

Can Sex Be Sacred?

"Transpersonal" sexuality—a meeting of souls rather than a mere melding of bodies—seemed far more elusive. "This is a way of thinking about sex as sacred," Lana noted. Based on the tantric view of sex as an exchange of energy between two people, it demands a heightened awareness. "You're giving and receiving energy," said Lana. "You're very aware of making love to the sacred being within your partner."

Glancing around the room, I saw some eyes rolling—including my husband's. I could understand why. Unfortunately, as spouses we see so much of each other that we forget to really look at the person we love, let alone think of him or her as sacred.

To help us refocus, Lana and David had the women and men stand opposite each other in concentric circles. As we moved around the circle and changed partners, the women were told to look for the little boy—vulnerable and sweet—inside the man before us; the men, to try to see the loving, lovely little girl inside the woman in front of them. We then tried to visualize our part-

ners as the men and women they are, filled with hopes, fears and dreams, and as the people they might still become. Finally, we pictured the person facing us as embodying a sacred life force.

There was something curiously touching about looking at relative strangers in this way. The men seemed boyishly appealing. The women, my husband noticed, took on a sort of inner glow. By the time we reconnected with our spouses, their familiar faces were the most welcome and radiant of all.

The Goddess Within

Certainly "goddess" had never had a career aspiration of the thoroughly modern women gathered at the workshop. But the more Lana and David discussed the goddess of sexual energy within every woman, the more appealing it sounded. One woman even added the word *goddess* to her name tag.

What qualifies a woman for promotion to a pantheon? "In the Eastern tradition," David explained, "sexual energy resides in the woman. Her lover's role is to unleash this powerful force by acknowledging and honoring her as a goddess. This is totally counter to the Western notion of sexual energy as something that men have and bring to women."

This also contradicts everything many of us were told about what nice girls do—and don't do. "Often women lock their sexual self away early in life," Lana noted. "They think, 'She's too dangerous.' I see a lot of women who are midlife virgins. They may have had sex thousands of times and given birth to children, but they've never experienced their sexual power or taken pleasure in being female."

It's never too late for a woman to find her inner goddess. "She must believe that she is entitled to experience a fulfilling sexual life," said Lana. She must then challenge any rigid attitudes that get in her way.

Yet the goddess gig can take some getting used to. We broke into all-male and all-female groups to get our instructions for a homework session dedicated to worshipping the deity. The men were taught fundamental tantric principles, such as massage of the "sacred spot" (otherwise known as the G-spot) in a woman's vagina. The women were told to lie back and enjoy. But when we reassembled again in same-sex groups, the goddesses were disgruntled. "We got into an argument because he kept insisting he'd found my G-spot and I kept saying he hadn't," said one. "It was so annoying, I was ready to pay to make him stop," groused another.

Afterward, I couldn't wait to talk to Bob. "The goddesses are angry," I reported. "How do the guys feel?" He looked at me in amazement. "They all bragged about how much their wives loved it," he said. We dissolved in laughter. Even goddesses and their worshipers, it seems, are from different planets.

Taking It Home

Each morning Lana discreetly asked for a brief "weather report" on the group members' psychological climate. The increasingly mellow "meteorologists" were reporting sunshine and clear skies, even a rainbow or two. One man crooned the opening lyrics of "Tomorrow" one day and "Oh, What a Beautiful Mornin'" the next.

When Lana and David asked the group to list the things that get in the way of love and loving in the real world, the first was a four-letter word: kids. Of all the conflicting roles in our lives, the women agreed, none collide more than goddess and mommy. Yet almost every couple in the group had managed to find ways to carve out some time for sex—by swapping child-sitting with neighbors, arranging visits to grandparents or installing locks on the bedroom door.

Ultimately, we had to admit that the most difficult challenges were intangible blocks like anger and fatigue. "Anger can poison your entire relationship," said Lana. "If you get mad at your spouse, admit it, deal with it and move on. If you hold on to it, sooner or later, you have to decide: Would I rather be right or be loved?"

Often the problem isn't temper, but tiredness. Should you forget about sex if you're too pooped for passion? Not at all, said David. "Sex can be a source of nourishment and energy, whether you feel sexy or not," he explained. Couples rarely regret rousing themselves to make love, Lana added. "For the short amount of time that sex takes, we get so much out of it. We sleep better. We feel better. There are tremendous chemical changes in the brain. Sex may be the single best thing you can do to feel better."

Gifts From The Heart

On the final day of the workshop, each couple had to create a drawing. A few husbands and wives immediately divided the paper in half and worked on independent creations. Some opted for abstractions—as Bob and I did. With a smile we realized that each time one of us would start to sketch a form, the other would complete it.

At the final celebratory circle, partners exchanged gifts (which could not be store-bought). One husband gave his wife a thorn to represent a problem that he had allowed to come between them for years. One woman presented her husband with an orange, in the hope that both of them would always be willing to peel away the tough outer layers to enjoy the sweetness underneath.

My husband [and] I still smile when we think back to our stay at Canyon Ranch. Even though we've found it impossible to re-create the sensual, mellow ambience, we try to set aside some precious moments each week just for each other. And we certainly haven't forgotten the enormous difference between having sex and making love. Now, if he'd only start calling me goddess.

Dianne Hales is a contributing editor of Ladies' Home Journal.

Celibate Passion

The hidden rewards of quitting sex

Kathleen Norris
The Christian Century

Kathleen Norris is the author of Dakota *(Ticknor & Fields, 1993).*

Celibacy is a field day for ideologues. Conservative Catholics tend to speak of celibacy as if it were an idealized, angelic state, while feminist theologians such as Uta Ranke-Heinemann say, angrily, that celibate hatred of sex is hatred of women. That celibacy constitutes the hatred of sex seems to be a given in popular mythology, and we need only look at newspaper accounts of sex abuse by priests to see evidence of celibacy that isn't working. One could well assume that this is celibacy, impure and simple. And this is unfortunate, because celibacy practiced rightly is not at all a hatred of sex; in fact it has the potential to address the troubling sexual idolatry of our culture.

One benefit of the nearly ten years that I've been affiliated with the Benedictines as an oblate, or associate, has been the development of deep friendships with celibate men and women. This has led me to ponder celibacy that works, practiced by people who are fully aware of themselves as sexual beings but who express their sexuality in a celibate way. That is, they manage to sublimate their sexual energies toward another purpose than sexual intercourse and procreation. Are they perverse, their lives necessarily stunted? Cultural prejudice would say yes, but I have my doubts. I've seen too many wise old monks and nuns whose celibate practice has allowed them to incarnate hospitality in the deepest sense. In them, the constraints of celibacy have somehow been transformed into an openness. They exude a sense of freedom.

The younger celibates are more edgy. Still contending mightily with what one friend calls "the raging orchestra of my hormones," they are more obviously struggling to contain their desire for intimacy and physical touch within the bounds of celibacy. Often they find their loneliness intensified by the incomprehension of others. In a culture that denies the value of their striving, they are made to feel like fools, or worse.

Americans are remarkably tone-deaf when it comes to the expression of sexuality. The sexual formation that many of us receive is like the refrain of an old Fugs song: "Why do ya like boobs a lot—ya gotta like boobs a lot." The jiggle of tits and ass, penis and pectorals assaults us everywhere—billboards, magazines, television, movies. Orgasm becomes just another goal; we undress for success. It's no wonder that in all this powerful noise, the quiet tones of celibacy are lost.

But celibate people have taught me that celibacy, practiced rightly, does indeed have something valuable to say to the rest of us. Specifically, they have helped me better appreciate both the nature of friendship and what it means to be married. They have also helped me recognize that celibacy, like monogamy, is not a matter of the will disdaining and conquering the desires of the flesh, but a discipline requiring what many people think of as undesirable, if not impossible—a conscious form of sublimation. Like many people who came into adulthood during the sexually permissive 1960s, I've tended to equate sublimation with repression. But my celibate friends have made me see the light; accepting sublimation as a normal part of adulthood makes me more realistic about human sexual capacities and expression. It helps me better respect the bonds and boundaries of marriage.

Any marriage has times of separation, ill health, or just plain crankiness in which sexual intercourse is ill advised. And it is precisely the skills of celibate friendship—fostering intimacy through letters, conversation, performing mundane tasks together (thus rendering them pleasurable), savoring the holy simplicity of a shared meal or a walk together at dusk—that help a marriage survive the rough spots. When you can't make love physically, you figure out other ways to do it.

The celibate impulse in monasticism runs deep and has an interfaith dimension. It is the Dalai Lama who has said, "If you're a monk, you're celibate. If you're not celibate, you're not a monk." Monastic people are celibate for a very practical reason: The kind of community life to which they aspire can't be sustained if people are pairing off. Even in churches in which the clergy are often married—Episcopal and Russian Orthodox, for example—their monks and nuns are celibate. And while monastic novices may be carried along for a time on the swells of communal spirit, when that blissful period inevitably comes to an end the loneliness is profound. One gregarious monk in his early 30s told me that just as he thought he'd settled into the monastery, he woke up in a panic one morning, wondering if he'd wake up lonely for the rest of his life.

From *Utne Reader,* September/October 1996, pp. 51-53. Originally from *The Christian Century,* March 20, 1996. Adapted from *The Cloister Walk* by Kathleen Norris. © 1996 by Kathleen Norris. Reprinted by permission of Riverhead Books, a division of The Putnam Publishing Group.

Another monk I know regards celibacy as the expression of an essential human loneliness, a perspective that helps him as a hospital chaplain when he is called upon to minister to the dying. I knew him when he was still resisting his celibate call. The resistance usually came out as anger directed toward his abbot and community, more rarely as misogyny. I was fascinated to observe the process by which he came to accept the sacrifices that a celibate, monastic life requires. He's easier to be with now; he's a better friend.

This is not irony so much as grace: In learning to be faithful to his vow of celibacy, the monk developed his talent for relationship. It's a common story. I've seen the demands of Benedictine hospitality—the requirement that all visitors be received as Christ—convert shy young men who fear women into monks who can enjoy their company.

Celibates tend to value friendship very highly. And my friendships with celibate men, both gay and straight, give me some hope that men and women don't live in alternate universes. In 1990s America, this sometimes feels like a countercultural perspective. Male celibacy, in particular, can become radically countercultural insofar as it rejects the consumerist model of sexuality that reduces a woman to the sum of her parts. I have never had a monk friend make an insinuating remark along the lines of "You have beautiful eyes" (or legs, breasts, knees, elbows, nostrils), the kind of remark women grow accustomed to deflecting. A monk is supposed to give up the idea of possessing anything, including women.

Ideally, in giving up the sexual pursuit of women (whether as demons or as idealized vessels of purity) the male celibate learns to relate to them as human beings. That many fail to do so, that the power structures of the Catholic Church all but dictate failure in this regard, comes as no surprise. What is a surprise is what happens when it works. For when men have truly given up the idea of possessing women, a healing thing occurs. I once met a woman in a monastery guest house who had come there because she was pulling herself together after being raped, and she needed to feel safe around men again. I've seen young monks astonish an obese and homely college student by listening to her with as much interest and respect as to her conventionally pretty roommate. On my 40th birthday, as I happily blew out four candles on a cupcake ("one for each decade," a monk in his 20s cheerfully proclaimed), I realized that I could enjoy growing old with these guys.

As celibacy takes hold in a person, as monastic values supersede the values of the culture outside the monastery, celibates become people who can radically **affect those of us out "in the world," if only because they've learned how to listen without possessiveness, without imposing themselves. In talking to someone who is practicing celibacy well, we may sense that we're being listened to in a refreshingly deep way. And this is the purpose of celibacy, not to attain some impossibly cerebral goal mistakenly conceived as "holi-** ness," but to make oneself available to others, body and soul. Celibacy, simply put, is a form of ministry—not an achievement one can put on a résumé but a subtle form of service. In theological terms, one dedicates one's sexuality to God through Jesus Christ, a concept and a terminology I find extremely hard to grasp. All I can do is catch a glimpse of people who are doing it, incarnating celibacy in a mysterious, pleasing, and gracious way.

The attractiveness of the celibate is that he or she can make us feel appreciated, enlarged, no matter who we are. I have two nun friends who invariably have this effect on me, no matter what the circumstances of our lives on those occasions when we meet. The thoughtful way in which they converse, listening and responding with complete attention, is a marvel. And when I first met a man I'll call Tom, I wrote in my notebook, "Such tenderness in a man . . . and a surprising, gentle, kindly grasp of who I am."

I realized that I had found a remarkable friend. I was also aware that Tom and I were fast approaching the rocky shoals of infatuation—a man and a woman, both decidedly heterosexual, responding to each other in unmistakably sexual ways. We laughed a lot; we had playful conversations as well as serious ones; we took delight in each other. At times we were alarmingly responsive to one another, and it was all too easy to fantasize about expressing that responsiveness in physical ways.

The danger was real but not insurmountable; I sensed that if our infatuation were to develop into love, that is, to ground itself in grace rather than utility, our respect for each other's commitments—his to celibacy, mine to monogamy—would make the boundaries of behavior very clear. We had few regrets, and yet for both of us there was an underlying sadness, the pain of something incomplete. Suddenly, the difference between celibate friendship and celibate passion had become a reality; at times the pain was excruciating.

Tom and I each faced a crisis the year we met—his mother died, I suffered a disastrous betrayal—and it was the intensity of those unexpected, unwelcome experiences that helped me to understand that in the realm of the sacred, what seems incomplete or unattainable may be abundance after all. Human relationships are by their nature incomplete—after 21 years my husband remains a mystery to me, and I to him, and that is as it should be. Only hope allows us to know and enjoy the depth of our intimacy.

Appreciating Tom's presence in my life as a miraculous, unmerited gift helped me to place our relationship in its proper, religious context, and also to understand why it was that when I'd seek him out to pray with me, I'd always leave feeling so much better than when I came. This was celibacy at its best—a man's sexual energies so devoted to the care of others that a few words could lift me out of despair, give me the strength to reclaim my life. Celibate love was at the heart of it, although I can't fully comprehend the mystery of why this should be so. Celibate passion—elusive, tensile, holy.

THE HEALING POWER
of Intimacy

Healthy long-term relationships offer big rewards—better health, longer life, even more sex than the single life offers. But less than 50 percent of couples stick together for the long haul. Here's how some therapists are teaching couples to use their relationship "hot spots" for greater intimacy and lasting love.

BILL THOMSON

Bill Thomson is Senior Features Editor of Natural Health.

Joe and Martha came to see couples therapist Seymour Boorstein when their relationship was in crisis. They'd been married many years but were locked in a terrible battle over the renovations of their guest cottage. Martha wanted a much bigger refrigerator and stove than Joe wanted. He was interested in aesthetics and insisted on less intrusive appliances. She became outraged at his refusal to go along with her plan. Caught in a deadlock, they went to Boorstein.

A psychiatrist and editor of a textbook on transpersonal psychology, Boorstein looks at marriage from a mind/body perspective. His wife and co-teacher, Sylvia, teaches meditation and has a new book out, *IT'S EASIER THAN YOU THINK: THE BUDDHIST WAY TO HAPPINESS* (HarperSanFrancisco, 1995). They've been together forty-three years.

In his work, Seymour has found that the majority of problems in couple relationships are caused when our primitive instinct for survival is triggered. When you or your partner get angry—whether you're peeved at him for burning the toast or outraged at her for wrecking the car—it is because the mind has perceived a threat and sent the body into a fight-or-flight mode.

"It's important for the couple to see that although they are disagreeing about

the size of a stove, they really aren't," says Boorstein. "It's an issue of survival. What's upsetting Martha is not so much the now, but what she's projected from the past into the now."

In therapy sessions with Boorstein, Martha learned that as a child she had not been fed regularly and needed to scream for food. As a woman, she had always been more comfortable with a well-stocked, large refrigerator.

"The instant she got that awareness," Boorstein says, "her rage disappeared." She saw the unreasonableness of her demand and was more comfortable with smaller appliances. Joe felt compassion for his wife. He sincerely told her to renovate the cottage and install appliances in a way that made her comfortable.

Because the parts of the brain that perceive threats, the limbic and reptilian brains, are the more "primitive" ones, which respond as if survival were at stake, our automatic tendency when we perceive a threat is to fight or flee—the two classic reactions during relationship struggles. A third part of the human brain, the neocortex, is the relational part of the brain which Boorstein believes is where our lovingness originates. The neocortex is able to distinguish between true threats to our survival and imposters, while the primitive parts of the brain (which develop in children before the relational part does) respond swiftly to anything even resembling a threat.

"When we get frightened on any primitive level," Boorstein explains, "the primitive brain overrides the neocortex and does what's necessary for survival. These are very different from the strategies we need to make a relationship work."

When two people—whether married, long-term heterosexual, or same-sex couples—begin to understand one another in this way, it becomes easier to override the primitive brain. As a couple learns to examine what's triggering their feelings, they slowly pull away from living in survival mode. Not only does this enable them to get along, they stop subjecting their bodies to the chronic stress that accompanies repeated fight-or-flight reactions.

Numerous studies have confirmed the effects of chronic stress, from high blood pressure to immune disorders to depression. From a health standpoint, in other words, the brain that's loving wins out over the brain that's stressing, every time. This explains, in part, why couples who work out their problems are likely to be healthier (*see* box "Marriage Will Make You Healthier, Wealthier, and Sexier").

Couples can learn strategies to understand their "hot spots"—the areas of conflict within their marriage or long-term relationship—and use them to strengthen bonds and build trust.

Indeed, the Boorsteins and other innovative therapists are now helping couples access issues from the past that set off the primitive brain and cause ranting and raving or splitting. Their work is

MARRIAGE WILL MAKE YOU HEALTHIER, WEALTHIER, AND SEXIER

While our national divorce rate—50 percent—might make you think marriage doesn't have much to offer, Linda J. Waite, Ph.D., a researcher at the University of Chicago, recently assembled some impressive data on the fate of unmarried versus married people. Consider the following evidence:

■ **Being single lowers life expectancy more than cancer.** For both men and women, being unmarried eats into life expectancy more than the risks of being overweight and getting cancer. For single men, bachelorhood is a greater risk factor than heart disease. They pay for their freedom with 3,500 days of their life (almost ten years) while heart disease, on average, takes only 2,100 days off their life. On average, the single life takes 1,600 days off a woman's life while cancer takes 980 days.

■ **Married men have fewer alcohol problems.** Married men have about half the alcohol-related troubles as their party-going single counterparts. In other words, the wedded average one-half incident per month while singles are getting into pickles one time a month. (Regardless of marital status, women have one-tenth the booze problems of men.)

■ **Married families save more money.** The median household wealth of marrieds is $132,000. It's less than one-third that for divorced, widowed, and the never married—around $40,000.

■ **Marriage reduces risk-taking behavior.** Both divorced men and women take risks—driving too fast, getting into fights, and practicing unhealthy lifestyle habits—at a higher rate than marrieds do (about 30 percent higher for men and 45 percent for women).

■ **Married people have sex twice as often.** If you're an average married man, you're having sex 6.84 times a month; if you're a woman, you're having sex 6.11 times a month. (These different figures raise questions about where men are getting the additional sex that the women aren't getting. But rest assured, this is a "statistical anomaly.") Single people have sex only about half as much—women, 3.23 times a month, and men, 3.63 times.

■ **Married men get more physical pleasure from sex.** Fifty-four percent of married men report being physically satisfied from sex with their wives while 43 percent of single men say they're satisfied with their sex. Married women, however, are only barely "statistically" happier than unmarried women.

■ **Married men and women are more emotionally pleased with sex.** Fifty-one percent of married men report emotional satisfaction from sex versus 36 percent of single men. For women, 44 percent of the marrieds are emotionally gratified with their love-making versus 33 percent of the single women.

Gray recalls, "I had one woman yelling at me on a radio show recently, 'I don't need a man. I've got a sperm bank!'

"Women are having careers to support themselves and be independent. They're feeling the same responsibilities their fathers felt, but they also want to create a beautiful relationship and have children and a home. Women are carrying a weight that is heavier than any woman in history has ever carried. Naturally, they are going to be unhappy."

Men, for their part, don't know what women want to make them happy. "After listening to couples again and again," Gray says, "right before they're about to get a divorce, the message I hear from men is 'I've given and I've given and I've given and no matter how much I give, it's not enough to maker her happy.'

"Women, when they're ready to give up say the same thing—'I've given and I've given and I've given, and no matter how much I give, I don't get back. I feel empty. I have nothing left to give.'"

"TILL DISSATISFACTION DO US PART"

"We are at a turning point in the history of couple consciousness," says John Welwood, Ph.D., a psychologist from Mill Valley, California, and author of several books on intimacy, including *JOURNEY OF THE HEART* (HarperCollins, 1990) and one to be released in January, *LOVE AND AWAKENING* (HarperCollins).

---

proving to help couples not only stick it out, but in the long run, make each of the partners stronger and healthier.

MARRIED, AMERICAN STYLE

Every fifteen minutes in America, sixty married couples untie the knot and opt for life alone, and untold others in relationships walk away from them. At the turn of the century, one out of fourteen marriages ended in divorce; today, every other one does. According to Census Bureau data, since 1970, the percentage of married Americans (among all adults eighteen and over) has declined 15 per-

cent, while the number of divorced has risen 300 percent.

Why aren't people staying together? John Gray, Ph.D, couples therapist and author of *MEN ARE FROM MARS, WOMEN ARE FROM VENUS* (HarperCollins, 1992), offers at least some insight.

Marital malcontent, he says, stems from a colossal shake-up in men's and women's roles. "Women don't need men the way they once did," says Gray, a forty-four-year-old former celibate monk who is now married with three kids. "A woman today doesn't need a protector—she can carry her Mace; she's got police forces; she's got lawyers; what does she need a guy for?"

The problem with basing marriage purely on pleasure and having your needs met is that those things come and go.

"In the past, marriage was a functional business that maintained the family and society," states Welwood. "During the last half century, people in the West have begun to look to marriage simply as a source of personal pleasure and need gratification. That's very new and we're seeing the limits of it."

Indeed, instead of "till death do us part," couples often stay together only "till dissatisfaction do us part." Also, divorce laws in the last several decades have been relaxed. Couples don't need to claim grounds of cruelty or abuse to get out of marriage. They can end it due to "irretrievable breakdown of the marriage," which can mean your spouse's sloppiness drives you crazy, or else you're just bored.

"The problem with basing marriage purely on pleasure and having your needs met is that those things come and go," Welwood says.

And when they go, disappointed partners look for insights on magazine racks and in bookstores—making books such as Gray's and Thomas Moore's *SOUL MATES* behemoth best-sellers. Alas, the popular newsstand solutions (often running along the lines of how to have "hotter, happier sex") are less than satisfying. Even Gray sometimes offers questionable cures. His advise that men must make women feel they're being heard (even if the guy has to *pretend* that he hears her) and that women must make men feel appreciated (however hard it is for her to imagine *why*) may win temporary peace in a relationship, but lasting love?

Welwood believes we need a new vision of intimate relationships if we are going to find lasting love. "There is a much deeper kind of happiness—which goes far beyond immediate gratification—that comes from realizing who you are and sharing that with someone you love," says Welwood. "*This* is the basis for healthy and satisfying relationships."

Welwood's definition of a healthy relationship involves working with the obstacles that arise when the going gets rough between partners. Indeed, hard times are the catalyst for healing emotional wounds that go back to childhood and that threaten not only our marriages but other arenas of our lives as well. In fact, recognizing and dealing with each partner's psychological wounds is necessary for a successful relationship.

As these wounds heal, instead of putting the blame for our marital difficulties on our partners, we learn to take responsibility for them, to "own them," the psychoanalyst would say. When we work to make this happen, we become

less stressed and the relationship—instead of dying out—grows into a trusting intimacy that we value both in spite of its troubles, and because of them.

FINDING A SOUL CONNECTION

Welwood's explanation of how relationship conflicts arise is different than Boorstein's, though he, like Boorstein, looks to the couple's past. Often as children Welwood explains, we build a psychological shell around us to protect ourselves from feeling pain. Born open and loving, as children we are often taught that some aspect of ourself is unacceptable. Maybe our exuberance wa squelched or our creativity was dampened. Or, maybe we were taught we had to behave a certain way in order to be good.

"No matter how much our parents love us," Welwood writes in *LOVE AND AWAKENING,* "they generally see their version of who we are, reflecting their own hopes, fears, expectations, and unmet needs." Instead of suffering the pain of rejection by our parents, we often develop a personality that will win their acceptance.

This adaptation, which is necessary for a child's psychic survival and integration into the family, forces children to build a false personality that they struggle to maintain throughout their lives. "The young child is like an open hand that gradually contracts and closes," says Welwood. "Eventually, we learn to shut ourselves down."

This protective tightening gets installed in our body and mind as a rigid set of defenses. "In this way," he says, "we inflict on ourselves the core wound that will haunt us the rest of our lives— we separate from our deeper spiritual nature, which is an openness to life."

Falling in love provides a glimpse of this spiritual nature. As Welwood details in *LOVE AND AWAKENING,* in love's early stages, feelings such as openness, peace, and expansiveness simply emerge, unbidden. We become inspired to commit ourselves to a new partner who is able to generate such feelings in us. When people are truly in love, which Welwood calls a "soul connection," they see behind the false facade of one another and connect on a deeper level. They connect with one another's "essential nature," which brings out the feelings of open-

ness and peace. One of the most complimentary things you can say about a partner is "I feel I can be myself with him." Or, simply, "He understands me. He gets who I am." This, says Welwood, is because when someone loves you in this way, they see through your facade and see who you really are. Being seen in this manner, however, can also bring about conflicts.

"If, for example, we harbor an image of ourselves as unlovable, then when the opportunity arises to be loved for who we really are, we won't know how to handle it," Welwood says. "Even though this is what we truly long for, it will also frighten us to death—because it threatens our whole identify." To let love enter, we have to give up who we think we are.

"I don't know any couples who have not suffered this fall from grace at some point, losing touch with the original bright presence that first drew them together," says Welwood. The longer we avoid these old psychological wounds and our rigid set of defenses, the greater becomes their hold on us. If left unresolved, we wind up living an exhausting charade, as Welwood calls it.

We resist our partner's confrontations because they threaten to blow our cover. But actually they're doing us a favor.

The antidote, Welwood says, is to let ourselves open to the feelings we fear the most. When people learn to open to their pain—within the context of an intimate relationship—there results a softening, a relaxation, and greater self-acceptance; it also deepens their connection with themselves and with each other, and can provide them a lifelong mutual path and direction.

"That's the real work of the relationship—and the real opportunity to develop deeper, lasting intimacy," says Welwood.

Of course, facing the challenges on this path takes great courage. As Welwood discusses in *LOVE AND AWAKENING,* in many ways, having a soul connection is like finding a worthy opponent. We have met our match, someone who won't let us get away with anything that is false or diminishes our being. This is often apparent in the first few years of a relationship, as the partners challenge each other, saying, in effect, "Why are you so stuck in your ways?"

If two partners confront each other like this in order to prove something or to get their own way, it will only result in a power struggle between two egos. Often we resist our partner's confrontations because they threaten to blow our cover, exposing parts of us we have a hard time acknowledging. Yet in blowing our cover, our partner is actually doing us a favor. This is what happened to Keith and Melissa, whose relationship Welwood describes in LOVE AND AWAKENING.

SACRED COMBAT

Keith was first attracted to Melissa because of her generosity of spirit. Everything about her—her warmth, her smile, her capacity to lavish affection, her emotional expressiveness—expressed this abundance. Although Keith loved these qualities in her, he felt threatened by them since he felt that these qualities were lacking in himself. In truth, Keith was very unexpressive because he had closed down his feelings as a child in order not to be overwhelmed by his emotionally intrusive mother.

In their typical conflict, Melissa would be unhappy about Keith's austerity and constrictedness while he became defensive, reacting in an angry, controlling manner. He would try to tone her down, while she remained intent on loosening him up. As the conflict between their different strategies escalated, their fights grew more fierce.

In examining the deeper source of their conflict, Keith eventually saw that Melissa was forcing him—by her very presence in his life—to confront ways in which he remained constricted. Melissa also saw that because she had grown up in a repressive family, she had come to believe that any self-restraint or detachment was a form of death. However, her emotional extravagance often veered into self-indulgence. When she was swept up in her feelings, she would exaggerate their significance, and this often left both of them feeling hurt and confused. Melissa had something important to learn from Keith in this regard— about not always acting out her feelings. By confronting Melissa's emotional

IN A LOVE CRISIS?

That's good! Use your relationship's "hot spots" to learn more about yourself and your partner. Here are nine ideas for dealing with love's day-to-day trials, taken from talks and writings by psychotherapists who specialize in working with couples: Seymour and Sylvia Boorstein, John Gray, and John and Jennifer Welwood.

1. Shut up. One thing that makes Gray's MEN ARE FROM MARS, WOMEN ARE FROM VENUS so popular is that he tells men a hundred different ways, LISTEN! This happens to be the single most powerful tool either sex has for averting trouble. If your partner wants to talk, let him or her talk. Don't interrupt. Don't vaccum. Don't answer the phone. Don't look to see what's on TV later. Listen.

2. Good happens. Students of Buddhism learn to observe that *everything* arises and passes. If you are angry or lonely or hurt and are distraught over your feelings and can't seem to get them resolved, allow them to pass before you act on them. They usually will pass. Your anger will somehow get soothed. Bad stuff happens. So does good.

3. Avoid the "67th argument." Every couple has had some particular discussion about sixty-seven times a year that *always* leads to an argument. You can see it coming. He says this, you say that, he says this again, and you know what's coming after you say that again: Mount Saint Helens erupts. So, change the script. It doesn't work. Do something else. Order a pizza, walk to the mail box, or watch the squirrels outside.

4. What are you afraid of? Beneath all anger is fear. If you understand this, then the next time you're so angry that you're ready to throw your plate of spaghetti at your lover's face, stop for a minute. Ask yourself, what am I so afraid of that I've gotten this mad? Or, if it's your partner who is brewing up a storm, try to feel empathy for the fear. What's he or she so afraid of? Compassion melts anger.

5. Feel lust, don't feed it. President Jimmy Carter made news when he confessed in *PLAYBOY* magazine that he had lusted in his heart. As he described his lusting, he had responded as a true Buddhist. He didn't act on his lust. He just felt it. Lust, like any powerful appetite, can never be fed enough. If you feed your lustful feelings in inappropriate ways, they will just want to be refed. Don't feed lust, feel it.

6. "Don't feed your lover a 150-pound burger." Boorstein says when you want to get a point across to your partner, you have to watch both the timing and the dosage of your efforts. Harping becomes nagging, which is counterproductive. Boorstein says, "You can't take a 150-pound hamburger and stuff it into a baby and get an adult. You have to put a little bit in. They chew a while, spit some out, swallow some. After a while, they grow a little."

7. The cure is in the poison. If your jealousy—or any strong emotion—is too much to bear, the most potent way of dealing with it is to walk right up to it and look it right in the eye. Say to yourself, "That's me. I am jealous." You feel the part of your body where it hurts. Your belly? Your neck? Your chest? Wherever it is, feel it and acknowledge it. Welwood and others say this is the entry point to meeting painful emotions head-on. If you confront them like this, they often back down.

8. It's up to you. One of the hardest things for people to accept and understand is that even in love, they're on their own when it comes to finding happiness. "Being responsible" means that you have to look at *your* issues and work them out with yourself. You may think the other person is the cause of the, or can be the answer. But that's generally not the case. What partners can do is *support* one another's struggles.

9. Pretty good is perfect. A woman in her late seventies, married for fifty years, heard another woman say, "My relationship is pretty good, but it isn't perfect." The older woman said, "Listen, when you're talking about relationships, 'pretty good' is perfect.

tyrannies, Keith had a grounding effect on her; in learning to reflect on her feelings before rushing into action, she was able to settle into herself in a new way.

As Keith and Melissa come to appreciate how they were each other's teachers, this helped them see their conflict in a new light—as part of a creative and fruitful "sacred combat"—rather than just a divisive struggle. This, says Welwood, is what a soul connection is about—two people joining together to nurture, stimulate, and provoke important steps in each other's unfolding.

RECOGNIZE YOUR SHADOW

Psychotherapists Kathleen Hendricks, Ph.D., ADTR, and Gay Hendricks, Ph.D., have counselled thousands of people with relationships problems over a fifteen-year period. One thing they say you can count on a relationship to do is to pull this kind of "unconscious stuff"—what psychoanalysts call your shadow—to the surface.

Robert A. Johnson, the author of many books on Jungian analysis, explains the shadow concept in OWNING YOUR OWN SHADOW. He writes, "We are born whole, but early on our way, we begin the shadow-making process; we divide our lives. We sort out our God-given characteristics into those that are acceptable to our society and those that we have to put away."

Johnson says we can hide these parts of ourselves, but they do not go away. "They only collect in the dark corners of our personality," he says. "When they have hidden long enough, they take on a life of their own." Our shadow can gain power over years. "If it accumulates more energy than our ego, it erupts as an overpowering rage or some indiscretion," says Johnson.

To remedy the problem, Hendricks explains, we teach couples to tell the "microscopic truth." Say, "my stomach is tight," or "I'm scared. I'm afraid of losing you when you do that." This is what psychoanalysts call "owning your shadow."

Johnson says, "The shadow is very important in marriage, and we can make or break a relationship depending on how conscious we are of this. We must come to terms with what we find annoying and distasteful—even downright intolerable—in the other and also in ourselves. Yet, it is precisely this confrontation that leads to our greatest growth."

Owning your shadow, say the Hendrickses, is about being truthful, with your partner and yourself. "It takes actual physical energy," says Kathleen, "to keep yourself from telling the truth. It can happen in a split second. You can suddenly be defensive without realizing that a fear has come up. You can withdraw, withhold, and project in an instant and suddenly it looks like the other person's fault."

Psychotherapists such as the Hendrickses and John Welwood, and his wife of ten years, Jennifer—also a psychotherapist who counsels couples—agree that the intimate partnership is the ideal setting where two people can support one another's inquiry into the recesses of the shadow. In an honest, open relationship, each partner summons the shadow—the anger, the hurt, the pain—and owns it, takes responsibility for it as his or her own, instead of "projecting" it onto others. When we project it, we're basically trying to dish it off to someone else, to disown it. All that this accomplishes, of course, is to arouse anger and reaction from the other person.

"What we found in the early years of our relationship," says Gay, "was that we had awesome barriers to overcome in learning to tell each other the truth, even the simplest truth, like 'I was angry when you wrecked my car.' That was hard for me to say because my programming was to be Mr. Reasonable. I was angry, but it took me weeks to get past being Mr. Reasonable. It was a big breakthrough for me, to say, 'I'm angry.' "

And this process is ongoing, says Kathleen, "In relationships, taking healthy responsibility is something you will have opportunity to do over and over."

COMPASSION FOR BUGABOOS

It's much easier for partners to take responsibility for their shadows when they're extending empathy—compassion—to one another. The Boorsteins learned this lesson in their own marriage.

"If we were criticized a lot early in life," Seymour says, "as I was by my mother, we tend to project onto people around us the image of the person who was critical of us. Even though she died ten years ago, my mother still follows me." Seymour often speaks in public, but he says if he sees disapproving looks in the audience, he gets nervous. The biggest problem he's had in marriage,

he says, is convincing his conscious mind that Sylvia is not his mother.

"Sylvia's not like my mother at all, but I've been sure at times that she was," he says. "It's gotten much better over the years, but I still slip up on occasion. I say to myself 'Ah-ha! I've been waiting forty-three years. I *knew* she would get like that.' "

Sylvia says she sees her mother too. But hers was approving, so she's not uncomfortable in front of audiences, she doesn't easily read criticism into innocent looks or comments, as Seymour might. Sylvia's bugaboo, however, is that she easily becomes fretful. Fifteen years ago, when their youngest daughter was studying theater dance in San Francisco, which required her commuting into the city, Sylvia could not sleep at night while worrying about the girl's safety.

"Seymour and I would be in bed and he'd fall asleep, and I'd get up at 10:45 when our daughter was to be home at 10:30 and I'd say to him, 'Get up. Worry.' He'd say, 'I have to work in the morning. I can't get up now.' He'd go back to sleep while I worried."

Couples seldom look for reasons *why* they're fretful or fearful. But doing so, says Sylvia, builds empathy, a foundation of successful relationships.

THE REASON FOR INTIMACY

Not a few people today wonder whether the struggles of a committed relationship are worth the troubles they seem to bring about. Jennifer and John Welwood have been together for ten years, and they've asked themselves what they give one another that they couldn't get on their own.

Jennifer says, "John creates an environment for me to develop as a human being. I'm very aware of needing him in my life to help me in this way. And it's mutual. That is what our relationship gives to both of us."

John adds, "When you find a larger purpose for your relationship—such as stimulating and supporting one another's deepest unfolding—that provides a bond that can hold two people together for a very long time. Then, whether things are going well this week or not, whether we're happy or not at any give moment, is secondary."

Reproduction

Birth Control and Abortion (Articles 27–30)
Pregnancy, Infertility, and Childbirth (Articles 31 and 32)

While human reproduction is as old as humanity, many aspects of it are changing in today's society. Not only have new technologies of conception and childbirth affected the *how* of reproduction, but personal, social, and cultural forces have also affected the *who*, the *when*, and the *when not*. Abortion remains a fiercely debated topic, and legislative efforts for and against it abound. Unplanned pregnancies and parenthood in the United States and worldwide, however, present significant, sometimes devastating, problems for the parents, children, families, and society.

In light of the change of attitude toward sex for pleasure, birth control has become a matter of prime importance. Even in our age of sexual enlightenment, some individuals, possibly in the height of passion, fail to correlate "having sex" with pregnancy. In addition, even in our age of astounding medical technology, there is no 100 percent effective, safe, or aesthetically acceptable method of birth control. Before sex can become safe, as well as enjoyable, people must receive thorough and accurate information regarding conception and contraception, birth and birth control. They must make a mental and emotional commitment to the use of an effective method of their choice. Only these measures can make every child a planned and wanted one.

Despite the relative simplicity of the above assertion, abortion and birth control remain emotionally charged issues in American society. While opinion surveys indicate that most of the public supports family planning and abortion, at least in some circumstances, there are certain individuals and groups strongly opposed to some forms of birth control and to abortion. Within the past few years, voices for and against birth control and abortion have grown louder, and on a growing number of occasions overt behaviors, including protests and violence, have occurred. Some Supreme Court and legislative ef-

forts have added restrictions to the right to abortion. Others have mandated freer access to abortion and reproductive choice and restricted the activities of antiabortion demonstrators. Voices on both sides are raised in emotional and political debate between "we must never go back to the old days" (of illegal and unsafe back-alley abortions) and "the baby has no choice."

Many of the questions raised in this unit about the new technologies of reproduction and its control are likely to remain among the most hotly debated issues for the remainder of this century. It is likely that various religious and political groups will continue to posit and challenge basic definitions of human life, as well as the rights and responsibilities of women and men regarding sex, procreation, and abortion. The very foundations of our pluralistic society may be challenged. We will have to await the outcome.

The articles in the *Birth Control and Abortion* subsection are designed to inform and update readers on available birth control methods as well as on the myriad of factors that go into individuals' and couples' choices and uses of them. The first two articles demystify the broad range of prescription and nonprescription contraceptives available to consumers. Each gives some guidelines for choices of primary and back-up contraceptive methods as well as times and situations where method changes may be indicated. In the fact-filled and comprehensive style that is well-known to its readers, *Consumer Reports* asks and answers the question, "How Reliable Are Condoms?" both for birth control and disease prevention. The final article explains nonsurgical abortion, supplementing facts with a personal, first-person account.

The first article in the *Pregnancy, Infertility, and Childbirth* subsection addresses the latest technological possibilities for human reproduction. While these advancements, which not so long ago would have seemed more like

This isn't the convertible he was saving for.

Make a baby—make a lifetime commitment.

science fiction, offer hope for some, they raise complex and difficult legal, ethical, financial, and social questions. The last article focuses on the joyous but often stressful and anxiety-filled period of a couple's life—post childbirth. It provides information and assistance for couples making the transition back to sexual intimacy.

Looking Ahead: Challenge Questions

In your opinion, what are the most important characteristics of a contraceptive? Why?

What personal feelings or expectations make you more likely to use contraception regularly?

Under what circumstances might a person not use contraception and risk an unintentional pregnancy?

Should contraceptive responsibilities be assigned to one gender or shared between men and women? Defend your answer.

How have recent events in the right-to-choose arena affected you? Have they changed your beliefs and/or attitudes?

What do you see as the important advantages and disadvantages of nonsurgical abortion methods?

Have you found a fairly comfortable way to talk about contraception and/or pregnancy risk and prevention with your partner? If so, what is it? If not, what do you do?

In the situation of an unplanned pregnancy, what should be the role of the female and the male with respect to decision making? What if they do not agree?

Do you know of a couple who has experienced infertility? If so, what do you think it was like for them? If you were unable to have a child, what treatments would you consider? Are there any you would not? Why? As a current and future taxpayer, do you feel infertility treatments should be insurance-covered expenses? Why or why not?

Protecting Against
Unintended Pregnancy
A Guide To Contraceptive Choices

by Tamar Nordenberg

I am 20 and have never gone to see a doctor about birth control. My boyfriend and I have been go- .ing together for a couple of years and have been using condoms. So far, everything is fine.

Are condoms alone safe enough, or is something else safe besides the Pill? I do not want to go on the Pill.
—Letter to the Kinsey Institute for Re-search in Sex, Gender, and Reproduc-tion

Image provided by © 1994 PhotoDisc. Inc.

This young woman is not alone in her uncertainty about contraceptive options. A 1995 report by the National Academy of Sciences' Institute of Medicine, *The Best Intentions: Unintended Pregnancy and the Well-being of Children and Families,* attributed the high rate of un-intended pregnancies in the United States, in part, to Americans' lack of knowledge about contraception. About 6 of every 10 pregnancies in the United States are unplanned, according to the report.

Being informed about the pros and cons of various contraceptives is impor-tant not only for preventing unintended pregnancies but also for reducing the risk of illness or death from sexually transmitted diseases (STDs), including AIDS.

The Food and Drug Administration has approved a number of birth control methods, ranging from over-the-counter male and female condoms and vaginal spermicides to doctor-prescribed birth control pills, diaphragms, intrauterine devices (IUDs), injected hormones, and hormonal implants. Other contraceptive options include fertility awareness and voluntary surgical sterilization.

"On the whole, the contraceptive choices that Americans have are very safe and effective," says Dennis Barbour, president of the Association of Repro-ductive Health Professionals, "but a method that is very good for one woman may be lousy for another."

The choice of birth control depends on factors such as a person's health, fre-quency of sexual activity, number of partners, and desire to have children in the future. Effectiveness rates, based on statistical estimates, are another key

From *FDA Consumer,* April 1997, pp. 20-26. Reprinted by permission of *FDA Consumer,* the magazine of the U.S. Food and Drug Administration.

About 6 of every 10 pregnancies in the United States are unplanned, according to the National Academy of Sciences.

consideration (see "Birth Control Guide"). FDA is developing a more consumer-friendly table to be added to the labeling of all contraceptive drugs and devices.

Barrier Methods

• *Male condom.* The male condom is a sheath placed over the erect penis before penetration, preventing pregnancy by blocking the passage of sperm.

A condom can be used only once. Some have spermicide added, usually nonoxynol-9 in the United States, to kill sperm. Spermicide has not been scientifically shown to provide additional contraceptive protection over the condom alone. Because they act as a mechanical barrier, condoms prevent direct vaginal contact with semen, infectious genital secretions, and genital lesions and discharges.

Most condoms are made from latex rubber, while a small percentage are made from lamb intestines (sometimes called "lambskin" condoms). Condoms made from polyurethane have been marketed in the United States since 1994.

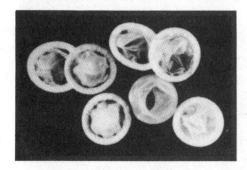

Except for abstinence, latex condoms are the most effective method for reducing the risk of infection from the viruses that cause AIDS, other HIV-related illnesses, and other STDs.

Some condoms are prelubricated. These lubricants don't provide more birth control or STD protection. Non-oil-based lubricants, such as water or K-Y jelly, can be used with latex or lambskin condoms, but oil-based lubricants,

such as petroleum jelly (Vaseline), lotions, or massage or baby oil, should not be used because they can weaken the material.

• *Female condom.* The Reality Female Condom, approved by FDA in April 1993, consists of a lubricated polyurethane sheath shaped similarly to the

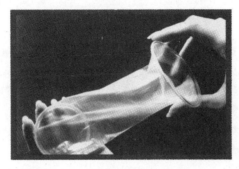

male condom. The closed end, which has a flexible ring, is inserted into the vagina, while the open end remains outside, partially covering the labia.

The female condom, like the male condom, is available without a prescription and is intended for one-time use. It should not be used together with a male condom because they may not both stay in place.

• *Diaphragm.* Available by prescription only and sized by a health professional to achieve a proper fit, the diaphragm has a dual mechanism to prevent pregnancy. A dome-shaped rubber disk with a flexible rim covers the cervix so sperm can't reach the uterus, while a spermicide applied to the diaphragm before insertion kills sperm.

The diaphragm protects for six hours.

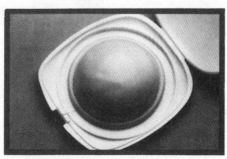

(Photos provided by Planned Parenthood Federation of America, Inc.)

For intercourse after the six-hour period, or for repeated intercourse within this period, fresh spermicide should be placed in the vagina with the diaphragm still in place. The diaphragm should be left in place for at least six hours after the last intercourse but not for longer than a total of 24 hours because of the risk of toxic shock syndrome (TSS), a rare but potentially fatal infection. Symptoms of TSS include sudden fever, stomach upset, sunburn-like rash, and a drop in blood pressure.

• *Cervical cap.* The cap is a soft rubber cup with a round rim, sized by a health professional to fit snugly around the cervix. It is available by prescription only and, like the diaphragm, is used with spermicide.

It protects for 48 hours and for mul-

tiple acts of intercourse within this time. Wearing it for more than 48 hours is not recommended because of the risk, though low, of TSS. Also, with prolonged use of two or more days, the cap may cause an unpleasant vaginal odor or discharge in some women.

• *Sponge.* The vaginal contraceptive sponge has not been available since the sole manufacturer, Whitehall Laboratories of Madison, N.J., voluntarily stopped selling it in 1995. It remains an approved product and could be marketed again.

The sponge, a donut-shaped polyurethane device containing the spermicide nonoxynol-9, is inserted into the vagina to cover the cervix. A woven polyester loop is designed to ease removal.

"In the population for which the IUD is appropriate—for those in a mutually monogamous, stable relationship who aren't at a high risk of infection—the IUD is a very safe and very effective method of contraception."
—Lisa Rarick, M.D., director of FDA's division of reproductive and urologic drug products

The sponge protects for up to 24 hours and for multiple acts of intercourse within this time. It should be left in place for at least six hours after intercourse but should be removed no more than 30 hours after insertion because of the risk, though low, of TSS.

Vaginal Spermicides Alone

Vaginal spermicides are available in foam, cream, jelly, film, suppository, or tablet forms. All types contain a sperm-killing chemical.

Studies have not produced definitive data on the efficacy of spermicides alone, but according to the authors of *Contraceptive Technology,* a leading resource for contraceptive information, the failure rate for typical users may be 21 percent per year.

Package instructions must be carefully followed because some spermicide

products require the couple to wait 10 minutes or more after inserting the spermicide before having sex. One dose of spermicide is usually effective for one hour. For repeated intercourse, additional spermicide must be applied. And after intercourse, the spermicide has to remain in place for at least six to eight hours to ensure that all sperm are killed. The woman should not douche or rinse the vagina during this time.

Hormonal Methods
• *Combined oral contraceptives.* Typically called "the pill," combined oral contraceptives have been on the market for more than 35 years and are the most

popular form of reversible birth control in the United States. This form of birth control suppresses ovulation (the monthly release of an egg from the ovaries) by the combined actions of the hormones estrogen and progestin.

If a woman remembers to take the pill

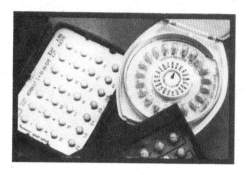

every day as directed, she has an extremely low chance of becoming pregnant in a year. But the pill's effectiveness may be reduced if the woman is taking some medications, such as certain antibiotics.

Besides preventing pregnancy, the pill offers additional benefits. As stated in the labeling, the pill can make periods more regular. It also has a protective effect against pelvic inflammatory disease, an infection of the fallopian tubes or uterus that is a major cause of infertility in women, and against ovarian and endometrial cancers.

The decision whether to take the pill should be made in consultation with a health professional. Birth control pills are safe for most women—safer even than delivering a baby—but they carry some risks.

Current low-dose pills have fewer risks associated with them than earlier versions. But women who smoke—especially those over 35—and women with certain medical conditions, such as a history of blood clots or breast or endometrial cancer, may be advised against taking the pill. The pill may contribute to cardiovascular disease, including high blood pressure, blood clots, and

blockage of the arteries.

One of the biggest questions has been whether the pill increases the risk of breast cancer in past and current pill users. An international study published in the September 1996 journal *Contraception* concluded that women's risk of breast cancer 10 years after going off birth control pills was no higher than that of women who had never used the pill. During pill use and for the first 10 years after stopping the pill, women's risk of breast cancer was only slightly higher in pill users than non-pill users.

Side effects of the pill, which often subside after a few months' use, include nausea, headache, breast tenderness, weight gain, irregular bleeding, and depression.

Doctors sometimes prescribe higher doses of combined oral contraceptives for use as "morning after" pills to be taken within 72 hours of unprotected intercourse to prevent the possibly fertilized egg from reaching the uterus. In a Feb. 25, 1997, *Federal Register* notice, FDA stated its conclusion that, on the basis of current scientific evidence, certain oral contraceptives are safe and effective for this use.
• *Minipills.* Although taken daily like combined oral contraceptives, minipills contain only the hormone progestin and no estrogen. They work by reducing and thickening cervical mucus to prevent sperm from reaching the egg. They also keep the uterine lining from thickening, which prevents a fertilized egg from implanting in the uterus. These pills are generally less effective than combined oral contraceptives.

Minipills can decrease menstrual bleeding and cramps, as well as the risk of endometrial and ovarian cancer and pelvic inflammatory disease. Because they contain no estrogen, minipills don't present the risk of blood clots associated with estrogen in combined pills. They are a good option for women who can't take estrogen because they are breast-

Being informed about the pros and cons of various contraceptives is important not only for preventing unintended pregnancies but also for reducing the risk of illness or death from sexually transmitted diseases, including AIDS.

feeding or because estrogen-containing products cause them to have severe headaches or high blood pressure.

Side effects of minipills include menstrual cycle changes, weight gain, and breast tenderness.

• *Injectable progestins.* Depo-Provera, approved by FDA in 1992, is injected by a health professional into the buttocks or arm muscle every three months. Depo-Provera prevents pregnancy in three ways: It inhibits ovulation, changes the cervical mucus to help prevent sperm from reaching the egg, and changes the uterine lining to prevent the fertilized egg from implanting in the uterus. The progestin injection is extremely effective in preventing pregnancy, in large part because it requires little effort for the woman to comply: She simply has to get an injection by a doctor once every three months.

The benefits are similar to those of the minipill and another progestin-only contraceptive, Norplant. Side effects are also similar and can include irregular or missed periods, weight gain, and breast tenderness.

(See "Depo-Provera: The Quarterly Contraceptive" in the March 1993 *FDA Consumer.*)

• *Implantable progestins.* Norplant, approved by FDA in 1990, and the newer Norplant 2, approved in 1996, are the third type of progestin-only contraceptive. Made up of matchstick-sized rubber rods, this contraceptive is surgically implanted under the skin of the upper arm, where it steadily releases the contracep-

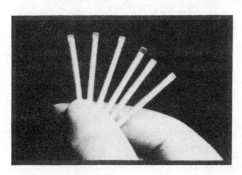

tive steroid levonorgestrel.

The six-rod Norplant provides protection for up to five years (or until it is removed), while the two-rod Norplant 2 protects for up to three years. Norplant failures are rare, but are higher with increased body weight.

Some women may experience inflammation or infection at the site of the implant. Other side effects include menstrual cycle changes, weight gain, and breast tenderness.

Intrauterine Devices

An IUD is a T-shaped device inserted into the uterus by a health-care professional. Two types of IUDs are available in the United States: the Paragard CopperT 380A and the Progestasert Progesterone T. The Paragard IUD can remain in place for 10 years, while the Progestasert IUD must be replaced every year.

It's not entirely clear how IUDs prevent pregnancy. They seem to prevent sperm and eggs from meeting by either immobilizing the sperm on their way to the fallopian tubes or changing the uterine lining so the fertilized egg cannot implant in it.

IUDs have one of the lowest failure rates of any contraceptive method. "In the population for which the IUD is appropriate—for those in a mutually monogamous, stable relationship who aren't at a high risk of infection—the IUD is a very safe and very effective method of contraception," says Lisa Rarick, M.D., director of FDA's division of reproductive and urologic drug products.

The IUD's image suffered when the Dalkon Shield IUD was taken off the market in 1975. This IUD was associated with a high incidence of pelvic infections and infertility, and some deaths. Today, serious complications from IUDs are rare, although IUD users may be at increased risk of developing pelvic inflammatory disease. Other side effects

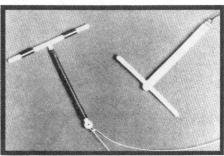

can include perforation of the uterus, abnormal bleeding, and cramps. Complications occur most often during and immediately after insertion.

Traditional Methods

• *Fertility awareness.* Also known as natural family planning or periodic abstinence, fertility awareness entails not having sexual intercourse on the days of a woman's menstrual cycle when she could become pregnant or using a barrier method of birth control on those days.

Because a sperm may live in the female's reproductive tract for up to seven days and the egg remains fertile for about 24 hours, a woman can get pregnant within a substantial window of time—from seven days before ovulation to three days after. Methods to approximate when a woman is fertile are usu-

ally based on the menstrual cycle, changes in cervical mucus, or changes in body temperature.

"Natural family planning can work," Rarick says, "but it takes an extremely motivated couple to use the method effectively."

• *Withdrawal.* In this method, also

Birth Control Guide

Efficacy rates in this chart are based on *Contraceptive Technology* (16th edition, 1994). They are yearly estimates of effectiveness in typical use, which refers to a method's reliability in real life, when people don't always use a method properly. For comparison, about 85 percent of sexually active women using no contraception would be expected to become pregnant in a year.

This chart is a summary; it is not intended to be used alone. All product labeling should be followed carefully, and a health-care professional should be consulted for some methods.

Type	Male Condom	Female Condom	Diaphragm with Spermicide	Cervical Cap with Spermicide	Sponge with Spermicide (not currently marketed)	Spermicides Alone
Estimated Effectiveness	88%[a]	79%	82%	64–82%[b]	64–82%[b]	79%
Some Risks[d]	Irritation and allergic reactions (less likely with polyurethane)	Irritation and allergic reactions	Irritation and allergic reactions, urinary tract infection	Irritation and allergic reactions, abnormal Pap test	Irritation and allergic reactions, difficulty in removal	Irritation and allergic reactions
Protection from Sexually Transmitted Diseases (STDs)	Except for abstinence, latex condoms are the best protection against STDs, including herpes and AIDS.	May give some STD protection; not as effective as latex condom.	Protects against cervical infection; spermicide may give some protection against chlamydia and gonorrhea; otherwise unknown.	Spermicide may give some protection against chlamydia and gonorrhea; otherwise unknown.	Spermicide may give some protection against chlamydia and gonorrhea; otherwise unknown.	May give some protection against chlamydia and gonorrhea; otherwise unknown.
Convenience	Applied immediately before intercourse; used only once and discarded.	Applied immediately before intercourse; used only once and discarded.	Inserted before intercourse and left in place at least six hours after; can be left in place for 24 hours, with additional spermicide for repeated intercourse.	May be difficult to insert; can remain in place for 48 hours without reapplying spermicide for repeated intercourse.	Inserted before intercourse and protects for 24 hours without additional spermicide; must be left in place for at least six hours after intercourse; must be removed within 30 hours of insertion; used only once and discarded.	Instructions vary; usually applied no more than one hour before intercourse and left in place at least six to eight hours after.
Availability	Nonprescription	Nonprescription	Prescription	Prescription	Nonprescription; not currently marketed.	Nonprescription

a   Effectiveness rate for polyurethane condoms has not been established.
b   Less effective for women who have had a baby because the birth process stretches the vagina and cervix, making it more difficult to achieve a proper fit.
c   Based on perfect use, when the woman takes the pill every day as directed.
d   Serious medical risks from contraceptives are rare.

Oral Contraceptives—combined pill	Oral Contraceptives—progestin-only minipill	Injection (Depo-Provera)	Implant (Norplant)	IUD (Intrauterine Device)	Periodic Abstinence	Surgical Sterilization—female or male
Over 99%[c]	Over 99%[c]	Over 99%	Over 99%	98–99%	About 80% (varies, based on method)	Over 99%
Dizziness; nausea; changes in menstruation, mood, and weight; rarely, cardiovascular disease, including high blood pressure, blood clots, heart attack, and strokes	Ectopic pregnancy, irregular bleeding, weight gain, breast tenderness	Irregular bleeding, weight gain, breast tenderness, headaches	Irregular bleeding, weight gain, breast tenderness, headaches, difficulty in removal	Cramps, bleeding, pelvic inflammatory disease, infertility, perforation of uterus	None	Pain, bleeding, infection, other minor postsurgical complications
None, except some protection against pelvic inflammatory disease.	None, except some protection against pelvic inflammatory disease.	None	None	None	None	None
Must be taken on daily schedule, regardless of frequency of intercourse.	Must be taken on daily schedule, regardless of frequency of intercourse.	One injection every three months	Implanted by health-care provider—minor outpatient surgical procedure; effective for up to five years.	After insertion by physician, can remain in place for up to one or 10 years, depending on type.	Requires frequent monitoring of body functions (for example, body temperature for one method).	One-time surgical procedure
Prescription	Prescription	Prescription	Prescription	Prescription	Instructions from health-care provider	Surgery

Women who smoke—especially those over 35—may be advised against taking the pill.

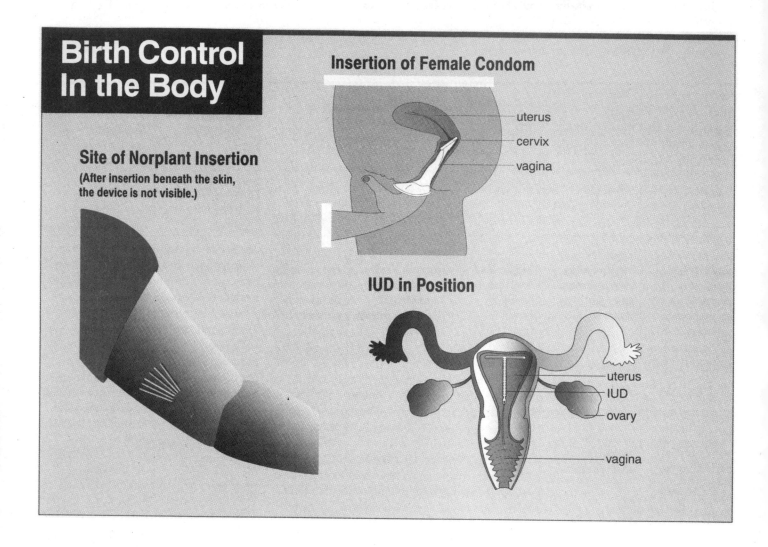

Birth Control In the Body

Site of Norplant Insertion
(After insertion beneath the skin, the device is not visible.)

Insertion of Female Condom

- uterus
- cervix
- vagina

IUD in Position

- uterus
- IUD
- ovary
- vagina

called *coitus interruptus,* the man withdraws his penis from the vagina before ejaculation. Fertilization is prevented because the sperm don't enter the vagina.

Effectiveness depends on the male's ability to withdraw before ejaculation. Also, withdrawal doesn't provide protection from STDs, including HIV. Infectious diseases can be transmitted by direct contact with surface lesions and by pre-ejaculatory fluid.

Surgical Sterilization

Surgical sterilization is a contraceptive option intended for people who don't want children in the future. It is considered permanent because reversal requires major surgery that is often unsuccessful.

• *Female sterilization.* Female sterilization blocks the fallopian tubes so the egg can't travel to the uterus. Sterilization is done by various surgical techniques performed under general anesthesia.

Complications from these operations are rare and can include infection, hemorrhage, and problems related to the use of general anesthesia.

• *Male sterilization.* This procedure, called a vasectomy, involves sealing, tying or cutting a man's vas deferens, which otherwise would carry the sperm from the testicle to the penis.

Vasectomy involves a quick operation, usually under 30 minutes, with possible minor postsurgical complications, such as bleeding or infection.

Research continues on effective contraceptives that minimize side effects. One important research focus, according to FDA's Rarick, is the development of birth control methods that are both spermicidal and microbicidal to prevent not only pregnancy but also transmission of HIV and other STDs.

Tamar Nordenberg is a staff writer for FDA Consumer.

Rethinking Birth Control

If you still believe the IUD is dangerous and the Pill is for women under 35, you may be stuck in a contraception rut. Here's a roundup of the most effective methods for midlife women.

JULIA CALIFANO

Through two years of dating, 10 years of marriage and two kids, Chris, a college professor in Syracuse, NY, relied almost exclusively on a diaphragm for birth control. Indeed, this 40-year-old would still be putting up with the hassle and mess if, at her last checkup, her doctor hadn't suggested she try an intrauterine device (IUD). Persuaded by his argument that it was highly effective, long-lasting and, for most women, nearly free of side effects, she switched. She hasn't regretted her decision. "It's such a pleasure not to have to plan ahead or get out of bed in the heat of passion," she says. "We don't even think about birth control anymore."

By the time a woman turns 35, she's moved an average of eight times, switched jobs seven times and had two children, yet there's only a 50–50 chance that she has ever thought about changing her method of birth control, according to a survey by Ortho Pharmaceutical. But the truth is she should. "A woman's contraceptive needs change as her life changes," says Anita Nelson, M.D., medical director of the Woman's Health Care Clinic at Harbor UCLA Medical Center in Los Angeles. "A barrier method may be great when you're 21 and concerned about AIDS and other sexually transmitted diseases [STD's], but it's probably not ideal when you're 35 and married with kids."

Perhaps more surprising is the staggering rate of unplanned pregnancies among women in their 40s: According to the Alan Guttmacher Institute in New York City, eight out of 10 pregnancies in this age group are unintended—the same rate as for women under age 20.

How can you tell if your current choice is still your best choice? Reassess your birth control periodically, taking your lifestyle, health, sex life and desire for children into consideration. Here's a guide to the options, plus expert advice on what to use when.

The IUD: Unfounded fear

What it is: The current IUD of choice is ParaGard, a piece of plastic with copper inside it that's put into the uterus to stop sperm from reaching eggs for up to 10 years. Another IUD called Progestasert contains hormones; it works for one year.

Benefits: Long-term, reversible, worry-free protection, and an insertion process that's only slightly more involved than a Pap smear. Progestasert also reduces menstrual cramps and the flow of monthly bleeding.

Drawbacks: The copper IUD can cause heavier than usual periods, won't protect you from STD's and shouldn't be used if you're not in a mutually monogamous relationship. Users with multiple partners are at increased risk for pelvic inflammatory disease (PID), an infection that can cause infertility.

What you may not know: Though most people still associate this device with the dreaded Dalkon Shield (an IUD that caused infection and infertility in thousands of women, along with a few deaths, in the '70s), ParaGard is considered one of the best and safest birth control options. In fact, it's the most popular form of reversible contraception outside the U.S., with 85 million users worldwide.

When to consider it: If you're in a mutually monogamous, long-term relationship and have had at least one child (for childless women there's a small risk that the device will be expelled). "An ideal time to switch to the IUD is when you've completed your family but don't want to take the irreversible step of sterilization," says nurse practitioner Kara Anderson, a medical consultant to the Planned Parenthood Federation of America in New York City.

The Pill: Now for Older Women

What it is: This oral contraceptive is a combination of two hormones, progestin and estrogen, that suppresses ovulation.

Benefits: Easy, reliable and offers a wealth of health benefits. After five

A Field Guide to Cost and Effectiveness

Barrier Methods

With perfect use, **two to six out of 100 users get pregnant.** Spermicides work best when used with a condom, diaphragm or cap. **Cost:** 30¢-$2.50 for condoms, $13-$25 for diaphragms and caps, $8-$18 for spermicide kit.

The Reality **Female Condom**

Five in 100 users will get pregnant with perfect use, 21 in 100 with typical use. **Cost:** $2.50 each.

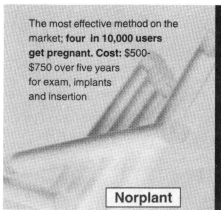

The most effective method on the market; **four in 10,000 users get pregnant. Cost:** $500-$750 over five years for exam, implants and insertion

Norplant

years the Pill halves your risk of endometrial and ovarian cancers, an effect that, for endometrial cancer, may last as long as 15 years after you stop using it. [Experts aren't sure how long the protective effects last for ovarian cancer.] It also reduces the risk of benign breast lumps, ovarian cysts, iron-deficiency anemia and PID.

Drawbacks: Side effects include breast tenderness, nausea, weight gain and headaches (though these usually clear up after two to three months). The Pill must be taken every day, and it doesn't protect against STD's. In addition, studies show it increases the risk of heart attack and blood clots in women over 35 who smoke. Some studies have also shown that the Pill increases breast cancer risk, though a recent analysis of 150,000 users found this risk to be negligible. In most cases, say experts, the health benefits far outweigh the risks.

What you may not know: A study at San Francisco State University found that women who use triphasic pills such as Orthonovum 7/7/7 (in which hormone levels vary throughout the course of the month) experience heightened sex drive compared with women on other types of pills.

When to consider it: If you're in a committed relationship and want a highly effective form of contraception. Contrary to what many believe, the Pill can be ideal for fortysomething non-smoking women. It eases the transition to menopause, says David Grimes, M.D., vice chairman of the department of obstetrics and gynecology at the University of California at San Francisco. "The Pill helps regulate periods, prevent hot flashes and protect against bone loss," he explains.

Norplant: A Five-Year Plan

What it is: Six flexible, matchstick-sized capsules inserted by a doctor just beneath the skin of the upper arm. They release progestin to suppress ovulation for five years.

Benefits: It's effective and convenient—you can't mess up. Norplant is also easily reversible; after removal, any remaining drugs leave the body in about three days. In addition, experts believe Norplant may be as good as the Pill at reducing the risk of endometrial and ovarian cancer.

Drawbacks: Norplant won't protect you from STD's, and it can cause ir-

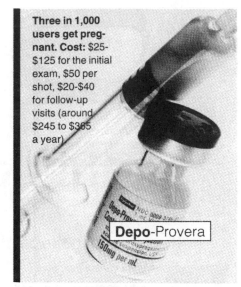

Three in 1,000 users get pregnant. Cost: $25-$125 for the initial exam, $50 per shot, $20-$40 for follow-up visits (around $245 to $365 a year)

Depo-Provera

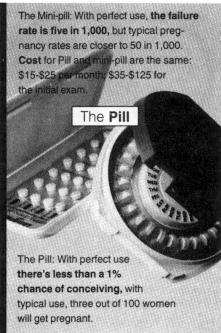

The Mini-pill: With perfect use, **the failure rate is five in 1,000,** but typical pregnancy rates are closer to 50 in 1,000. **Cost** for Pill and mini-pill are the same: $15-$25 per month; $35-$125 for the initial exam.

The **Pill**

The Pill: With perfect use **there's less than a 1% chance of conceiving,** with typical use, three out of 100 women will get pregnant.

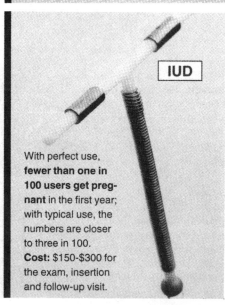

IUD

With perfect use, **fewer than one in 100 users get pregnant** in the first year; with typical use, the numbers are closer to three in 100. **Cost:** $150-$300 for the exam, insertion and follow-up visit.

Among women who are in their 40s, a staggering eight out of 10 pregnancies are unintended—the same rate as for women under age 20.

regular bleeding during the first year. There have also been a number of lawsuits filed by Norplant users, primarily because of problems such as pain or scarring upon removal. Despite the bad press, experts say such problems shouldn't arise if you use an experienced doctor. (For referrals, call your local Planned Parenthood clinic.)

What you may not know: Norplant is very expensive if used for fewer than three years.

When to consider it: If you're breast-feeding (unlike estrogen in the Pill, progestin doesn't reduce milk flow) and plan to wait several years before having another child or if you've completed your family. You also may want to try it if you absolutely don't want to worry about an accidental pregnancy.

Depo-Provera: Convenience Without Long-Term Commitment

What it is: This injection of synthetic progestin suppresses ovulation for 11 to 13 weeks.

Benefits: Depo-Provera provides many of the health perks of the Pill, and you don't have to take it every

day. After about a year, periods may stop completely, which many women consider a welcome side effect.

Drawbacks: Doctor's visits are required four times a year to get the shots, and the effects are not immediately reversible (fertility may not return for an average of 10 months after the last dose). Side effects may include headaches, weight gain, depression and heavier, more frequent periods. Depo-Provera also provides no protection against STD's.

What you may not know: Though many American women think of this method, approved here in 1992, as new, Depo-Provera has been used by more than 30 million women in 100 other countries over the past 30 years.

When to consider it: If you're nursing or trying to space out the arrival of new children, or you can't remember to take the Pill every day.

The Reality Female Condom: Women in the Driver's Seat

What it is: The Reality Condom is a floppy polyurethane tube with an in-

ner ring at the closed end that fits over the cervix, like a diaphragm, and an outer ring at the open end that hangs outside the vagina.

Benefits: Protection against AIDS and other STD's; more spontaneity than with male condoms, since it can be inserted in advance.

Drawbacks: It has about as much sex appeal as a sandwich bag.

What you may not know: The device is reputed to squeak during use (adding a little extra lubricant can alleviate this distraction).

When to consider it: If you're not in a stable relationship or you have a partner who refuses to wear a condom.

Tubal ligation: No More Hassles

What it is: This surgical procedure blocks the fallopian tubes so that sperm and egg never meet.

Benefits: No-worry, contraceptive-free sex for the rest of your life. And, after the cost of the surgery ($1,000-$2,500), you'll never spend another dime on birth control.

Drawbacks: This procedure isn't foolproof: Though only five in 1,000 users become pregnant in the first year, surprisingly, over 10 years the failure rate is one in 50 (2%). And, as with any surgery, the procedure carries risks. Finally, depending on how it's done it can't easily be undone.

What you may not know: Sterilization is the most popular method of birth control in the U.S., chosen by a whopping 42% of contraceptive users.

When to consider it: If you're *sure* you don't want any more children.

The Mini-Pill: Fewer Annoying Side Effects

What it is: This pill contains no estrogen and a very small dose of progestin—hence the name.

Benefits: Since it contains no estrogen, the mini-pill has fewer side effects than the Pill and is not associated with any increased risk of blood clots or breast cancer. It also causes lighter than normal periods, making it a good choice for women who are anemic or who tend to bleed heavily.

Contraception 911

Condoms break, diaphragms slip and even the most responsible woman sometimes misses a Pill. The good news is that post-coital contraceptive options are expanding. An FDA advisory panel recently agreed unanimously that the Pill can safely be used as a morning-after contraceptive. The procedure—taking two doses of two or four pills each, depending on the brand, within 72 hours of unprotected sex—reduces the risk of pregnancy by 75%, though nausea and vomiting are common side effects. Several different Pill brands can be used; check with your doctor for specifics. Note: Don't try this on your own.

An emergency IUD insertion can also be done within five to seven days of unprotected sex and is more than 99% effective. Contact your doctor or Planned Parenthood, or call the new 24-hour Emergency Contraception Hotline (800-584-9911) for a list of doctors who provide emergency contraception in your area. You'll also find a list of local providers on the Internet at http://opr.princeton.edu/ec/.

Alternatives to surgical abortion are on the way. The long-awaited French abortion drug mifepristone, better known as RU 486, is expected to be available in this country later this year. The drug blocks progesterone and causes the uterus to discard its lining

along with the implanted egg. It can be used up to nine weeks into pregnancy and may also be used as emergency birth control up to three days after unprotected sex, with fewer side effects than oral contraceptives.

On the horizon: Two FDA-approved drugs already on the market, methotrexate (a chemotherapy drug) and misoprostol (used to prevent stomach bleeding), induce abortion when combined. Since research is still limited on this method, few doctors use it, but that may soon change. Planned Parenthood has received FDA clearance for a large-scale clinical trial to test the technique's safety and effectiveness.

Women who use triphasic birth control pills report experiencing a heightened sex drive.

And it doesn't require a waiting period to get pregnant after you stop taking it.

Drawbacks: It can cause irregular bleeding, offers no protection against STD's and has a significantly higher failure rate than combined oral contraceptives, particularly if you have trouble remembering to take a pill every day.

What you may not know: This method has almost no margin for error. Missing even one day can result in a pregnancy.

When to consider it: If you're nursing (which naturally reduces—but doesn't rule out—fertility); it also seems to slightly increase the quantity and quality of breast milk.

Barrier Methods: STD Protection

What they are: This group includes condoms; diaphragms and cervical caps used with spermicidal jellies or foam; inserts and film. All prevent sperm from reaching eggs.

Benefits: They're safe, cheap and available without a prescription; barrier methods also guard against STD's. Latex condoms provide the best protection against the AIDS virus.

Drawbacks: They interfere with spon-

taneity and can be messy, and your partner may complain of lessened sensation during sex with condoms. Also, caps can be tricky to insert and diaphragms may increase the risk of urinary tract infections in women.

What you may not know: Lubricated condoms and spermicides help counteract vaginal dryness, a common perimenopausal and postpartum problem.

When to consider them: If you're breast-feeding, planning to get pregnant relatively soon or having sex infrequently. Condoms are the best choice if you want iron-clad protection against AIDS and other STD's. Barrier methods are also handy backups when you forget to take a Pill.

Julia Califano is a writer in Hoboken, NJ

Six Reasons to **Switch**

If you've been using the same contraceptive since college, it's probably time to take a fresh look at your birth control options. Here are some compelling reasons to reconsider your method:

1. You've settled down with one partner. Provided neither one of you has a sexually transmissible disease, you can switch from condoms to a method you both like better and will use consistently.

2. Your health has changed. If you develop heart disease, high blood pressure or diabetes, you should re-evaluate your current method with your doctor.

3. You're breast-feeding. Consider a nonhormonal contraceptive, such as condoms, a diaphragm or a copper intrauterine device (IUD), or a progestin-only method, such as the minipill, Norplant or Depo-Provera.

4. You've completed your family. Sterilization is only one long-term option. Also consider Norplant, Depo-Provera, the IUD and the Pill.

5. You're contemplating pregnancy. If you're on the Pill, doctors recommend stopping two to three months before conceiving to re-establish your natural cycle. If you use Depo-Provera, it can take up to a year after your last shot to conceive.

6. You dislike your current method. If you hate inserting your diaphragm or can't remember to take the Pill every day, don't grin and bear it—switch.

HOW RELIABLE ARE CONDOMS?

They're the best protection against sexually transmitted diseases. But several popular varieties failed our tests.

Every day some 6000 people around the world become infected with HIV, most of them through sex. In the U.S., more than a million people carry the virus that causes AIDS, and the count rises by one every 13 minutes. Nearly everyone knows how AIDS is spread—and how to stop it. Three out of four Americans now know that latex condoms, used correctly and consistently, will block AIDS and other sexually transmitted diseases, says Melissa Shepherd, who heads AIDS education efforts at the Federal Centers for Disease Control and Prevention.

Condom sales, driven by the fear of AIDS, have climbed to 450 million a year in the U.S. Once only whispered about, condoms are now routinely advertised on cable TV and in magazines, are sold in supermarkets, and come in a dizzying variety of styles. (One brand alone promotes nine variations: lubricated, mint-scented, spermicidal, studded, sensitive, ribbed, colored, black, and snug.)

Yet many people who should use condoms still don't, apparently put off by the inconvenience or the feel. A recent survey of people with multiple sex partners, for instance, found that those who never use condoms,

or use them inconsistently, outnumbered those who always use them by 11 to 1.

Now there's more bad news: Couples who do use condoms may not be getting all the protection they think they are. How well a condom works is in good part up to the users—some people are more likely than others to break condoms through misuse. But some breakage may be due to real differences among the brands and varieties.

To assess their reliability, we bought and tested 6500 latex condoms—37 different kinds. Among our findings:

■ A half-dozen types of *Trojans,* the best-selling brand, too often flunked an air-inflation test. Long part of many other countries' condom standards, that test was adopted by U.S. inspectors last year after we bought our condoms. Had such guidelines been in place when these condoms were made, and had Government inspectors checked production lots as we did, some lots of those *Trojans* probably would not have made it out the factory door. (One variety of *LifeStyles* condoms failed the same test.)

■ Several condoms promoted as "stronger" did not do as well as others in our inflation tests. Inflating condoms checks their elasticity,

which experts say is the quality that tends to keep a condom intact during intercourse.

■ Several condoms promoted as "thin" are not especially so, according to our measurements. And the condoms that really are thinnest, although they passed the basic inflation test, tended to break more easily than did the other condoms we tested. They may not provide as much protection as their thicker counterparts.

A protective barrier

It may not be obvious from the packaging, but all condoms are pretty much the same. They're nearly all made of latex, in the same basic shape, according to industry standards for size and thickness.

Latex condoms are produced by dipping a cylindrical form in liquid latex and heating it. Machines shape and trim the condom's ring; then the new condoms are washed and aged for a number of days, a "curing" that lets the rubber complete the chemical reactions that strengthen the latex. The final steps: rolling and wrapping individual condoms. The basic process hasn't changed much in 50 years.

The industry standards say a condom's width should be no greater than 54 millimeters—about 2⅛ inches—to prevent slippage; "snugger" condoms are about 10 percent narrower. The minimum length is 160 millimeters, roughly 6⅓ inches, but some products are up to 2 inches longer.

Condoms for contraception

As a contraceptive, condoms are cheap and easy to obtain, and usually cause no side effects. (A very small number of people are allergic to latex—see box "Two Ways to Avoid Latex.")

They are not, however, perfect. The condom's reliability in preventing pregnancies depends on how it's measured. Researchers don't count the number of individual con-

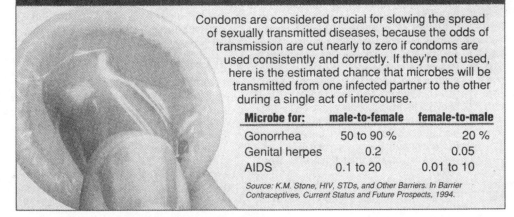

FOR PREVENTION OF DISEASE

Condoms are considered crucial for slowing the spread of sexually transmitted diseases, because the odds of transmission are cut nearly to zero if condoms are used consistently and correctly. If they're not used, here is the estimated chance that microbes will be transmitted from one infected partner to the other during a single act of intercourse.

Microbe for:	male-to-female	female-to-male
Gonorrhea	50 to 90 %	20 %
Genital herpes	0.2	0.05
AIDS	0.1 to 20	0.01 to 10

Source: K.M. Stone, HIV, STDs, and Other Barriers. In Barrier Contraceptives, Current Status and Future Prospects, 1994.

From *Consumer Reports,* May 1995, pp. 320-325. © 1995 by Consumers Union of U.S., Inc., Yonkers, NY 10703-1057. Reprinted by permission.

doms that fail; instead they define contraceptive failure as the percentage of women who use a given method but nonetheless become pregnant over a year's time. For condoms, the typical rate is about 12 percent, somewhat worse than birth-control pills but better than the diaphragm (see graph below). But researchers know that, as with other methods, the failure figures include many couples who don't use contraception every time.

If couples used condoms consistently and correctly, researchers estimate, the condom's failure rate would plummet to 2 or 3 percent, or perhaps even less. One way some couples might further reduce the failure rate—to an estimated one-tenth of a percent, if used consistently—is to use condoms in combination with a vaginal spermicide.

Stopping germs

As a means of preventing the transfer of disease causing microbes between sex partners, condoms have no equal. The condom shields the penis from cervical, vaginal, oral, or rectal secretions. At the same time, the partner is protected from potentially infectious semen and any lesions on the penis.

The need for such protection is apparently greater than many people realize: Every year, 12 million Americans—one-fourth of them teenagers—come down with sexually transmitted diseases. Chlamydia, the most common such disease but often unrecognized, can lead to tubal scarring that experts believe is a key factor in the quadrupling of ectopic pregnancies in the last 10 years. And AIDS is still increasing in the U.S., particularly among women. (Gay men still account for the largest number of AIDS cases; there's concern that condom use is falling among younger gay men.)

Chlamydia, gonorrhea, and AIDS—as well as other sexually transmitted diseases—are virtually 100 percent preventable with proper condom use. So well do latex condoms block germs that, since 1987, the U.S. Food and Drug Administration has allowed condom boxes to list all the diseases condoms help avert. More recently, the FDA told companies that the disease-prevention message was so crucial, they should also print it on the wrappers of individual condoms. Condom boxes warn that the product is intended for vaginal sex, but health officials say it's crucial to use condoms in anal and oral sex, too.

Preventing sexually transmitted disease is in some ways a more rigorous test of condoms than is preventing pregnancy. While conception is a concern only a few days a month, diseases can be caught all the time. Over the decades since the latex condom's introduction, epidemiologists have amassed considerable evidence that it does cut disease rates, but not quite to zero. A 1992 review in the American Journal of Public Health, summing up the results of many varied studies, found that condoms on average cut the risk of infection in half. But the authors said the studies included many couples who failed to use condoms properly or consistently.

When couples are strongly motivated to use condoms every single time, the score greatly improves. Herbert Peterson, chief of the CDC's women's health and fertility branch, cited two recent "blockbuster" studies on condoms' use against HIV. Both focused on heterosexual couples, with one partner carrying HIV at the start of the study, who continued to have sex regularly for two years or more.

In the first study, Italian researchers followed more than 300 healthy women in stable, monogamous relationships with HIV-positive men, questioning the women closely about condom use and testing them periodically for HIV. Among women whose partners never or inconsistently used condoms, 12 percent eventually were infected with HIV. By contrast, fewer than 2 percent of the women whose partners always used condoms became infected.

The second report, from the European Study Group, showed even better results for some 250 uninfected men and women with HIV-positive partners. Among the half who used condoms inconsistently, 10 percent of the previously uninfected partners acquired HIV. When condoms were used all the time, however, HIV was never passed on to the healthy partner—even though the average couple had sex about 120 times over the course of the study.

"If everyone used condoms correctly and consistently, we could break the back of the AIDS epidemic," Peterson told us.

When they fail

An estimated 2 to 5 percent of condoms tear during use. Most of those failures are thought to stem from misuse, not inherent product flaws. (And misuse is common: When the British Consumers' Association asked some 300 Englishmen to demonstrate putting a condom on a model penis, nearly one in five got it wrong—they tried to unroll the condom from the inside out.) Bruce Burlington, who heads the FDA's Center for Devices and Radiological Health, which is responsible for condoms, told a CU reporter that the difference in quality between the best and worst condoms on the market is "tiny compared with the problems that users introduce."

When condoms do break despite being used correctly, it's probably caused by hidden weaknesses in the rubber. Both manufacturers and the Government take steps to catch flawed condoms before they can leave the factory.

Manufacturers test each lot of condoms for leaks and for strength, according to voluntary guidelines set by the American Society for Testing and Materials, the major U.S. standards-setting organization. Those tests, however, which destroy the condoms being examined, can be used only to spot-check a

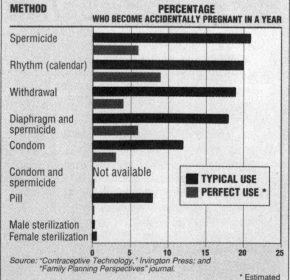

FOR BIRTH CONTROL

As a contraceptive, condoms are more effective than the diaphragm, less so than the Pill. Below are percentages of women relying on each method who nonetheless become pregnant over a year's time. If birth control is used perfectly—consistently and correctly—failures can be cut dramatically. If no birth control method is used, 85 percent become pregnant.

METHOD	PERCENTAGE WHO BECOME ACCIDENTALLY PREGNANT IN A YEAR
Spermicide	
Rhythm (calendar)	
Withdrawal	
Diaphragm and spermicide	
Condom	
Condom and spermicide	Not available
Pill	
Male sterilization	
Female sterilization	

■ TYPICAL USE
■ PERFECT USE *

0   5   10   15   20   25

Source: "Contraceptive Technology," Irvington Press; and "Family Planning Perspectives" journal.

* Estimated

Shapes vary The brands we tested included plain condoms (Ramses), contoured (Saxon Gold), textured (Trojans Ribbed), and an unusual pouch (Pleasure Plus).

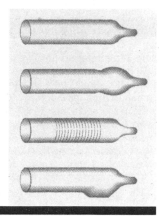

batch of condoms, not to check individual condoms before packaging and sale.

Companies can test every condom for leaks, with a gentler but telling electrical procedure. In one variant of the test, each condom is placed on a charged metal form and swept over by a soft, conductive brush. Minute holes in the condoms trip circuitry that shunts many "leakers" aside. Sometimes this test finds thin spots as well.

The FDA, which regulates condoms as medical devices, sends inspectors to factories unannounced. They review production records and examine stock at random, checking for cracked, moldy, dry, or sticky rubber. The inspectors also test the condoms—until now primarily with a water-leakage test. In this protocol, they pour 10 ounces of water into a condom, then press and roll it along blotter paper. Should leaks turn up in the equivalent of more than 4 per 1000 con-

doms in a run, the manufacturer must scrap the entire lot, perhaps tens of thousands of condoms.

In 1993, the latest year for which we could obtain data, the FDA rejected 2 of the 44 lots of domestic condoms it checked for leakage. The FDA tests every batch of imported condoms as well, though imports account for very few condoms used in this country.

Although the smallest hole the water test can find is 100 times bigger than the HIV virus, officials believe the test is sufficient. The laboratory and clinical studies of HIV persuade them that smaller holes are rare or possibly even nonexistent. Such minute holes are a problem for "skin" condoms, however (see box on next page).

How we tested condoms

When we last tested condoms, in 1989, none of the brands we checked failed the water test. This time, we concentrated on air-burst testing, which we think better predicts breakage in use. Condoms are locked onto an apparatus that slowly inflates them until they're bigger than a watermelon and finally burst with the bang of a gunshot. Meters record the volume of air and amount of pressure the condom withstand.

Unlike tests of tensile strength—done by stretching a band cut from the condom—air-burst testing stresses the entire condom. Last year, the FDA added the air-burst test to its inspectors' repertoire, and asked the companies to include it

in their internal quality-control regimens. The testing guidelines are expected to be adopted shortly as the industry standard.

Published research has linked a condom's air-burst volume to its resistance to breakage during use. Scientists believe that a condom's "extensibility"—its stretchiness—is what helps keep it whole during intercourse. The air-burst test assesses that vital quality.

We tested about 120 individual condoms for each of the 37 styles we bought. To see as many lots as possible for each product, we generally combined samples from five different lots, identifiable by date codes on boxes.

As the Ratings show, our tests were designed to answer two questions: whether a condom passes a minimal standard and, if so, how well it performs on a tougher test, a measure of a product's tendency to break in use. To make the first cut, our combined lots of each product had to pass the new Government air-burst requirement. That rule allows no more than 1½ percent of condoms in a lot to fall short of the required pressure and volume limits. Average-sized condoms, for instance, are supposed to inflate to at least about 16 liters (it varies with condom width) before breaking. Using statistical techniques, inspectors can sample a production run and project a failure rate for the entire lot.

Seven products we tested did not meet that minimal requirement. In each case, at least 4 out of 120 condoms broke too soon during infla-

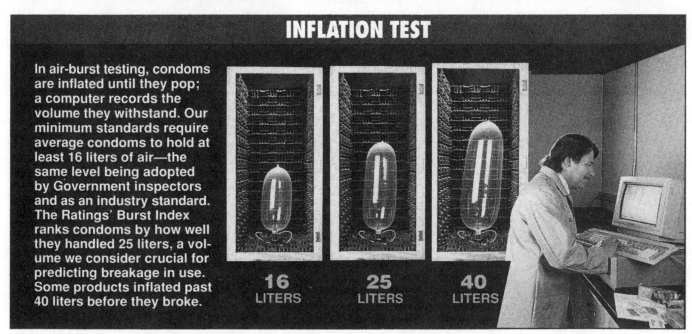

INFLATION TEST

In air-burst testing, condoms are inflated until they pop; a computer records the volume they withstand. Our minimum standards require average condoms to hold at least 16 liters of air—the same level being adopted by Government inspectors and as an industry standard. The Ratings' Burst Index ranks condoms by how well they handled 25 liters, a volume we consider crucial for predicting breakage in use. Some products inflated past 40 liters before they broke.

16 LITERS 25 LITERS 40 LITERS

tion. Based on statistical projections, we believe that more than 1½ percent of condoms in at least some of those products' manufacturing lots would not have inflated to the required minimum volume of air. The products include six styles of *Trojans*—including, ironically, *Trojans Extra Strength*—and *LifeStyles Ultra Sensitive*. We downrated all seven in the Ratings.

For the 30 products that passed that initial screening, we then ranked condoms by a "burst index"—the percentage of samples that withstood at least 25 liters of air. This volume is much greater than the standards specify, but we consider it a crucial measure. In a key study in the journal Contraception—which relied on 260 couples who used 4600 condoms—breakage

was more likely among products from manufacturing lots whose condoms typically could not hold 25 liters of air before rupturing.

Condoms with higher scores on this index should offer greater protection. Three products turned in perfect scores in our tests: *Excita Extra Ultra-Ribbed Spermicidally Lubricated, Ramses Extra Ribbed Spermicidally Lubricated*, and the U.S.-made

---

OTHER CONDOM OPTIONS

TWO WAYS TO AVOID LATEX

If latex condoms irritate your skin, the culprit may be the lubricant, the spermicide, or the materials used in processing; try switching brands. If that doesn't work, you may be among the small percentage of people whose skin is sensitive to latex itself. You have two other choices in condoms, each with pluses and minuses.

'Skin' condoms

Made from a natural pouch in lambs' intestines, these condoms cost several times as much as latex ones. The membrane is especially strong and may enhance sensitivity. The downside: They have small holes.

The microscopic pores can be up to 1.5 microns across. Since sperm cells are twice as wide as that, skin condoms still make an effective contraceptive. But viruses and some bacteria are far smaller than these pores (see diagram). Lab work has shown that HIV and the herpes and hepatitis-B viruses can pass through skin condoms. So these condoms must bear a warning that they are not intended for disease prevention.

We examined *Fourex* and *Kling-Tite Naturalamb* brands. *Fourex* condoms come folded, not rolled, inside plastic

capsules (the condom is pulled on, like a glove). We found the capsules surprisingly hard to open. *Kling-Tite* may be easier to don because it's rolled, like a latex condom. Skin condoms might slip off some men during intercourse because both *Fourex* and *Kling-Tite* are significantly wider than the latex condoms we tested: 78 and 68 millimeters, respectively (latex condoms average 52 millimeters). The *Fourex* has a rubber band rolled onto the base of the condom to prevent slippage. The *Kling-Tite's* elastic band is sewn on more securely.

Polyurethane condoms

Last year, on the basis of limited testing, the FDA gave Schmid Laboratories approval to sell its new *Avanti* brand, a clear condom made of polyurethane. The agency justified approving the product because it felt a pressing public-health need to offer latex-sensitive people an alternative that could prevent disease as well as pregnancy. The *Avanti* condoms first appeared in Western states and should be available elsewhere by summer. But it's unclear just how much protection they offer. A label on the foil packet declares it "effective" against pregnancy and sexually transmitted diseases, while the label on the box warns that "the risks of pregnancy and STDs . . . are not known for this condom." The FDA says it has noted the discrepancy; the packet label will be changed to match the box.

The manufacturer says it has demonstrated to the FDA that *Avanti* does block viruses and neither slips nor breaks

more often than latex. Studies of its contraceptive value are under way.

We bought *Avanti* and *Avanti Super Thin*, which cost us $1.75 each, more than the most expensive latex condoms. Both products are in fact the same condom; the *Super Thins* come with more lubricant.

In the lab, we found the condoms thinner than any conventional condoms tested—roughly 0.04 millimeters. They are also among the shortest of condoms but wider than even larger-size latex brands (60 millimeters versus 55 or 56). That's probably because polyurethane doesn't stretch as much as latex. Despite the company's statements to the contrary, we suspect some men might have slippage problems. When we placed the *Avanti* on a model of an average-sized penis, we found we could pull the condom off quite easily.

Since *Avanti* isn't latex, the label claims that any lubricant may be used safely. We cannot comment on the *Avanti's* strength. Because synthetic condoms are so new, researchers don't know how to compare their performance in standard tests against that of latex condoms.

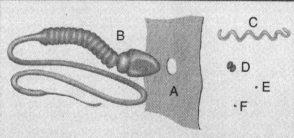

Partial protection Condoms made from lamb membrane (A) block sperm (B), but have natural pores that may be large enough to let through the syphilis (C) and gonorrhea (D) bacteria, and the herpes (E) and AIDS (F) viruses.

Mixed messages
The box and packets of this new polyurethane condom bear conflicting messages about users' risks of disease or pregnancy. The correct answer, the FDA says: The risks are unknown.

Highly ranked condoms
Products that did especially well in our air-burst tests were Excita Extra Ultra Ribbed, the domestic version of Sheik Elite, and Ramses Extra Ribbed. We judged Touch from Protex, which costs less than 35 cents each, A Best Buy.

version of *Sheik Elite Lubricated* (distinguished from the Japanese-made version by a label on the box). The other high-scoring condoms include a mix of *LifeStyles, Ramses, Sheik,* and *Trojans* brands with varied lubricants, both straight and contoured.

Recommendations

Latex condoms work well—both to prevent pregnancy and to avoid sexually transmitted diseases. Unless you know your partner is uninfected, the CDC recommends—for disease prevention—that you use condoms, start to finish, for all sex—vaginal, anal, and oral.

Here are important factors to consider when selecting a condom:

Strength. Among the 30 products that passed our initial screening, those with a higher Burst Index should minimize the possibility of breakage during sex. Our findings don't match the claims on several packages, however. Five condoms we tested claim to be strong (or stronger than some other brand), but only one of those products—*Ramses Extra Ribbed Spermicidally Lubricated*—earned a top score on our Burst Index.

Sensitivity. When researchers asked a national sample of men in their 20s and 30s about condoms, the biggest gripe concerned sensitivity: Three out of four complained that condoms reduce sensation.

Some brands claim to enhance sensitivity, but it's not clear how they do. Some makers say a snug condom helps, but others say it's a looser fit (*Pleasure Plus* has a floppy pouch near the head, for instance). As a group, condoms promising sensitivity aren't especially thin, by our measurements.

What's more, even if a thin condom does heighten sensitivity, thin is not necessarily desirable. The thinnest products—*Beyond Seven,* a Japanese import; and *Sheik Super Thin* and *Ramses Ultra Thin,* both American—had some of the lowest burst scores; they passed our minimum standards, but may not always hold up as well as higher-ranked condoms. When inflated, one-fourth to one-third of those thinner condoms did not reach the crucial 25-liter mark before bursting.

If sensitivity is an issue for you, be aware that this is a poorly defined term. If you want to try some "sensitive" products, it's safest to start with the higher-scoring condoms that make this claim—such as the top-rated *Excita Extra Ultra-Ribbed*—before trying thinner ones.

Size. Size does matter. If a condom is too tight, it can be both uncomfortable and more likely to break; too loose, and it is more likely to slip off. We measured the condoms: Width varied by 12 percent, product to product; length, by almost 20 percent. (The two types we tested that claim to be larger than average—*Trojan-Enz Large* and *Trojan Magnum*—were in fact longer and wider.) The Ratings give the details.

Lubricant. Many condoms come coated with various preparations that feel like oil, glycerine, or surgical jelly. Using a lubricated condom is largely a matter of preference. If couples wish to add their own lubricant, they should be certain not to use petroleum- or mineral-oil-based products, which rapidly weaken latex. (See "Using Condoms Wisely," at left.)

Spermicide. Many condoms' lubricants include a small amount of nonoxynol-9, a spermicide that

USING CONDOMS WISELY

Most of the products we tested provide adequate instructions, often including pictures. But some print the information on the inside surface of the box, which must be torn apart before the instructions can be read. That's unfortunate—good instructions are key for people unaccustomed to using condoms.

Here are the most important points to remember:

■ Open an individual packet only when ready to use the condom—and open it gently, to avoid tearing the contents. If the rubber feels brittle or sticky or looks discolored, discard the condom—it's spoiled.

■ Don the condom when the penis is erect but before sexual contact. Place the tip of the rolled-up condom over the penis. If there is a reservoir tip, first squeeze out the air. If there is no tip, leave a half-inch space at the end for semen, and squeeze the air out.

■ Unroll the condom down the entire length of the penis (uncircumcised men should first pull back the foreskin).

■ Right after ejaculation, grasp the condom firmly at the ring and withdraw before losing the erection, to prevent spillage.

■ Use a new condom for each act of intercourse—never reuse condoms.

■ Store condoms in a cool, dry place. Heat, light, and air pollution can all hasten deterioration.

■ If you want additional lubrication, use only water-based lubricants, such as surgical jelly. Petroleum jelly and mineral-oil products (baby oil, cold cream, many hand lotions) all rapidly weaken latex. Even some lotions that easily wash off with water may contain oils; check the label.

■ If a condom does fail, both partners should wash their genitals with soap and water. Urinating may also help to avoid infections. If the breakage is discovered after ejaculation, having a separate spermicide handy to apply quickly may help. Or a doctor can prescribe an intense dose of birth-control pills, which will block most pregnancies if used within 72 hours of intercourse.

RATINGS Latex condoms

Listed in order of air-burst performance [5]

Product	Cost PER CONDOM	Burst Index	Lubricant feel	Spermicide	Size (LENGTH X WIDTH)	Thickness	Comments
Excita Extra Ultra-Ribbed, spermicide	$1.00		glycerine	8%	193 x 53 mm	0.07 mm	Textured. Product renamed Sheik Excita Extra Ribbed.
Ramses Extra Ribbed, spermicide	0.99		glycerine	5	187 x 52	0.07	Textured.
Sheik Elite [1]	0.53		oily	—	187 x 52	0.07	Renamed Sheik Classic.
LifeStyles Vibra-Ribbed	0.44		glycerine	—	188 x 54	0.08	Wider than most. Textured.
Ramses Extra, spermicide	0.75		glycerine	15	200 x 51	0.07	Spermicide now 5%.
Ramses Sensitol	0.83		oily	—	192 x 52	0.07	—
Sheik Elite Ribbed, spermicide	0.68		oily	8	190 x 51	0.07	Textured. Renamed Sheik Classic.
Sheik Elite, spermicide	0.59		oily	8	190 x 51	0.07	Renamed Sheik Classic.
Trojan-Enz Large	0.75		jelly	—	214 x 56	0.07	Wider, longer than most.
Trojan-Enz Nonlubricated	0.47		—	—	191 x 53	0.07	—
LifeStyles	0.46		glycerine	—	186 x 54	0.07	Wider than most.
Touch from Protex, **A BEST BUY**	0.31 [2]		oily	—.	193 x 52	0.07	—
Trojan-Enz, spermicide	0.64		jelly	5	202 x 51	0.07	Heavier lubrication than most.
Saxon Gold Ultra Lube	0.43		jelly	—	191 x 51	0.08	Contoured.
Trojan Magnum	0.69		oily	—	205 x 55	0.07	Wider, longer than most. Heavier lubrication than most.
Trojan Very Sensitive	0.62		oily	—	206 x 50	0.07	Longer but narrower than most.
LifeStyles, spermicide	0.45		glycerine	7	189 x 54	0.06	Wider than most. Heavier lubrication than most.
Trojan Ribbed	0.64		oily	—	199 x 53	0.07	Textured.
Rough Rider Studded	1.04 [3]		glycerine	—	186 x 53	0.10	Textured. Heavier lubrication than most.
LifeStyles Extra Strength, spermicide	0.65		oily	7	191 x 53	0.09	—
Gold Circle Coin Nonlubricated	0.60 [4]		—	—	184 x 52	0.09	Shorter than most.
Sheik Elite [1]	0.53		oily	—	188 x 51	0.06	Discontinued.
Trojan Naturalube Ribbed	0.66		jelly	—	205 x 53	0.07	Longer than most. Textured.
Class Act Ultra Thin & Sensitive	0.33 [2]		oily	—	193 x 53	0.06	Wider than most.
Kimono	0.39		glycerine	—	193 x 52	0.07	Contoured. Lighter lubrication.
Pleasure Plus	0.98		glycerine	—	197 x 51	0.09	Textured, with floppy pouch.
Beyond Seven	0.50		oily	—	194 x 50	0.05	Narrower than most. Lighter lubrication than most
Gold Circle Rainbow Coin Nonlubricated	0.67 [4]		—	—	180 x 51	0.08	Various colors, contoured.
Sheik Super Thin	0.62		glycerine	—	193 x 51	0.05	—
Ramses Ultra Thin	0.88		glycerine	—	190 x 51	0.05	—
The following products, listed alphabetically, had an overall burst volume defect rate that exceeded 1.5%.							
LifeStyles Ultra Sensitive	0.46	—	glycerine	—	187 x 53	0.06	—
Trojan Extra Strength	0.78	—	oily	—	198 x 53	0.07	—
Trojan Mentor	*1.08 [4]	—	glycerine	—	181 x 52	0.07	Contoured. Has applicator and adhesive band.
Trojan Plus	0.66	—	oily	—	196 x 52	0.07	Contoured.
Trojan Very Thin	0.64	—	oily	—	195 x 53	0.06	Lighter lubrication than most.
Trojan-Enz	0.58	—	jelly	—	201 x 54	0.07	Wider than most.
Trojans Nonlubricated	0.49	—	—	—	200 x 53	0.06	No reservoir tip.

[1] Higher-rated product made in U.S.; lower-rated, in Japan (box flaps are marked).
[2] Purchased in boxes of 13.   [3] Purchased in boxes of three.   [4] Purchased in boxes of six.

[5] *Products tested were manufactured prior to the FDA's air-burst test requirements, which should reduce the defect rate.*

Notes on the table

Cost is the estimated average, based on a national survey. An * indicates the price we paid. Except where noted, we purchased boxes of 12.
Burst Index is the percentage of condoms that inflated to at least 25 liters in air-burst testing. Products with higher scores should offer greater assurance against breakage in use.

Lubricant feel indicates which substances feel like oil, glycerine, or surgical jelly.
Spermicide in the lubricant may offer some extra safety against disease and pregnancy if a condom breaks; the extent of this protection is unknown. Figure given is the concentration of nonoxynol-9.
Size was measured on unrolled, flattened condoms and are averages of several samples. Proper fit

affects comfort and may help avoid breakage or slippage.
Thickness is the average of three measurements along the length of the condom. The typical condom we tested is about 0.07 millimeters thick.
Comments identify textured condoms—which have raised bumps or rings—and contoured condoms—which generally flare out near the head of the condom.

promises extra protection. It's a promise without much proof behind it. In the test tube, the chemical does kill sperm and inactivate a range of microbes, including HIV. But no one knows if it works as well in real use and if there's enough of it to make a difference if the condom breaks. (The CDC says it's optional,

that the latex barrier alone should offer sufficient protection.)

Age. As condoms age, the rubber in them may weaken, so it's a good idea to avoid packages that are more than a few years old. (We found no sign of aging among the condoms we tested, which were all less than three years old.) Un-

fortunately, different brands date products differently. Bear this in mind when you're checking the label: Products containing spermicide are given a shelf life of roughly two or three years (to assure that the spermicide still works), while other condoms are allowed as many as five years on the shelf.

THE drug-induced ABORTION

"I was saved from having surgery"

Within a year, you may not need to have surgery—or cross a picket line—to have an abortion. Two common prescription drugs, used together, are being tested as a surgery alternative. The story of one woman who underwent the procedure

AS TOLD TO LAURA ZIV

My boyfriend and I have always been careful about birth control in the three years we've been together. The first year, we used condoms; then we switched to a diaphragm. I got pregnant on the only occasion I failed to put my diaphragm in. It was the end of my period and my boyfriend just pulled out. I didn't think anything would happen, even though I certainly knew better. It was a stupid thing to do.

When I didn't get my period the following month, I was in denial. I didn't take a pregnancy test until the fifth week. But when the test came back positive, I was on the telephone with my gynecologist immediately.

There was no way I could consider having this baby. Even though I intend to have children one day, this just wasn't the right time. I'm not married, I'm just about to start my career, and it would have been wrong to have a child that I couldn't love and take care

of in the right way. Also, I've been pro-choice my whole life and have never had any moral problem with abortion. I was brought up in a very liberal family—my parents have always considered abortion to be the critical issue in determining whom they would vote for.

My gynecologist told me that she couldn't perform a surgical abortion until the ninth week of my pregnancy. She wanted to be certain that she was removing everything during the suction, and a six-week pregnancy—the stage I was at—is considered early for this method. But she wanted to do the abortion right in the middle of my exams, and I couldn't wait that long. **I wanted to get it over with and not be pregnant anymore. On the other hand, I was petrified of surgical termination. For some reason, I've always felt it would be hard for me to get pregnant and I didn't want any damage done to my body. With the suction method, there's al-**

A STUDY conducted by Dr. Hausknecht reported that drug-induced abortions were safely performed on 96 percent of the patients in the trial.

ways a slight risk of puncturing the cervix, which may affect your ability to conceive in the future.

The weekend after I spoke with my doctor, I was at my friend's house. On her coffee table was an issue of *New York* magazine, with a cover story about nonsurgical abortions. I read it, trying to look totally nonchalant. (My friend had no idea I was pregnant.) The article featured Richard Hausknecht, M.D., an eminent New York gynecologist and obstetrician and associate professor at the Mount Sinai School of Medicine, and his experimental work using the drugs methotrexate and misoprostol to induce abortion. It mentioned a study Dr. Hausknecht published in the *New England Journal of Medicine* in August 1995.

That afternoon, I pulled that article up on my home modem. In his study, Dr. Hausknecht reported that he had safely performed drug-induced abortions on 96 percent of his patients in an independent trial. I called Dr. Hausknecht's office to find out whether it was possible to have a drug-induced abortion. I was surprised when I was told to come in the next day. It turns out nonsurgical abortions are safest in the first six weeks of pregnancy (although the procedure can be performed until the eighth week). That's one of the advantages of nonsurgical abortion: You can have one as soon as you find out you're pregnant.

My boyfriend went with me to my appointment. In the waiting room, I was teary-eyed, scared at the prospect of doing something completely new and fearful of the unknown. But as soon as I met Dr. Hausknecht, I trusted him immediately. He has a very caring bedside manner and I knew everything would be OK. I was determined to go ahead with a drug-induced abortion.

"If you think [this method] is going to be easy, it's not," he said when I told him I was afraid of surgical abortion. "It's going to hurt; it won't be comfortable." He also said that nonsurgical abortion isn't foolproof—there's a failure rate of approximately 4 percent, and in these cases, a suction termination is subsequently performed.

I read the ten-page consent form, line by line, five times. What stood out most in my mind was the possibility of needing a surgical termination after all. My boyfriend was nervous about it. "Are you sure you want to do this? Why do you want to do something new?" he asked. But drug-induced abortion scared me much less than surgery did.

After signing the waiver form, I had a vaginal sonogram to make sure that I was no more than eight weeks pregnant. I asked how big the embryo was and what it looked like. Dr. Hausknecht showed me seven millimeters on a ruler. I told him that I didn't have an attachment to anything that's seven millimeters. A lot of people may think my response offensive, but I'm sarcastic by nature and my gallows humor was my way of dealing with the situation.

The worst moment was the methotrexate shot in my backside. I hate injections. Unlike the French abortion pill, which blocks the hormone needed for maintaining a pregnancy, methotrexate stops the fetal cells from dividing and growing. After the shot, psychologically, I no longer felt pregnant. Now, it was a matter of expelling the embryo. That's the job of the second drug, misoprostol, a suppository-like tablet, which induces uterine contractions. The process, Dr. Hausknecht explained, is like a chemically induced miscarriage.

Dr. Hausknecht gave me four misoprostol tablets, all to be inserted into my vagina five days later. Usually, you go back for a second visit to have the tablets inserted by the doctor, but Dr. Hausknecht was going out of town and I had to do it myself. He told me, "If you can put in a diaphragm, you can do this."

During that five-day waiting period, I suffered absolutely no side effects from the methotrexate. But I found the actual physical act of inserting the misoprostol tablets distressing.

the abortion drug HOW SAFE? HOW SOON?

Like the French abortion pill RU-486, the combination of the prescription drugs methotrexate and misoprostol chemically induces an abortion. Unlike RU-486, which antiabortion activists have successfully kept out of this country, the two drugs cannot be banned from the market, because they have already been approved by the Food and Drug Administration for other uses: methotrexate for cancer and arthritis and misoprostol for ulcers. Because doctors are allowed to prescribe drugs for "off-label purposes," a methotrexate termination, as the procedure is called, is not illegal.

The procedure goes as follows: Within the first eight weeks of conception, the patient gets a shot of methotrexate, a folic acid blocker which stops fetal cells from multiplying. Five to seven days later, the patient inserts four misoprostol vaginal tablets, which cause the uterine contractions that expel the embryo.

Some doctors and antiabortion activists are concerned about the safety of methotrexate, a toxic drug for abortion purposes.

Doctors in favor of drug-induced abortion point out that it has been used for over a decade to end ectopic pregnancies (when the fetus grows outside the womb) with no adverse effects and that the dose used to induce abortion is much lower than that used to treat cancer.

In a 1995 study by Dr. Richard Hausknecht, a New York obstetrician and gynecologist, 178 women underwent the procedure. Ninety-six percent successfully ended their pregnancies. (The others had surgical abortions.) Side effects included mild irritation of the lips and gums, a brief period of diarrhea, and nausea.

Last summer, the FDA allowed Dr. Hausknecht to conduct a formal nationwide trial. To date, approximately 2,000 women have undergone the procedure in the U.S. Planned Parenthood hopes to offer drug-induced abortion by the end of 1996—after the drug has been approved by the FDA for that purpose and enough doctors have been trained in the procedure. For more information, contact Dr. Hausknecht at 212-369-1116.

When I held them in my hand, I started to cry. I wasn't sure where to stick them in and I was worried that they would fall out. At first I thought, "I can't do this." My boyfriend offered to put them in, but finally I did it myself. It took all of five seconds. The tablets stayed put and eventually dissolved.

Misoprostol is like a time-release capsule: It kicked in six hours after insertion, as Dr. Hausknecht said it would. After inserting the tablets at 10 A.M. on a Sunday, I spent the day working on an important project that I wanted to hand in the following day. I also bought enough food for the rest of the week just in case I was sick in bed. At exactly 4 P.M., I broke into a little sweat and vomited once. I crawled into bed. From 5:30 to 8 P.M., I had terrible cramps, like a combination of a really bad period and flu. I was hot, cold, then hot again. I took some codeine—the only pain-killer you are allowed to take in combination with misoprostol. Still, the fact that I was aborting at home didn't panic me. My boyfriend was with me if anything happened. I went to sleep and the cramps continued throughout the night.

It's over

The next morning, I was running around, feeling fine. I was bleeding heavily, but it just felt like I had my period. Instead of using tampons, I had to wear sanitary pads. Dr. Hausknecht explained that I would see blood clots, clumps, and tissue, and that's exactly what I saw. I thought it might freak me out to see what was being expelled from my body, but it looked just like a heavy period. I bled a lot for two whole weeks and toward the end, I must admit, it did get a little irritating. But I didn't miss a single day of school and I wasn't walking around thinking, "I'm in the middle of a two-week abortion." No one knew.

In all, the abortion cost me $550. (I didn't try to see whether it was covered by my insurance plan, although some insurance companies do pay for the procedure.) The two drugs are cheap (they cost less than $10) and the bulk of the fee is for the doctor's visits.

I had my follow-up examination, to make sure the abortion was completed, four days after inserting the misoprostol. Someone in training from Planned Parenthood watched the exam with my permission. I think it's important that this type of abortion become available as another option to women nationwide. When it does, women who live in rural areas won't need to travel to faraway, violence-prone abortion clinics because they'll be able to have the procedure performed by their local doctor.

Having the choice

Yes, nonsurgical abortion is still new. Methotrexate hasn't yet been approved by the FDA for abortion. There may be long-term, unknown side effects. A friend asked me, "What if you grow a third breast in ten years?" But, actually, the chances of developing adverse side effects are very slim. Methotrexate has been around for more than 40 years and is commonly prescribed in much higher doses for cancer and arthritis. My friend's mother has been taking it for 20 years for her arthritis and nothing's happened to her. And methotrexate has also been safely used for ten years to terminate ectopic pregnancies (where the fetus grows in the fallopian tube).

Although I hope never to need another abortion, I would choose this method again if I had to. My experience with it was easy, though I don't know whether it will be that way for everyone. To me, drug-induced abortion feels more natural than surgery. The doctor is present, but you don't really need him. I did everything myself, except for injecting the methotrexate. I felt in control.

Some women experience abortion as a loss, but I saw it as a gain: I gained my life back. I think methotrexate is a miracle drug—I feel like I've participated in something revolutionary that will make a difference to women's reproductive rights. In 20 years, I hope Dr. Hausknecht will be known for radically changing abortion in this country. I'm glad that my abortion was accessible, private, and trauma-free, and that I didn't run the risk of getting bombed in an abortion clinic.

Infertility, Inc.

As thousands of couples desperate for a child gamble their life
savings on unproven, high-tech treatments, often the only ones
who stand to gain are the clinics. A heartbreaking report
on the multimillion-dollar business of baby making.

Ford Fessenden

*Ford Fessenden is an award-winning
reporter for* Newsday *in Melville,
New York.*

Diane Porter's hopes ran high
as she awaited the surgery
that could give her and her
husband, Grosvenor, the child they
longed for. The couple had traveled
one thousand miles from their home
near Omaha to seek treatment from
one of the nation's top infertility specialists, Ricardo Asch, M.D., at University of California at Irvine's center
for Reproductive Health. After giving
Diane hormones to stimulate her
healthy ovaries, Asch told her that
she might produce forty eggs, maybe
even fifty—plenty for several tries at
in vitro fertilization (IVF), a high-
tech procedure that has produced almost twenty-six thousand babies
over the last seventeen years.

"I thought, Oh, my gosh, I'm going
to have lots of chances [at having a
baby]," recalls Diane, thirty-three.

For years, she and Grosvenor, thirty-
nine, a former University of Nebraska
football player who goes by the nick-
name Budge, had been trying to have
a child, with no luck. Budge had been
injured in a game twenty years ago,
and suffered from quadriplegia until
1991. During those years of paraly-
sis, low-grade infections wreaked
havoc with his sperm count.

But Asch was hopeful. He told Diane she would have a one-in-four
chance of getting pregnant—almost
the same odds a couple with no fertility problems would have each
month. He also seemed to have the
skills necessary to produce a miracle:
He was affiliated with a reputable
university and had pioneered an infertility procedure known as gamete
intrafallopian transfer, or GIFT
(which involves depositing sperm and
egg into one of the woman's fallopian
tubes, where fertilization occurs, at
an average cost of $7,800 per at-
tempt) in the mid-eighties. GIFT's
profitability brought him tremendous
wealth, and even greater self-confi-
dence. He told one patient, who had
experienced ten years of failure in
other infertility programs, "You will
be pregnant." She was.

"I really felt good about Dr. Asch,"
Diane remembers.

Cool and authoritative, Asch entered the recovery room after Diane's
surgery. "How'd I do?" she asked. It
wasn't as fruitful a harvest as they
had hoped, he told her—they'd collected just twenty-two eggs. Still, he
reassured Diane that was plenty for
several attempts at IVF, in which her
eggs would be combined with Budge's
sperm in a laboratory dish and the
resulting embryos implanted in her
uterus. (Often, multiple embryos are

inserted in the hope that one will implant.)

But to the Porters' disappointment,
the IVF failed—twice. (Statistically
speaking, this is not surprising;
about 80 percent of IVF attempts
fail.) Asch recommended that the
couple work with doctors in Omaha.
They did, and in 1993, Diane finally
became pregnant. Now she and Budge
have a little girl named Claire.

Two years later, the couple was
horrified to learn that Asch had
never told them about other eggs he
had harvested from Diane—eggs
that, according to medical records,
were combined with the sperm of a
stranger whose wife eventually had
twins. Medical records indicate the
twins aren't biologically related to
the Porters; apparently, another patient's eggs were also used. But that
hasn't taken the edge off their anger
and pain.

"It was bad enough to go through
the process [of infertility treatment]
all these years," says Diane. "Then
to find out we were betrayed. . . . It
makes me so angry."

The theft of Diane's eggs is just
one horror emerging from the practice of Asch and his two partners,
Jose Balmaceda, M.D., and Sergio
Stone, M.D. More than sixty patients
at the Irvine clinic unknowingly do-
nated eggs to other patients or re-

ceived the wrong eggs themselves. The doctors also have been accused of using a non-FDA-approved fertility drug. And in some cases, harvested eggs may have been sent to a university for embryo research.

The scandal was uncovered last May when two former employees of the clinic came forward. In June, the university filed a lawsuit against Asch and his two partners and closed the clinic. The Porters, along with twenty other couples, are suing the three doctors and are fighting to learn what happened to their eggs.

Investigations are being conducted by no fewer than seven federal, state and local agencies, as well as a California state senate committee, and records have been seized from the doctors' homes and offices. But there has been no criminal action against Asch and his partners, because there are no laws against embryo theft. (A bill to criminalize it is likely to be introduced in the current session of the California legislature.) All three doctors deny any wrongdoing, and Asch is now practicing in Mexico City.

"When you see this happen at a world-renowned clinic," says Diane, "you wonder, What's happening in the rest of the country?"

In the wake of the Asch scandal, that very question resonates in the minds of the 5.3 million infertile couples across the nation.

The baby business

Seventeen years after the world's first test-tube baby was born, the $350-million infertility business is booming. The number of clinics has mushroomed from just thirty in 1985 to about three hundred in 1995, and infertility doctors, known as reproductive endocrinologists, are now the highest paid medical specialists.

It's not just doctors who are making money on the infertile. For years, men have been paid to donate sperm to fertility clinics. Now women can sell their eggs for as much as $3,000 to others with poor-quality eggs. (The donor eggs are combined with sperm in a petri dish, and the resulting embryo is implanted in the infertile woman's uterus.)

No wonder the business has become so profitable: A glut of baby boomers in the thirty-five to forty-four age group—the childbearing years during which infertility rates are highest—has created an explosion in demand. (About 8 percent of women aged fifteen through forty-four are infertile at any given time.) Although about 43 percent of women with impaired fertility are seeking medical assistance for their problem, most are not filling their empty bassinets: Success rates for assisted-reproduction procedures remain low (about 25 to 30 percent per treatment cycle).

And when it comes to unexplained infertility, a large number of infertile couples get pregnant *without* treatment. "To a great extent, the treatments are still shots in the dark," says John A. Collins, M.D., professor of obstetrics and gynecology at McMaster University, in Hamilton, Ontario.

Compounding the general lack of scientific understanding is the fact that the infertility business remains largely unregulated. Clinics are not government-inspected, and they may exaggerate success rates, a problem that caught the attention of the Federal Trade Commission, which, since 1990, has obtained cease-and-desist orders against five clinics.

Ethical standards are lacking as well. In 1992, Cecil Jacobson, M.D., an infertility specialist in Vienna, Virginia, was sentenced to five years in prison for fraud by failing to tell his patients that he had inseminated them with his own sperm and falsely telling other patients they were pregnant when they weren't.

So what lures couples to spend thousands on treatments that are often painful, emotionally wrenching and unsuccessful? Aside from the hope that persistence will produce a baby, extensive publicity about new, high-tech treatments convinces couples that doctors can solve any infertility problem, no matter how tough.

Science falls short

The shocking truth is that "our ability to diagnose infertility is still stuck in the nineteenth century," says John Collins.

And the value of treatment has never been clearly established. In a 1994 review of infertility research in *The New England Journal of Medicine*, Howard W. Jones, M.D., and James P. Toner, M.D., of the Jones Institute for Reproductive Medicine, in Norfolk, Virginia, stated that a surprising number of pregnancies occur without intervention. In a 1993 study published in the journal *Fertility and Sterility*, 40 percent of pregnancies in previously infertile women still occurred without treatment.

Experts say one reason science falls short is that the federal government has not funded embryo research that might answer key questions, such as why some embryos don't implant in the uterus.

The numbers game

Despite the lack of scientific understanding, emotionally fragile couples are often lured into clinics by bullish marketing. The desire to capture a portion of the sizable profits (the cost of a live birth can range from $10,000 to $100,000, and some clinics may profit by as much as 40 percent) has ignited intense competiton among clinics. In big cities, they advertise like car dealers, often touting misleading success rates. The best hospitals aren't immune: In 1994, Mt. Sinai Medical Center, in New York City, paid former patients $4 million to settle a lawsuit stemming from false claims regarding success rates. The clinic advertised that its take-home baby rate was 20 percent when it was much lower—about 13.7 percent.

The Fertility Clinic Success Rate and Certification Act of 1992 mandates that clinics publish consistent success rates (the number of treatment attempts per live birth). But the law hasn't been implemented because of lack of financing.

Janice and Rick Byer of Clifton, Virginia, were fooled by misleading statistics when, starting in 1990, they underwent two attempts at IVF. The couple wound up spending around $25,000 over two years on the baby chase, largely because a doctor told them they had roughly a 40 percent shot at having a child. But with

The Stork Market

A Guide To Infertility Services

t he following tips can help ensure quality treatment:

1. Consider your odds of conceiving. If you are under forty and have at least one ovary capable of responding to fertility drugs, have a normal uterus and endometrial lining, have been pregnant before and your husband's sperm function is normal, your odds are good. Talk to your gynecologist.

2. Get a second opinion. Seek a referral from RESOLVE, a nonprofit, national support group for infertile couples. Call the National Helpline at 617-623-0744.

3. Find out about insurance coverage. Currently, about ten states mandate some level of coverage. If your insurer says you are covered, request a written statement.

4. Choose a clinic carefully. Your best bet is a clinic that's recognized by the American Society for Reproductive Medicine (ASRM), 1209 Montgomery Highway, Birmingham, AL; 35216-2809; 205-978-5000. Be

sure to investigate its success rates, which should be classified as number of treatment attempts per live birth. Keep in mind, clinics that have been using a procedure longest may have the best rates of success. Talk to patients who have completed the clinic's programs.

5. Know the treatment options:
● *In vitro fertilization (IVF),* in which eggs and sperm are united in a laboratory dish and then transferred to the uterus. Success rate: 18 percent.
● *Intrauterine insemination (IUI),* in which sperm is injected directly into the uterus. Success rate: 10 percent.

If you plan to use sperm from an anonymous donor, be sure he has been screened for HIV, the virus that causes AIDS. Check with your state to be sure it mandates donor testing, and ask the fertility clinic about their screening procedures.
● *Gamete intrafallopian transfer (GIFT),* in which eggs and sperm are injected into one fallopian tube, where fertilization occurs.

Success rate: 28 percent.
● Best for low sperm counts and sluggish sperm: *zygote intrafallopian transfer (ZIFT),* in which fertilized eggs are transferred directly into a woman's fallopian tube, or *intracytoplasmic sperm injection (ICSI),* in which healthy sperm are injected directly into eggs in the laboratory. The resulting embryos are placed in the uterus. Success rates: 24 percent.

6. When you begin treatment, consider a stress-reduction program. Alice Domar, Ph.D., staff psychologist at Deaconess Hospital, in Boston, has shown that stress levels of infertile women rival those of women with cancer.

7. Use the Net. If you have a computer, go to the Internet's Usenet news group in your on-line provider, and follow the instructions to sign up with alt.infertility. Or, participate in an E-mail "chat" group on infertility by subscribing to majordomo@acpub.duke.edu.

—F.F.

---

transferring them to the uterus). Those aged thirty-six to thirty-nine pay the most—$16,400—because they are less likely to become pregnant. Of all the women who qualify, about half get pregnant, says Geoffrey Sher, M.D., executive medical director.

The problem with this setup, according to infertility experts, is that some women—especially those who get pregnant on the first try—may pay more than they would at other clinics. "It's like buying insurance," says Eldon Schriock, M.D., director of the IVF program at the University of California at San Francisco (UCSF). The UCSF clinic, for instance, charges women who get pregnant on the first try about $7,500 for the same services PFC offers. "The patient who gets pregnant on her first try at PFC pays about $5,000 more," Schriock adds. "She pays for those who *don't* get pregnant."

Would UCSF implement the same kind of program? "We've thought about it," Schriock says. "But the AMA [American Medical Association] has a written policy that it's unethical to tie the success of a medical therapy with cost."

Fortunately, things may soon change: At an AMA meeting last November, a Federal Trade Commission representative said one goal for this year was to investigate infertility clinics' advertising and marketing claims.

Of ethics and embryos

The absence of government regulation has also hampered the development of ethical standards in the infertility business, says experts. Crucial questions remain unanswered, such as who owns embryos once they are created in the lab. The confusion is evident in U.S. courts. In 1992, a Tennessee court ruled that a divorced man had the right not to have children, so he was granted custody of the fertilized embryos he and his ex-wife had produced during their marriage. (He later had them destroyed.) But last year, in a different case, a New York court determined that a

---

Janice' age (forty) and the type of infertility problem they had (Rick's low sperm count), their actual chance was less than 5 percent.

"We wasted thousands of dollars on false hopes, " Janice says.

And even when success rates are legitimate, women can be misled by marketing ploys, experts say. Take, for instance, the Pacific Fertility Center (PFC), which has offices throughout California. In the clinic's In Vitro

Fertilization Partnership Plan, IVF patients are offered a 90 percent refund if they don't become pregnant. To qualify for the program, a woman must have a healthy uterus, and her ovaries must be capable of being stimulated by hormone drugs. And price varies by age: Women thirty-five and under pay $12,500, excluding drugs to stimulate the ovaries, for one egg retrieval (which includes the cost of freezing embryos and

husband had no such right and awarded custody of the embryos to his ex-wife.

Embryo custody after divorce seems a simple issue compared to the perplexing questions the Asch scandal has raised: To whom do embryos—and eventually babies—belong when they are created by unrelated, unwilling participants? Those who contribute the genetic material or those who give birth?

The Asch episode has certainly brought talk of reform. The American Society for Reproductive Medicine has published guidelines that call for hiring personnel with expertise in reproductive technology and equipment

maintenance. This year, the organization plans to publish guidelines on proper treatment for different fertility problems.

The AMA is also stepping in. In December, they established the AMA Task Force on Ethical Issues in Reproductive Technology to examine the current clinical and ethical guidelines and explore possible ways to enforce them. However, standards set by the AMA would not be as effective as federal laws.

But don't look for federal regulation any time soon. With the exception of the Asch hearings, Congress and state legislatures have shown little interest in dealing with the larger

issues at stake. "Americans don't like to regulate reproduction," explains Arthur Caplan, Ph.D., a bioethicist at the University of Pennsylvania, in Philadelphia. "We don't want to interfere with someone's right to have a child. Also, the field has fought any attempts at regulation because it's lucrative."

Unfortunately, infertile couples must suffer the consequences. Diane and Budge Porter's daughter has "helped lessen the blow [of the scandal]," says Budge. "But she also makes us painfully aware of the other [eggs] that could have given us more children in the future."

Making Love again

Judith Newman

New moms and dads reveal the truth about sex after the baby.

You've got to be kidding...

DAVID GOLDIN

"Sex after childbirth?" asks my friend Maria, trying to calm her overtired 6-month-old son. "Well, if I ever have sex again, I'll be sure to give you a call."

"Sex after childbirth?" echoes Emily, mother of 1-month-old Sam. "Who cares? How about doing a story on sleep after childbirth?"

"I have only two words for you," says new mom Amanda. "K-Y Jelly."

To a woman who's trying to get pregnant for the first time, writing a story on sex after childbirth is somewhat like watching a series of car wrecks before going for my driver's license. The spectacle isn't pretty.

According to a 1993 survey conducted by Dwenda K. Gjerdingen, M.D., at the University of Minnesota in Minneapolis, about 40 percent of women report some difficulty with sex three months after delivery, and 20 percent continue to have problems for up to a year. Such complications can result from any of a number of factors, including discomfort caused by an episiotomy that hasn't yet healed, uneasiness over a body that's decidedly less than perky, or that universal state of new parenthood: bone-deep exhaustion.

Fortunately, the vast majority of these difficulties eventually go away. But not necessarily without a fight.

The First Time

Most doctors recommend waiting four to six weeks after delivery before resuming sexual intercourse. In addition, you will need to consider a few other very scientific factors, such as "How amorous am I feeling?" and "How much longer can I stand to listen to my husband whine?"

The biggest obstacle, of course, is simple: fear of pain. Let's face it. Something the size of a pot roast has just come out of you, and you're not sure you're eager to see anything go back in. What's more, your body has been on a hormone high for nine months, and now, with the sudden drop in estrogen levels after childbirth, your nether regions may feel as dry as the Sahara Desert (breastfeeding generally prolongs this condition).

"After a horrendous labor and delivery that required a two-mile-long episiotomy," says Linda, a gynecologist in Tampa, Florida, "I waited the requisite six weeks and then turned to my eager husband and said, 'Honey, I love you. But if you hurt me, I will personally give you a vasectomy.'" Fortunately, Linda's husband was gentle and had no aversion to generous dollops of K-Y.

"It was so scary," says Deirdre, a graduate student in Milwaukee. Deirdre had lost a good deal of blood during delivery and had needed a transfusion. Her husband, Jason—"a guy who had to walk out of *Jurassic Park* during the scary parts"—had been there to witness the whole event. And then there was the freakish allergic reaction to the adhesive on the back of her panty liners that caused her to break out in hives.

"So when, after eight weeks, we had sex for the first time, it wasn't like we could just pick up where we left off," she says. "We were both still traumatized. But we wanted to prove to each other that we could still do it." And they could. But Jason, seconding his wife, admits, "We were more relieved than anything else. After that **one time, we didn't do it again for months.**"

Women who've delivered by Caesarean section have their own set of concerns. "Sex after a C-section is much different than sex after a vaginal delivery," says Meghan, a marketing executive in Austin, Texas, who's had one of each. "For one thing, you can feel something. With a vaginal delivery, what came out at birth was probably five times larger than anything your partner can offer, and you're stretched to the size of the Holland Tunnel. With a C-section, that's not a concern. Instead, you worry about whether your stitches will hold up—especially if you have sex prior to the doctor's okay, which I did. Fortunately, everything turned out fine."

Occasionally, women wait so long to resume having sex that they feel like born-again virgins. My friend Maria's son was 6 months old when I interviewed her for this article—and she still hadn't done it with her husband. But to oblige me, she finally did—and admitted it was great (her husband sent me flowers). "I'm not sure why I waited," says Maria, who's a lawyer in Baltimore. "I guess it's just that you receive so much touching

grotesquely swollen ankles. Then he got to witness my shrieking like a banshee during childbirth. Afterward, everything sagged and I was so stretched I needed a diaphragm the size of a Frisbee. And he still wanted to have sex as soon as possible. How could that be?" It took Nina four months before she felt good enough about her body to be interested again.

The ZZZZ Factor

As you can see, "sexy" and "passionate" are not the first words that usually slip off the tongue of most new mothers. It's far more common to hear things like "sleep deprived" and "tired to the bone." Indeed, it is complete and utter exhaustion, probably more than any other single factor, that makes having sex at this stage about as appetizing as a chocolate sandwich with ketchup and string beans.

"At 8 weeks, my son was still waking up about every two hours throughout the night," says Amy, an executive recruiter in Berkeley, California. "So the first time my husband and I had sex, I was *soooo extreeeeemely*

might as well have been making love to a rocking chair. My attitude was like, 'If this helps you, I'm glad to be of assistance. But I don't think you can possibly help me.'

"I certainly wanted to reestablish relations with my husband," she adds, "but sheer physical exhaustion prevented me. I think this is true of most new mothers: You covet sleep more than the most fantastic sexual experience of your life."

Indeed, even the most passionate women agree that for the first few months after your baby is born, sex is more like a plate of meatloaf and mashed potatoes than champagne and caviar. "It's comfort sex," explains Angela, a public relations consultant in Santa Cruz, California. "You save those wilding experiences for when the kid's a little older."

But sleep isn't the only deterrent to a postpartum roll in the hay. If the couples that I've talked to are any indication, one thing seems absolutely certain: Children do not want siblings. Thaisa, a short-story writer who lives in San Francisco, explains it this way: "Kids seem to know that sex between parents has only one purpose: that of getting them into this world. As far as they're concerned, once this sole goal has been accomplished, parental intimacies are no longer necessary. In fact, they are completely undesirable and must be stopped at all costs. Children are therefore programmed to wake up and cry whenever their parents attempt to repeat this act."

Hildie, a high school teacher in Minneapolis, agrees. "My husband and I think our 9-month-old son is going to be a comedian because he has this incredible sense of timing. It was particularly acute when he was an infant. As soon as you sat down, he woke up. As soon as your head hit the pillow, he cried. As soon as you . . . well, you know . . . he started wailing. We had to wait until I felt comfortable enough to leave him with a babysitter before we could have sex again—and then it was in one of those 'no-tell motels.' "

Even now, Hildie and her husband have to work hard to psych

When you feel like a moo-cow, how can your husband still *find you appealing?*

from a child that your senses are overloaded. At the end of the day, the thought of being touched some more is just—yuck."

Maria adds that after all that time, sex was quite an experience. "I was so used to changing Daniel's diaper that when I saw my husband it was like, *woah!* I had forgotten what an adult guy looked like."

Feeling Frumpy

Like Maria, many women find that they lose their sense of sexuality after giving birth. It's common to see yourself in an entirely different role—a role my friend Emily sums up as "moo-cow"—and it's virtually impossible to understand how your husband can still view you as a bedroom diva.

Nina, a magazine editor in New York City, explains it this way: "Adam watched me gain 55 pounds. He saw me spend the last month with these

tired that I told him not to take it personally if I fell asleep. And I did.

"I woke up when he indulged in what he claimed is every man's fantasy: nursing. And then I made him stop, fearing he'd deplete our baby's milk supply." ("Amy need not have worried," notes William Sears, M.D., a pediatrician in private practice in San Clemente, California, and co-author of *The Baby Book*. "Your partner won't deplete your milk—or increase the risk of infection to the baby.")

"I had the next day off from work," Amy adds, "and that evening we got together earlier—and somewhat more successfully than before."

"The funny thing is, I was in some sort of deranged estrogen frenzy while I was pregnant, and sex was just incredible," says Marissa, a homemaker living in Princeton, New Jersey. "After I gave birth, Keith

their young son out. "We do make love," she says, "but it's not exactly a regular thing."

Adds Marissa, "It's like your brain has been rigged to hyper-respond to a child's cry, and that cry is always, *always* timed to when you and your husband are having sex. Even if you can manage to divert your attention to something other than your role as 24-hour baby attendant—no small feat, I can tell you—you just can't give your undivided attention to The Act."

rediscovering the
Joy of Sex

If You Feel **Pain During Intercourse**

Allow yourself time to heal. Try oral and manual love play instead.

Use lubricants, such as K-Y Jelly or Astroglide, to relieve dryness.

Start with a woman-on-top position so you can control the speed and degree of penetration.

Bear down during penetration (imagine pushing out a tampon) to counteract painful muscle tightening.

If You Feel **Lack of Desire**

Remind yourself of how wonderful sex can be by recalling romantic interludes from the past.

Engage in emotional foreplay. As clichéd as it sounds, sexy lingerie, candles and erotica might be just the stimulation you need.

Think of sex as something you're doing for yourself—not your partner—and expect to get something out of it.

If You Feel **Fatigue**

Make "dates" with your mate and plan accordingly. Try to take a nap. Have a babysitter come by for a few hours so you can rest. Ask your husband to come home early to help with the baby.

Don't push too hard. No matter how good a relationship is, the sexual aspect always dips during the first three to six months. Don't worry. This is normal.

If You Feel **Unattractive**

Tell yourself over and over again that the current state of your body is a temporary side effect resulting from one of the greatest things you've ever done.

Let your partner be the judge. Since he is interested in having sex with you, your body is not a problem for him, so why make it difficult for yourself? Think of sexual attractiveness as being in the eye of the beholder.

If You Have **Sore Nipples and Tender Breasts**

Apply pure lanolin or vitamin E oil to soothe sore nipples. (Both are safe for babies and don't need to be washed off before nursing.)

Make sure your baby has the entire areola (dark area) in her mouth. Sucking on the nipple only is painful for you and makes it hard for the baby to get milk.

Source: Lonnie Barbach, Ph.D., a San Francisco psychologist and author of several books, including *The Erotic Edge.*

Some Passions Never Wane

Lest you think every woman on the planet looks upon sex after childbirth as a chore only marginally more enjoyable than undergoing root canal, think again. Though they do seem to be in the minority, there are those randy women who can't wait to get back in the saddle, so to speak.

"I remember asking my ob/gyn how soon after delivery I could do it," says Lacey, a musician in Miami. "He smiled and said, 'That depends on whether you have a private or semi-private room.' And he was right—although we did end up waiting a week or so."

Then there's Angela. She had one of those earth-mother, no fuss, no muss deliveries that most moms fantasize about: a three-hour labor yielding twins, delivered vaginally, without drugs. But because she was carrying twins, she and her husband hadn't been able to have sex since the fourth month of her pregnancy. "I was so tired of oral sex," says Angela. "Just having my husband lie on top of my flat—well, sort of flat—stomach was such a thrill."

So you see, there's at least one thing about postpartum sex to look forward to.

Judith Newman is a freelance writer based in New York City.

Sexuality through the Life Cycle

Youth and Their Sexuality (Articles 33–36)
Sexuality in the Adult Years (Articles 37–39)

Individual sexual development is a lifelong process that begins at birth and terminates at death. Contrary to popular notions of this process, there are no latent periods during which the individual is nonsexual or noncognizant of sexuality. The growing process of a sexual being does, however, reveal qualitative differences through various life stages. This section devotes attention to these stages of the life cycle and their relation to sexuality.

As children gain self-awareness, they naturally explore their own bodies, masturbate, display curiosity about the bodies of the opposite sex, and show interest in the bodies of mature individuals such as their parents. Exploration and curiosity are important and healthy aspects of human development. Yet it is often difficult for adults (who live in a society that is not comfortable with sexuality in general) to avoid making their children feel ashamed of being sexual or showing interest in sexuality. When adults impose their ambivalence upon a child's innocuous explorations into sexuality, fail to communicate with children about this real and important aspect of human life, or behave toward children in sexually inappropriate ways, distortion of an indispensable and formative stage of development occurs. This often leaves profound emotional scars that hinder full acceptance of self and sexuality later in the child's life.

Adolescence, the social stage accompanying puberty and the transition to adulthood, proves to be a very stressful period of life for many individuals as they attempt to develop an adult identity and forge relationships with others. Because of the physiological capacity of adolescents for reproduction, sexuality tends to be heavily censured by parents and society at this stage of life. Societal messages, however, are powerful, conflicting, and confusing: Just Say No . . . Just Do It; billboards and magazine ads using adolescent bodies provocatively and partially undressed; "romance" novels, television shows, and movies with torrid sex scenes. In addition, individual and societal attitudes place tremendous emphasis on sexual attractiveness (especially for females) and sexual competency (especially for males). These physical, emotional, and cultural pressures combine to create confusion and anxiety in adolescents and young adults about whether they are okay and normal. Information and assurances from adults can alleviate these stresses and facilitate positive and responsible sexual maturity if there is mutual trust and willingness in both generations.

Sexuality finally becomes socially acceptable in adulthood, at least within marriage. Yet routine, boredom, stress, pressures, the pace of life, work or parenting responsibilities, and/or lack of communication can exact heavy tolls on the quantity and quality of sexual interaction. Sexual misinformation, myths, and unanswered questions, especially about emotional and/or physiological changes in sexual arousal/response or functioning, can also undermine or hinder intimacy and sexual interaction in the middle years.

Sexuality in the later years of life is also socially and culturally stigmatized because of the prevailing misconception that sex is for young, attractive, and married adults. Such an attitude is primarily responsible for the apparent decline in sexual interest and activity as one grows older. Physiological changes in the aging process are not, in and of themselves, detrimental to sexual expression. A life history of experiences, good health, and growth can make sexual expression in the later years a most rewarding and fulfilling experience, and today's aging population is becoming more vocal in letting their children and grandchildren know that *old can be sexy!*

The articles chosen for the *Youth and Their Sexuality* subsection address several difficult and somewhat controversial issues related to sexuality, society, and children. The first unit article, "Age-by-Age Guide to Nudity," dramatically shows that children are born as sensual and sexual people, and that adults' verbal and nonverbal messages about nudity and bodies can have powerful effects. "Raising Sexually Healthy Kids" emphasizes that "the talk" about sex is not the only crucial role parents play in their child(ren)'s sexual development. "Could Your Precious Child Be Gay?" was written by a pediatric nurse who shares expert, professional, and personal experiences (one of her four children is gay) about the developmental states and needs of straight and gay children. The final

tions of the National Middle School Association for helping these young people.

The *Sexuality in the Adult Years* subsection deals with a variety of issues for individuals and couples who are twenty-something, thirty-something, or ninety-something. The first article, "Men and Sex at 20, 30, 40," lets men tell you how sex and relationships have changed for them. "Great Married Sex" exposes the negative and potentially damaging myth that married sex is less exciting, less satisfying, or basically inferior sex. The next two articles not only challenge readers to replace their old-is-dried-up or over-the-hill perceptions of aging; they tell readers how to have full, healthy, and satisfying sex no matter what their age.

Looking Ahead: Challenge Questions

Do you remember trying to get answers about your body, sex, or similar topics as a young child? How did your parents respond? How did you feel?

As an adolescent, where did you get answers to your questions about sex? Are you still embarrassed at any lack of information you have? Why or why not?

Would you like to be a junior or senior high school-aged young person today? Why or why not? In what ways is being a young teen easier than when you were that age? How is it more difficult? In what ways is being a young male different? A young female? A young person discovering that she or he is not heterosexual?

How do you view sex and sexuality at your age? In what ways is it different than when you were younger? How do you perceive the changes—positively, negatively, not sure—and to what do you attribute them? Are there things you feel you have missed? What are they?

Close your eyes and imagine a couple having a pleasurable sexual interlude. When you are finished, open your eyes. How old were they? If they were younger than middle age, can you replay your vision with middle-aged or older people? Why or why not? How does this relate to your expectations regarding your own romantic and/or sexual life a few decades from now?

article in the subsection addresses an often-neglected minority in our adolescent population that many would, it seems, prefer to believe does not exist. "Breaking through the Wall of Silence: Gay, Lesbian, and Bisexual Issues for Middle Level Educators" details the lonely, confusing, stigmatized, and, sometimes tragic experience of growing up gay, lesbian, or bisexual and includes the recommenda-

age-by-age guide to nudity

Families differ when it comes to modesty, but how much privacy do kids (and parents) really need?

Anthony E. Wolf, Ph.D.,
with Ellen H. Parlapiano

Contributing editor Anthony E. Wolf, Ph.D., is the author of "It Isn't Fair" . . . A Guide to the Tougher Parts of Parenting. *Ellen H. Parlapiano is a writer and mother of two.*

Three-year-old Malcolm stripped off his swimming trunks and began to romp in the nude at the crowded beach he was visiting with his parents. "Look, Mommy, now everybody can see my weeny!" he declared with pride. Of course, we want our kids to feel good about their bodies. We want them to be proud of how they look—but maybe not quite that proud! How do we help them become confident and comfortable with nudity, yet at the same time teach them that their bodies are private and not for public show? And how do our own attitudes and reactions to nakedness affect our children's physical confidence? The following guide to body-bar-ing behaviors, from infancy through the grade-school years, reveals what you can expect and how best to handle nudity—your kids' and your own.

Birth to 18 months
Bare-All Babies

"Where's Amy's nose?" Dad asked his 13-month-old as he bathed her. But Amy couldn't have cared less about her nose right then—she was investigating the territory between her legs instead.

Being naked helps infants learn about their bodies by giving them the opportunity to see and touch their various parts. Even if it's embarrassing to you as an onlooker, you shouldn't underestimate the value of this type of exploration. A child's gaining a clear sense of her physique is an integral part of good emotional and intellectual development.

The learning process is gradual. Newborns don't even know they have a body. But as they grow, so does their self-awareness. Their tactile and visual senses increase, and their muscle control strengthens. Little by little, babies realize that their body parts belong to them. They can reach out and touch things, experience what it feels like to be touched back, and learn about themselves and how they are connected to the world around them.

How can you help your baby learn about her body? The bathtub and the changing table are the most logical places to provide your little one total access to her body. There, she can regularly see and touch herself all over while she interacts with you. Let her explore herself freely, and don't take her hands away from her private areas.

Don't be afraid to let your baby be naked at other times, too. As long as she's in a place that's safe and warm, she'll be fine. Let her go diaperless in the

Toddlers love taking their clothes off. Being naked gives them a sense of freedom and helps them feel independent.

crib or on the playmat. Allow her to learn what it feels like to be bare-bellied on a flannel sheet or bare-bottomed on the smooth kitchen floor. At this stage, the big issues about nakedness are that your child gets to experience it at least some of the time and that she learns to recognize and point to most of her body parts.

18 months to 3 years
Should Toddlers Run Naked?

Two-year-old Kenny was playing in the front yard with his mother. As soon as she turned her back to say hello to an elderly couple strolling by, Kenny whipped off his clothes and streaked across the lawn exuberantly—giving the senior citizens quite a surprise. "I just can't seem to keep his clothes on lately!" Kenny's mother explained with a sheepish grin.

Toddlers love taking off their clothes. Wearing clothes can feel confining and uncomfortable, while being naked gives them a sense of freedom and helps them feel independent. But since it's too early to teach toddlers rules about nudity, the responsibility of deciding whether they can be naked or not falls to you. No matter how much children enjoy being nude, there are simply some times and places where you have to see to it that they keep their clothes on.

First, determine when and where nudity is appropriate, according to what you are most comfortable with: Some parents allow their toddlers to be nude in the front yard, for example, while others do

not. Of course, your personal policy should be in keeping with the norms of society. Allowing a nude toddler to romp in the front yard may be no big deal, but bringing a naked tot to the supermarket would surely raise some eyebrows! Be respectful of other people's sensibilities and avoid practices that would be considered shocking by most people. It's not fair to your children to impose countercultural rules upon them.

Your next job is clothes management. If Kenny's mother doesn't want him to be nude in the front yard, she has to matter-of-factly say, "When we're in the front yard, we need to wear our clothes." If he refuses to put his clothes on, she should calmly do it for him. Avoid saying things that imply that nudity is bad. And certainly don't get into a power struggle about it, as this can easily escalate into a battle of wills in other areas besides dressing.

Do designate some places—such as the backyard—where your toddler can bare all. Many parents find this is a great time to play "name that body part." Romps in the nude can also be helpful during these accident-prone toilet-training years. When they cavort in the nude, keep the potty nearby. Then, when the urge strikes, they

can get to it quickly and easily without having to fumble with clothing.

3 to 6 years
Becoming Body Conscious

Denise's father was taking a shower when she came into the bathroom to chat. In the past, he hadn't worried if his daughter, now 4, saw him naked. But lately he'd been finding himself increasingly uncomfortable. What's more, Denise had begun asking him lots of questions about his private parts. Should he be more discreet?

In the preschool years, children are not only more aware of the differences in people's bodies but more inquisitive about them. That may leave

"Mommy, what are those big bumps on your chest?" It's natural for preschoolers to ask questions about what they see.

Words That Hurt

A negative reaction to your child's nudity can have a big impact on how comfortable she'll be with her body.

Never make statements that express:

Shame "It's not nice for little girls to run around naked."

Shock "I can't believe you're doing that in front of your Aunt Louise! Put some clothes on!"

Insensitivity "I don't understand why you're so nervous about undressing in gym class."

Good-natured teasing "Too bad. You've got thunder thighs just like your mom."

Negative comparisons "Your brother was much more muscular at this age."

you wondering just how much of your own body to bare, particularly if your child is of the opposite sex. Should you cover up when preschoolers see you naked in the bathroom or bedroom? Should you discourage them from entering a room when you're getting dressed?

It all depends on your personal philosophy and style. What's most important is that you convey a sense of confidence, not uneasiness, about your body. So do what makes you feel the most comfortable. If you're the uninhibited type who often walks around in the buff, you needn't stop. But do tune into your child's feelings about it. If she seems bothered by your nudity, you'll want to start limiting her exposure to it.

On the other hand, if you feel uncomfortable about your child's seeing you nude, now is the time to establish some privacy boundaries. Show her that in some places—specifically bathrooms and bedrooms—you want privacy. But teach this lesson in a low-key way. Denise's dad might say something like, "We'll talk as soon as I get out of the shower, honey." He shouldn't get anxious or angry, and he certain-ly shouldn't ban Denise from the room. Eventually, preschoolers will learn to respect the boundaries on their own.

Still, it's natural for children this age to be curious and make comments about what they observe. Be prepared for questions like, "What are those big bumps on your chest, Mommy?" or "How come you're so hairy there?" The best response is always a matter-of-fact one. You don't have to go into great detail, but you should acknowledge and answer questions like these with simple, straightforward responses. For example, you could say, "They're called breasts," and, "Because grown-ups have hair there."

6 to 9 years
Modesty and Manners

Seven-year old Joseph was changing in his room when his mom appeared in the doorway with clean socks. "Don't come in! I'm naked!" he screamed, jumping up to close the door.

Joseph's mom was surprised. He'd never been self-conscious about his body before. Why the sudden desire for privacy?

Modesty emerges in the early grade-school years. In order to feel good about their bodies, kids this age need to know that they have some control over

When Mom and Dad Disagree

You're always careful to cover up in front of your kids, but your spouse parades around stark naked. You think he's an exhibitionist, and he wonders why you're such a prude. How should parents with differing philosophies handle nudity? Here are some secrets to minimizing conflict and conveying a healthy message.

Respect each other's styles. Don't be judgmental about your partner's beliefs. No one is right or wrong on this issue. You simply have different comfort levels, and it's important to recognize that.

Don't worry about having different points of view. It's all right for kids to see that their parents have opposing opinions on an issue, as long as the two of you remain calm and matter-of-fact about your differences. Your children will learn that, in this world, people don't always agree on things.

Don't criticize your spouse in front of the kids. Not only will it put a negative spin on nudity, but children will feel that they have to take sides.

Playing Doctor
and Other Dicey Issues

Is it proper to undress in front of your kids? Up to what age can you take your son into the ladies' room with you? A good rule of thumb is to do whatever you feel most comfortable with, keeping in mind what's considered acceptable by society, and being sensitive to your child's feelings.

Should you:	Allow children to play doctor?	Let kids touch themselves?	Bathe siblings of the opposite sex together?	Take a child of the opposite sex into a public restroom with you?	Undress in front of your kids?
Things to think about:	This is normal for preschoolers. But if kids are playing this game excessively, stop the activity in a calm and nonjudgmental way. Be particularly vigilant if grade-school kids are playing with their younger siblings.	Teach kids that this behavior is okay and that it's something they can do at home when they're in a private place, but that they shouldn't do it in public. If your child is doing it excessively, mention it to your pediatrician.	Take into account the children's ages and awareness levels. It's fine when they're really young, but as they approach school age, it's best to bathe them separately.	Consider the child's age and competency level. Kids are generally able to go into public restrooms alone by age 5 or 6. If you're worried about your child's ability or safety, though, bring him in with you.	Take stock of your kids' gender, awareness level, and feelings. Be more discreet as your kids reach the grade-school and preteen years, particularly if they're of the opposite sex.

To feel good about their bodies, school-age kids need some control over who sees them naked. Parents need to respect that.

who sees them naked. As a parent, you need to respect that. Clue in to your child's feelings, and be sensitive to his growing need for privacy. If he doesn't want you or his siblings to see him nude, go along whenever it's practical. It's important that grade-school kids have a place where they can undress without interruptions. Simple gestures, like knocking before entering the bedroom or bathroom, will show your child that you value his feelings.

If grade-schoolers are being bothered by siblings who insist on barging in on them, set some family rules. Tell the sibling, "Your brother doesn't want you coming into his room when he's dressing. I need you to respect that." But don't get too involved in enforcing this. It's best for siblings to resolve such issues on their own.

Be aware, too, that grade-schoolers are likely to become increasingly uneasy about seeing you in the nude. Start being more discreet when you dress and undress—especially with kids of the opposite sex—but don't get so obsessed with covering up that you become aloof or send the message that nudity is bad.

And never tease or judge kids about their modesty or self-consciousness. A positive, nurturing attitude that reflects supportiveness and sensitivity will help your child develop a healthy body image that will last a lifetime.

Raising **sexually** healthy kids

Everything from **bathtime** to how often you **kiss your husband** shapes your child's future **relationships**.

By Jennifer Cadoff

Talking about sex makes most parents—even the chatty ones—very nervous. How much do kids need to know? When should the topic be introduced? How can we help our children grow up prepared to form happy, healthy sexual relationships?

Too often, when we do attempt to broach the topic, we find ourselves fumbling through awkward explanations of the mechanics of sex or "how babies grow," all the while sensing that we are, somehow, missing the real point—that sex is an expression of love. It's not about sperm swimming up vaginas; it's about tenderness, the desire to please someone we care about. It's about being completely at ease with another person—and feeling good about that.

Children certainly do need to learn the "facts of life," but experts say that even more important is raising them to be confident, compassionate, and kind, which will teach them more about how to behave in their adult relationships than any discussion of anatomy.

"Good values are good values," says Karen Shanor, Ph.D., a Washington, D.C.–based clinical psychologist who has written several books on human sexuality. Teaching thoughtfulness and courtesy in any situation will eventually translate into how kids behave in future relationships. "If, for example, you don't teach your children to be respectful of others when you take them out for dinner, it generalizes itself later in many ways, including that child's future approach to sexual situations."

Some of the most important things we teach our children—about love and trust and physical pleasures—we do naturally, starting the day they're born. When your baby cries, you pick her up gently and speak softly. You feed her if she's hungry, tuck an extra blanket around her when it's chilly. All this teaches your baby a profound lesson: That people who care about her will respond to her needs.

Sex Ed starts at birth

For the sheer sensual delight of it, we sniff and nuzzle a powdery neck, stroke a delicious, peachy cheek, smooth the downy fuzz on a tiny head. And as we do, we are also teaching our newborns about the pleasures of another person's touch.

At the same time, you need to be aware of your baby's responses to your ministrations. "Each child, from infancy, is his own human being, with his own temperament," says Martin J. Drell, M.D., head of infant, child, and adolescent psychiatry at Louisiana State University Medical School, in New Orleans. "Some babies don't want to cuddle."

But all infants do have reflexive, sexual responses from day one. "Little boys have erections from infancy.

From *Parents* magazine, February 1997, pp. 55-58. © 1997 by Jennifer Cadoff. Reprinted by permission.

The physical response in both girls and boys is in place very early on," notes Shanor. They frequently explore their genitals, for instance, and by the age of 10 months can deliberately fondle themselves.

And from infancy, they observe our own attitudes. "Babies understand what you're saying before they can talk, and they are exquisitely sensitive to nonverbal communication. When you scrunch up your face at a stinky diaper, it conveys clearly to your baby what you feel about a very natural process," says Drell.

By the time kids do start to talk, one of the first things we teach them is the names of body parts. What toddler can resist a rousing rendition of "Head and Shoulders, Knees and Toes"? To that lineup, experts agree, we need to add the correct terminology for a child's sexual

Marty Klein, Ph.D., a Palo Alto–based sex therapist and lecturer, enjoins his audiences to repeat "vagina," loud and clear. "They think I'm kidding, at first," he admits. "But we have a responsibility for the education of our children. I'm sympathetic to parents who find talking about sex embarrassing. But instead of avoiding the topic, we need to become comfortable with it."

Learning about boundaries and privacy

Two- and 3-year-olds are often exuberantly physical. They are likely to be enthusiastic huggers, cuddlers, and masturbators, and they love to parade around buck naked.

"By age 3, you can start introducing the concept of public versus private behavior," says E. Mimi Schrader, Ph.D., a psychologist and sex therapist in Boulder,

Raising sexually healthy boys

Discomfort with intimacy and an inability to express affection in nonsexual ways are top problems sex therapists see in the adult men they treat. The following can help young boys grow up to be more comfortable with physical and emotional closeness. Foster empathy in boys by encouraging them to think about how others might feel in various situations, particularly in response to their own actions. Praise boys when they are kind, gentle, and considerate of others. Teach boys that girls have a right to say no ... and that boys, too, can decline the advances of girls. Allow boys to express their full range of feelings, including pain, fear, and timidity. "When little boys fall down, we tend to tell them not to cry, that it doesn't hurt. That teaches them from very early on to deny their feelings, even to themselves," says Karen Shanor, Ph.D., a Washington, D.C.–based clinical psychologist. Instead, acknowledge the hurt, then reassure the child it will feel better soon.

also let her know that you need a little privacy every once in a while."

"One of the biggest jobs parents have is teaching children what's appropriate under what circumstances," says Klein, who is also the author of *Ask Me Anything: A Sex Therapist Answers the Most Important Questions for the '90s* (Pacifica). "Just as there are rules about when and what we eat and names for the body parts connected with eating, there are rules about sex, too. Playing on the floor is okay; eating on the floor is not okay. Rubbing between your legs is okay in your room but not okay in line at the grocery store."

But rub they will: Preschoolers, freed from diapers, will often touch, hold, or massage themselves, sometimes as a way to unwind. It soothes them much the same way rocking or cuddling does. Children this young can even have very pleasurable sensations—a feeling of physical release. Some children actually say, "I'm finished" when they're ready to stop.

Besides setting privacy limits, parents should allow their children to have more independence and more decision-making power as they

get older. "If a child doesn't want to cuddle and doesn't want a kiss, you need to respect that and not force them," says Jamie Wasserman, a New York City psychoanalyst. "By your respecting their boundaries, they learn to respect their own boundaries. They learn it's okay to say no to people. They learn to pay attention to their own needs and desires, instead of allowing someone else to move in and overwhelm them." Similarly, parents should respect a child's desire for privacy, letting him use the bathroom and get dressed on his own, if he wishes, as early as they can.

Teach by example

Children learn how to form happy, loving relationships by growing up in a happy, loving home. "From their parents' hugs, passing kisses, and friendly pats, a child sees love in operation," explains Schrader. "I see so

Two-year-olds are enthusiastic cuddlers and huggers, and they love to parade around naked.

parts. It's not likely your little boy hasn't noticed that he has a penis or your daughter that she has a clitoris. Not giving them names implies that they are forbidden.

Colorado. "You might talk about using some words discreetly, or when it's okay for them to touch their private parts. If you're irritated with a child this age barging into your bathroom, you can

Raising sexually healthy girls

There's no mystery to what prevents most adult women from fully enjoying sex: Therapists say it's most often low self-esteem and body-image problems.

The following are ways parents can help girls to grow up feeling good about themselves. Talk to little girls about how healthy, strong, and capable their body is. As they grow, encourage athletics so their sense of physical prowess develops. Let them wear overalls, get dirty, "play rough." Try not to focus too much on a girl's weight or appearance. Instead, applaud school and other accomplishments so she learns to value who she is and what she can do above what she looks like. Appreciate girls when they are outgoing, determined, and spirited. Teach girls that they have a right to say no to unwanted advances—even yours. A little girl who is taught always to submit to your hugs and kisses could grow up to be a woman who doesn't believe she has the right to say no.

"From their parents' hugs, passing kisses, and friendly pats, a child sees love in operation."

many adults whose families never expressed affection. They just don't know how."

If warmhearted squeezes and smooches "in front of the kids" don't come naturally at your house, remember that the practice is likely to benefit your children as much as your marriage. And if your child wants to turn it into a group squeeze, let her join in and be assured there's plenty of love to go around.

"Affection is always the best context for sexuality," Shanor says. "If the father doesn't usually greet his wife with a kiss or ignores her, or the mother constantly complains that he's never home, those are sexual lessons. If, on the other hand, children see their par-

ents trying to be kind, that, too, is a lesson."

Help children handle our sex-permeated society

"This is a much more sexually stimulating culture than the one we were raised in," says Drell. "It's almost impossible to protect children from it." What parents can do is set standards for what we believe is appropriate for children at what age—in terms of television and movies—and to at least occasionally sit down and watch together. "The world," says Drell, "is not going to convey your values. That's something you have to do."

As children get older, they will need help handling the social aspects of sex. "If you

want kids to make sexually responsible decisions, you have to teach them good decision-making skills," says Klein. "We gradually give children more responsibility for crossing streets as they get older, and we need to do the exact same thing with sex. If a 12-year-old girl is worried about kissing a boy, you can't just say, 'It's bad, don't do it.' Talk to her about whether she likes the way that person treats his friends. Does she like the way he talks about them? If he brags, she can count on the whole school finding out if she makes out with him," Klein says. Without such decision-making skills, he says, your child is left to her own devices.

In very fundamental ways, Shanor concludes, "teaching healthy sexuality works in the same format as raising healthy children in general. You teach them about love and respect and empathy by treating them with love, respect, and empathy. You're not afraid to create structure and rules that make them feel safe. If you help your children develop a strong sense of themselves and respect of themselves and respect for their own bodies, then your children, in turn, will respect other people, their bodies, and their feelings."

---

*Health writer **Jennifer Cadoff** has a 6-year-old son and a 9-year-old daughter.*

HOME FRONT

Could Your Precious Child be Gay?

BY HARRIET A. RICKERTSEN CALKINS

There are understandable reasons why discussions of homosexuality are often taboo in the black community, not the least of which is the prevailing respect for parents' wishes shown by young people. Many pressures confront black youth, with gay, lesbian, and bisexual youth carrying additional burdens. This significant minority (Kinsey reported 10 percent) has much to offer. Beyond consideration for the personal suffering involved, the community may not want to abandon these young people for lack of knowledge and resulting prejudices.

I am a Registered Nurse with primarily pediatrics experience, wife of a psychiatrist, mother of three straight children and one gay son, and grandmother of three. I have two additional gay relatives, and have befriended a number of gay men and lesbians, some who remain closeted, passing as straight because of the restraints imposed partially by those of us who do not give it much thought.

Certainly very few parents want to think about it, for who in this culture would include homosexuality among their dreams for the future of a beloved son or daughter? But it is a fact that some of the children now growing up in our homes, neighborhoods, soccer teams, scout troops, Sunday schools, and schools are, or will realize some day they are, gay or lesbian. Our son, like many, realized at a very early age, long before he knew very much about sexuality.

A child should not be required to go through the stages of that kind of discovery alone. My greatest regret is that our son had to work out who he was, and eventually had to teach us what we needed to know in order to understand and support him. And we were the parents!

Could your precious child be gay or lesbian? Of course. Anyone's child can. Homosexuality has existed throughout the ages, in virtually all cultures; and has often been repressed and vilified as it is by many today in this culture. Causes remain unknown, with many theories having been promulgated, but the fact of its existence is not questioned.

Even so, no parent wants to face it. We love our children too much to want them to encounter more discrimination. We also have deeply seated fears about homosexuality based on what we have learned from society including churches during our own formative years. We are very likely to have passed these fears and even revulsion on to our children.

Society and religions have sometimes denied the existence of gays and lesbians. If recognized, gay men and lesbians are often disrespected and hated which denies their validity as humans.

Consider the devastating trauma of being a person who has assimilated homophobic attitudes, who then begins to haltingly realize that, maybe, just possibly, he or she might be homosexual.

If children begin to believe they could be gay or lesbian, and then wish to talk about it, parents must be ready. Parents who have not considered it, or, worse, refused such thoughts, will not be able to react in helpful and supportive ways. In fact, where knowledge and resulting understanding are absent, the family environment is capable of criticizing and ostracizing the child before words are ever spoken about the subject. Under these circumstances, many gay youth commit suicide.

This is not about sorting out who is and who is not gay or lesbian. Ultimately each person will conclude for himself or herself. If a child is gay, he will learn about it as he develops and will probably first live alone with it in fear and self-loathing. But if he shares it with parents: 1) Their judgmental attitudes will stand in the way, or 2) Their acceptance will be empowering.

If parents are fortunate enough to share in this secret, they can increase their child's fear and self-loathing by rejecting him and assuming those traits themselves, or parents and children can walk forward together into a family, and eventually a community and world, that accepts and supports all people, even those who are gay, lesbian, or bisexual.

Children reach their full potential in families that nurture, value, and accept them. Parents or parent substitutes bestow vital self-esteem by loving children, who then know their lives are meaningful to others. Such children can depend on affirmation if they are kind or generous, and will know they have someone to stand with them when they are hurting.

Many parents desert gay and lesbian children. Many are told to leave home ("You are dead to us"), others are asked to keep their life a secret from extended family and friends. Still others, of course, are embraced in the fullness of their being and are loved along with their partner—if they have one—as parents usually love, in joy for whom their children are and for all they embody. But arrival at this latter choice too often takes precious and painful time.

Instead parents and others can become knowledgeable, then supportive and accepting, in order to lessen, or at least not increase, the burdens of those who are gay or lesbian. Since most believe they have no choice regarding their sexuality, they can decide only to suppress who they really are, or to stay in the closet or come out. The most easily available choice is how we as parents, relatives, friends, neighbors, and citizenry regard their presence among us.

The action of not taking others seriously and acknowledging their realities because of our own discomfort compels gays and lesbians to continue to live in stuffy, airless, dark, lonely closets. Happy, well-adjusted people find closets unbearably stifling. It is unconscionably rude and inconsiderate, even cruel, to subject others to closeted lives due to our unwillingness to encounter them in the sunlight and fresh air.

Parents and children who can communicate and share, who can accept and usually understand each other, can succeed with this big one, too.

But it helps to think ahead.

IF I COULD DO IT AGAIN, THIS TIME I WOULD . . .

1. Understand that a community accepting of all people is healthier for all children.
2. Learn to know gay men and lesbians.
3. Say "sexual orientation" instead of "sexual preference" because for most, it is not a choice.
4. Have family discussions of news stories about gays and lesbians as well as those about race relations.
5. Speak up when others tell racist, sexist, or homophobic jokes.
6. Tell others to ask about our gay son just as they inquire about our other children. "He has not died. He's only gay."
7. View the AIDS quilt and go to to AIDS fund-raisers recognizing this devastating disease occurs throughout the population.
8. Buy children's books featuring various non-traditional families, and encourage schools to do the same.
9. Become involved in organizations like PFLAG (Parents and Friends of Lesbians and Gays).
10. Discourage participation in organizations that have discriminatory policies, and work go to change them.
11. Talk with our children about hearing all minority viewpoints.
12. Vote against legislation that discriminates, and work for policies and legislation that promote justice.
13. Support hiring and protecting the jobs of openly gay and lesbian school teachers, youth group leaders, ministers, and others influential to children, realizing that one person can increase understanding among all children, and particularly help those who may later discover they are gay or lesbian.
14. Stop making assumptions about others, and, instead, check with them, listen and hear, then form attitudes that provide new awareness, helping to open mind and heart to receive increased knowledge and understanding.

Breaking Through the Wall of Silence: Gay, Lesbian, and Bisexual Issues for Middle Level Educators

Norma J. Bailey and Tracy Phariss

Norma J. Bailey is a doctoral student at the University of Northern Colorado, Greeley.
Tracy Phariss teaches at Creighton Middle School in Lakewood, Colorado.

"When I was in the Pearl River Middle School from sixth to eighth grade ... I did not know I was gay. I did have a feeling I was different from everyone else. These three years were my worst years in school. I was constantly called a faggot. I did not have many friends. I was very lonely and insecure. The worst part was that I could not talk to teachers ... about my feelings" (Whitlock, 1989, p. 3).

"During junior high and in my freshman year of high school, I was very depressed. Feeling alone and isolated from the rest of the world, I managed to fail three of my five majors that year" Matthew, 18 (Governors Commission, 1993, p. 17).

"I felt as though I was the only gay person my age in the world. I felt as though I had nowhere to go to talk to anybody. Throughout eighth grade, I went to bed every night praying that I would not be able to wake up in the morning, and every morning waking up and being disappointed. And so finally I decided that if I was going to die, it would have to be at my own hands" Steven, 18 (Governors Commission, 1993, p. 12).

On November 6, 1993, at the Annual Business Meeting of the National Middle School Association in Portland, Oregon, the membership adopted a resolution that encouraged middle level schools to gather information on school policies and programs addressing the needs and problems of gay, lesbian, and bisexual youth so that these schools could "organize and conduct staff development initiatives designed to elevate staff awareness and sensitivity in order to ensure safe and equitable school environments for youth of every sexual orientation."

The question raised at the Open Resolutions Hearing the previous day and at the Annual Business Meeting was "Why?" Why is it necessary for NMSA to include a resolution regarding gay, lesbian, and bisexual youth in its list of resolutions which serve to focus the Association's efforts during the coming years? This may be a question that you raised as you read that this resolution was passed. Why does my *middle school* association have to deal with this issue? Surely, homosexuality is not a big concern for young adolescents. And besides, should the middle school be dealing with such an issue anyway? And, if it should, in what ways can it do that? To answer these questions is the purpose of this article.

Current Problems Regarding Gay and Lesbian Youth

In 1972 Kinsey reported that an estimated 10% of the population "has more than incidental homosexual experiences" and identifies as a gay male or lesbian in their lifetime. Although there is controversy related to sexual identity, cause and effect, most of the available evidence indicates early determination of sexual orientation, but not necessarily early recognition or acknowledgment by the individual. Nevertheless, researchers have generally accepted consistently that 10% of the population is gay or lesbian and that this portion represents every race, creed, class, ability, and disability (Grayson, 1987).

This means, therefore, that a significant proportion of the educational population throughout the nation, teachers and students included, is also gay or lesbian. Leaving teachers aside, it is estimated that there are 2.9 million gay or lesbian adolescents in the United States (Colorado Department of Health, 1992; Dunham, 1989). These students, again from every race, creed, class, ability, and disability, found in urban, suburban, and rural schools, have for the most part sat passively through years of school education where their identities as gay and lesbian people have been ignored or even denied. They have done this because of their own fears and isolation and because of the failure of a society, full of cultural taboos and fear of controversy, to take up their cause (Rofes, 1989). This has resulted in an "invisible" minority within our schools whose needs are just beginning to be addressed.

Suicide is the leading cause of death among gay male and lesbian youth ... they are five times more likely to attempt suicide than their heterosexual peers.

The growth of gay activism in the 1980s and 1990s has yielded a new assertiveness on the part of gay and lesbian youth that has forced individual schools and sometimes entire school systems, particularly in large cities, to grapple with the reality that gay and lesbian youth are in the schools and are not going to go away (Rofes, 1989). More importantly, however, and more widespread in its impact, is the fact that helping professionals are beginning to realize that these "invisible" students are becoming more visible each day through increased numbers of referrals to school counselors, school social workers, substance abuse personnel, and various other support staff. Individual reasons for these referrals are diverse, but among the most common concerns are efforts to clarify sexual orientation, anxiety, attempted suicide, substance abuse, low self-esteem, family conflict, and emotional isolation (Dunham, 1989). In other words, these students are finally being recognized as among our most "at risk" populations.

The normal trials of growing up as an adolescent in today's society are trying enough, but it is particularly trying for young people who experience difficulties in understanding what may be a developing homosexual orientation, in part because of the stigma attached to homosexuality in contemporary American society. These youth face problems in accepting themselves due to internalization of a negative self-image and the lack of accurate information about homosexuality and the lack of positive role models. They often face physical and verbal abuse, rejection, and isolation from family and peers. They often feel totally alone and socially withdrawn out of fear of adverse consequences. As a result of these pressures, lesbian and gay youth are more vulnerable than other adolescents to psychosocial problems including substance abuse, chronic depression, school failure, early relationship conflicts, and being forced to leave their families prematurely (Dunham, 1989).

Suicide

Each of these problems presents a risk factor for suicidal feelings and behavior for any adolescent. However, the 1989 Department of Health and Human Services Report on the Secretary's Task Force on Youth Suicide reported that suicide is the leading cause of death among gay male and lesbian youth. Furthermore, it was estimated that gay and lesbian youth are five times more likely to attempt suicide than their heterosexual peers. A majority of the suicide attempts by homosexual youth took place at age 20 or younger, with nearly one third occurring before age 17 (Gibson, 1989). It is also estimated that of the more than 5,000 annual suicides committed by young adults in the United States, about 30% are committed by gay or lesbian youth or youth dealing with issues of sexual orientation and sexual identity (Gibson, 1989; Harbeck, 1992; Hunt, 1986; Rofes, 1989; Russell, 1989; Sears, 1989; Whitlock, 1989).

Substance abuse

Even if gay or lesbian adolescents do not choose suicide as an avenue of escape (or a cry for help), they face many other problems which put them at high risk. If they are closed about who they are, they may be able to pass as "straights" in their schools and communities, but they face a tremendous internal struggle to understand and accept themselves, especially in that they feel "different" from their peers. With little or no access to information which portrays the homosexual in a positive light, they often buy in to society's stereotypic negative views of the homosexual, and thus begins the internal erosion of self-worth which ultimately leads to a sense of inferiority, disregard for personal self, and loss of identity (Dunham, 1989). In response to these negative self-images, many gay and lesbian youth become involved in substance abuse to reduce the pain and anxiety of the internal conflicts (Dennis & Harlow, 1986; Dunham, 1989; Gibson, 1989; Harbeck, 1992; Lenskyj, 1990; Russell, 1989; Sears, 1991). In the Report of the Secretary's Task force on Youth Suicide, it is estimated that gay and lesbian youth are three times more likely to abuse substances and that 58% of the adolescent gay males studied suffered from substance abuse disorder (Gibson, 1989).

Sexual activity

Young adolescents who suspect they may be gay or lesbian often engage in frequent sexual involvements in order to either deny their homosexuality or to experiment to affirm it. Although both male and female adolescents will engage in opposite-sex relationships to deny their homosexuality, some (lesbians) purposely get pregnant in order to "disprove it" (Dunham, 1989; Gibson, 1989; Harbeck, 1992; Lenskyj, 1990; Rofes, 1989).

Because a high percentage of gay and lesbian youth experiment sexually in a search for their identity, this increases their risk of infection from STDs and of the transmission of HIV (Rofes, 1989; Russell, 1989; Whitlock, 1989). Although the vast majority of all adolescents have the "can't happen to me" attitude regarding HIV infection, gay and lesbian youth give even less attention to prophylactics because the fear of pregnancy is not present with same-sex sexual activity (Colorado Department of Health, 1992).

Family and homelessness

If young gays or lesbians are "out," there are additional problems which may occur. Although they may feel some sense of internal integrity and security within themselves, they may face tremendous external conflicts with family and peers.

The loss of family support is a tremendous blow to a young gay or lesbian, but it happens quite frequently because many families are unable to reconcile their child's sexual identity with moral and religious values. Because of this, many are often forced to leave their homes as "pushaways" or "throwaways" rather than running away on their own (Gibson, 1989). Thus, the incidence of homelessness among gay and lesbian youth

is very high (Andrews, 1990; Dennis & Harlow, 1986; Grayson, 1987; Rofes, 1989; Whitlock, 1989), with some estimates as high as 50% of homeless youth being gay or lesbian (Colorado Department of Health, 1992).

The shame of ridicule and the fear of attack make school a fearful place, resulting in frequent absences and sometimes academic failure.

When gay youth are forced out of their homes, they often flee to large cities, hoping to find families and friends to replace the ones that did not want them or could not accept them. Here, however, they become street kids and enter a world that presents serious dangers and often an even greater risk of suicide. Without adequate education, many are forced to become involved in prostitution in order to survive. Thus they face physical and sexual assaults on a daily basis and constant exposure to sexually transmitted diseases including AIDS (Dennis & Harlow, 1986; Dunham, 1989; Gibson, 1989; Russell, 1989).

The education of gay and lesbian youth: harassment and violence issues

Besides the home, school is the other primary social institution where all young people should be able to feel safe. For openly gay or lesbian youth, or those "suspected" or "accused" of being so, however, this is not in any way the case. For these students, middle school, junior high school, and high school most often mean cruel harassment from fellow students, ridicule from teachers, and refusal from school personnel to punish verbal and physical attacks upon them. The shame of ridicule and the fear of attack make school a fearful place, resulting in frequent absences and sometimes academic failure. These and other school practices undermine the ability of gay students to learn in school and frequently cause them to forfeit an education altogether (Dennis & Hawlow, 1986; Gibson, 1989).

In schools across the country, even very young children learn those words which are sure to deliver an insult or to keep someone in line—*queer, lezzy, faggot,* or *sissy.* Children may not always know what these words mean, but they know the demeaning power of this language (Whitlock, 1989). By the time students are in the secondary schools, this kind of name calling, while still directed indiscriminately at times to any student one dislikes, becomes a virulent form of verbal harassment when directed against gay and lesbian youth, and it is often accompanied by physical assaults such as shoving into lockers and beatings. (Colorado Department of Health, 1992). In a recent national survey done by the National Gay Task Force, approximately 20% of lesbians and 50% of gay males reported that they had been harassed, threatened, or physically assaulted in secondary schools (Gibson, 1989; Lenskyj, 1990).

While some teachers and administrators harass, ridicule, and unfairly punish gay students, the predominant feature of the discriminatory school environment for gay youth is the failure of school officials to provide protection from peer harassment and violence (Dennis & Harlow, 1986; Grayson, 1987). By far the most common form of this failure is when teachers, who would most often confront instances of racist or sexist name calling or jokes, make no effort to intervene when they hear homophobic name calling or jokes. Non-gay students have reported that teachers have observed verbal or physical harassment and done nothing to intervene on behalf of gay or lesbian students (Lenskyj, 1990). When school personnel fail to protect gay students from verbal or physical harassment, for whatever reason, they fail in their duty to provide for the welfare of *all* students.

Counseling issues

Since the school guidance counselor may often be the first person within the educational community with whom the gay or lesbian adolescents choose to disclose (or at least explore) their sexual orientation, these educators are in important positions to provide confidential and supportive personal counseling to gay and lesbian youth. However, for a variety of reasons, this is not what often occurs. Unfortunately, counselors are often engaged in too many administrative duties that leave little time for personal counseling and that convey a message of unapproachability to all students, especially to gay students who are already extremely hesitant to approach any adult with issues of sexuality (Sears, 1989). Second, because in most schools and communities homosexuality is still a forbidden subject so that the presence of homosexuals among the student population is tacitly denied or because the school population and the general public are still rather hostile toward homosexuals, most school counselors are often uncomfortable with discussing homosexuality (Powell, 1987). Third, many counselors are not trained by the counselor education programs of their colleges and universities around the needs of the gay and lesbian population, especially in terms of the coming-out process. Neither are there sufficient inservice programs available to allow school counselors to upgrade their knowledge to provide quality services to gay youth (Powell, 1987).

Fourth, because most counselor training programs have not dealt with these issues, most counselors have not thoroughly examined their own knowledge, beliefs, values, prejudices, and biases about homosexuality. Therefore, they are not comfortable when dealing with these students (Krysiak, 1987). Worse yet, some counselors further undermine conditions for these youth because they are unwilling to acknowledge or support an adolescent's homosexual identity exploration, instead giving students inaccurate information, reinforcing the myths, encouraging them to "change" their identities, or forcing them into therapy and mental hospitals under the guise of "treatment" (Gibson, 1989).

Curriculum issues

Another school practice which needs to be addressed in order to provide a more equitable education for gay and lesbian youth is the "conspiracy of silence" which envelops most schools (Sears, 1991). In most schools neither curriculum content, including sex education classes, nor library resources provide students, gay or non-gay, with accurate and positive information about homosexuality.

If homosexuality were to be discussed anywhere in the curriculum, one would expect to find it in the health or sex education curriculum. However, in reviews of representative textbooks used in these kinds of classes, researchers found few references to the subject of homosexuality and many of those references had a homophobic bias. Even those texts that treated homosexuality in at least a neutral manner tended to "ghettoize" it by discussing the topic in a condensed section or by switching from a personalized "you" voice to a detached "they" format, thus implying the inferiority of homosexuality as a form of human sexuality (Sears, 1989; Whitlock & DiLapi, in Gordon 1983). This assumption only serves to reinforce the sense of isolation experienced by many lesbian and gay adolescents. Also, because of the initial, and often yet believed, image of AIDS as a "gay disease," as well as the attitude of a society which does not want "these" issues discussed in schools, access to straightforward and clear information about AIDS, HIV, and safe sex practices, which is essential for the survival of all youth, is truly limited (Whitlock, 1989).

Given these attitudes and beliefs, it is little wonder that other subjects taught in the curriculum are devoid of references to gays or lesbians or the topic of homosexuality. Just as with the experience of Blacks 30 years ago, the experiences and contributions of lesbians and gay men are not acknowledged in the curriculum, thus depriving gay and lesbian youth of positive role models from history. Although some might argue that homo-

Table 1

Mean Age of Coming Out

	Males	Female
1971	19.3	—
1980	16.3	—
1982	15	20
1987	14	—
1993	13.1	15.2

sexuality is not relevant to the accomplishments of these men and women, the argument does not hold up when these biographies are examined nor when compared to the relevance of race, gender, or religion in other biographies (Sears, 1989).

A school library or media center is very important to support the curriculum and to meet the individual needs of students in a school. Based on Kinsey's 10% figure, a school of one thousand students might have approximately one hundred students needing information about their own homosexuality. However, finding books that present accurate information about homosexuality or a positive view of gay and lesbian life can be very difficult for adolescents, even in large cities (Whitlock, 1989). In the first place, holdings on homosexuality may be very limited. In a study designed to examine the holdings of school libraries on sensitive topics such as child abuse, incest, and homosexuality, the responding schools reported the fewest holdings on homosexuality, regardless of format (fiction, non-fiction, vertical files, or professional titles) (VanMeter, 1991). Second, access to gay and lesbian library materials is difficult because the standard cataloging classifications do not fully nor easily identify these materials by means of contemporary subject headings which would make it easier for young people to find these materials (Berman, in Gordon, 1983). Third, even encyclopedias, which adolescents questioning and assessing their own sexual identity often consider to be a safe (i.e., private) resource, tend to have inaccurate, misleading, and often biased information about homosexuality and gay and lesbian people, especially considering the fact that most school libraries tend to maintain outdated editions of encyclopedias in their collections (Burke, in Gordon, 1983).

Middle school connection

Maturation of all young people has been occurring earlier in successive generations due to several factors. "As a result of earlier maturation, sexual relations, pregnancy, and sexually transmitted diseases are now issues of con-

cern at the middle school, whether or not educators and parents prefer it" (George & Alexander, 1993, p. 5).

This is true for the lesbian and gay population as well. Although the problem of sexual minority youth engaging in high-risk behaviors and the failures of schools to address these problems are more acute later in adolescence, they are becoming more prevalent and relevant at the middle level. Studies have shown that the mean age of coming out of sexual minority youth is declining, at least in urban areas (Table 1).

Other studies also show that homosexuality, or the struggle with sexual identity, is a middle level issue. Most gay and lesbian youth report having experienced the feeling of being "different" long before the onset of puberty, some as early as first grade (Herdt & Boxer, 1993). In a comprehensive national study in which the researchers interviewed over 4400 gay men and lesbians, Jay and Young (1979) reported significant evidence concerning the incidence of adolescent homosexuality. Their findings revealed that the majority of gay and lesbian adults reported knowing about their homosexuality prior to the age of 18, with approximately 30% reporting knowing prior to the age of 13.

Many studies have shown that gay and lesbian youth are self-identified (recognize their same-sex attraction and have same-sex fantasies) before they have had a same-sex experience (Herdt & Boxer, 1993; Remafedi, 1987), just as heterosexual youth could identify themselves as heterosexual before engaging in opposite-sex activity. In a Chicago study of a sample of lesbian, bisexual, and gay male youths done by Boxer, Cook, and Herdt (1989), they reported that first homosexual attraction occurred at average age 9.6 for males and 10.1 for females, with first homosexual fantasy occurring at average age 11.2 for males and 11.9 for females. It is clear "that gay and lesbian youth exist during childhood and early adolescence—with or without homosexual behavior and/or homosexual identity" (Savin-Williams, 1990, p. 204).

That homosexuality, or the struggle with sexual identity, is a middle level issue is also strongly supported by the results of a 1992 large-scale study of adolescent sexual orientation surveying nearly 35,000 junior and senior high school students from diverse ethnic, geographic, and socioeconomic strata in Minnesota (Remafedi, Resnick, Blum, & Harris, 1995). They reported that at 12 years old, 25.9% of the students were "unsure" about their orientation; at 13 years old, 17.4%; at 14 years old, 12.2%; and at 15 years old, 7.0% (declining to 5% in 18 year olds). It seems clear that this is an issue that educators avoid to the detriment of their young adolescent students.

The middle school philosophy is based on the principle that middle schools accept the responsibility to try to meet the needs of all the young adolescents in their care (National Middle School Association, 1995). This responsibility should be interpreted to include the

Resource Guide

Organizations

The Gay, Lesbian, and Straight Teachers Network (GLSTN). GLSTN is a national organization that brings together gay and straight teaches in order to combat homophobia in their schools as well as to support gay teachers. For information, contact GLSTN, 2124 Broadway, Box 160, New York, NY 10023, (212) 387–2098.

Parents and Friends of Lesbians and Gays (P-FLAG). P-FLAG offers support to family members of gay people. Its national office can refer you to local chapters: PO Box 27605, Washington, DC 20038, (202) 638–4200.

The Hetrick-Martin Institute, a New York-based social service agency, has long been a leader in providing services for gay youth. They also publish *You Are Not Alone: The National Lesbian, Gay, and Bisexual Youth Directory*, which is available for a $5 fee. Address: 2 Astor Place, New York, NY 10003-6998, (212) 674–2400.

The Bridges Project of the American Friends Service Committee facilitates communication among gay youth service providers through its newsletter and other activities. Address: c/o AFSC, 1501 Cherry St., Philadelphia, PA 19102, (215) 241–7133.

Project 10 is an on-campus counseling program in the Los Angeles Unified School District which responds to the needs of adolescent lesbians/gays in the educational system. It also produces a resource directory for teachers, guidance counselors, parents, and school-based adolescent care providers. For informa-tion, contact Virginia Uribe, Fairfax High School, 7850 Melrose Avenue, Los Angeles, CA 90046, (213) 651–5200.

Publications

Looking at Gay and Lesbian Life by Warren Blumen-feld and Diane Raymond is a good general intro-duction.

Is It a Choice?: Answers to Three Hundred of the Most Frequently Asked Questions about Gay Men and Lesbians by Eric Marcus is a good starting point as well.

Making Schools Safe for Gay and Lesbian Youth, the *Education Committee Report of the Massachusetts Gover-nor's Commission on Gay and Lesbian Youth* surveys the needs of gay youth and presents detailed recommen-dations for action by schools to meet those needs. Its recommendations were adopted as state educational policy by the Massachusetts Board of Education in May 1993. Write the Commission at State House Room 111, Boston, MA 02133, to receive a copy.

Understanding Sexual Identity: A Book for Gay Teens and Their Friends by Janice E. Rench is geared for grades 6–12.

Two Teenagers in Twenty: Writings by Lesbian and Gay Youth edited by Ann Heron are the writings of youth, ages 12 to 14 years old.

Gay Men and Women Who Enriched the World by Thomas Cowan consists of biographies of positive role models throughout history.

needs of those youth who are struggling with their sexual identity, as well at all youth who have the right to have accurate information about one of the human diversities, sexual orientation. Since early adolescence is a time of searching for personal identity; of ques-tioning and testing; of building beliefs, attitudes, and values; of building, consolidating, confirming, and af-firming identity and self-concept; and of building so-cial skills, it is right for middle level schools to address the issues of homosexuality and the existence of gay and lesbian youth.

Recommendations

So what should be an appropriate response to meeting the needs of gay and lesbian youth? What can school officials do to improve the atmosphere in our schools so that all our students can receive a safe and equitable education?

There seem to be several factors which serve as bar-riers to making changes which would allow for the de-velopment of services to meet the needs of gay and lesbian youth, including a lack of courage from adults, both gay and non-gay; a lack of information available about the needs of these young people; and the failure of school systems to confront controversial matters, especially in the area of youth sexuality. Rofes (1989) outlines several things that will need to change if schools are truly going to meet the needs of the gay and lesbian student population. He contends that schools are going to have to focus on the needs of young people rather than on the demands of parents or the larger community. In light of STDs and HIV, issues of sexuality must move from the taboo into a public forum. Teachers will need to be helped to become comfortable with gay and lesbian issues through sensitive training, including exploring their own beliefs about sexuality and sexual orientation. School curricula will need to be integrated to include the historical contributions of gay men and lesbians in order to provide positive messages and role models to our sexual minority youth. Finally, educators must abandon the myth that by discussing homosexuality in a positive way, they will cause young people to grow up to be gay or lesbian.

Professional educators, regardless of their moral or political convictions, are duty bound to protect and promote the human and civil rights of all people within the classroom.

Sears (1987) approached the task of making these changes occur by listing several steps that he believed socially responsible educators must take in order to have a positive impact upon the quality of life in school for all students, especially for gay and lesbian youth. As a first step, educators must examine their own attitudes toward homosexuality. When people become comfortable with their feelings, they more easily educate themselves about this subject. The second step is educating others about homosexuality, with particular emphasis on replacing myths with accurate information. This means communicating with the school board, parents, and community groups, as well as with students. As a third step, concerned educators must be responsive to the needs of gay and lesbian youth. This means providing young people with a nonjudgmental atmosphere in which they can process their feelings and come to terms with their sexuality and know that they are "okay," as well as providing a curriculum and educational resources which should in-

clude information about sexual orientation and people who are gay and lesbian.

Fourth, Sears believes that professional educators, regardless of their moral or political convictions, are duty bound to protect and promote the human and civil rights of all people within the classroom. This implies enforcing responsible standards of professional and student conduct in terms of verbal and physical harassment of gay and lesbian students, as well as combating the ignorance and fear engendered by the AIDS health crisis. The fifth step that educators can take is to encourage the hiring of and to provide support for gay and lesbian educators who will be healthy role models for such students. Finally, Sears (1987) contends that educators, as articulate citizens of the community, must speak out in favor of legislation that bars discrimination against homosexual men and women. He believes, "The struggle for social change must begin with a critical examination of arbitrary, narrow, and socially constructed categories in our lives as well as an assessment of how those categories affect the lives of those around us. Only when human beings accept themselves and respect the dignity of others can a genuine commitment to social justice be possible" (p. 96).

Jennings (1995), executive director of the Gay, Lesbian, and Straight Teachers Network, a national organization based in New York City, describes several specific steps that he believes teachers and schools can take to provide safe and inviting learning environments in schools. They are:

1. *Guarantee Equality.* Schools should add "sexual orientation" to their non-discrimination statements in all school publications as a way to communicate their commitment to equal treatment for all.
2. *Create a Safe Environment.* Schools must make it clear that neither physical violence nor harassing language like "faggot" and "dyke" will be tolerated, just as they are not for any other group. Clear harassment policies, which include sexual orientation, must be developed and then publicized to the entire school community, so that the consequences of and procedures for dealing with such behavior are clear to all.
3. *Provide Role Models* Studies consistently show that personal acquaintance with gay and lesbian people is the most effective means for developing positive attitudes toward acceptance. Both gay and straight students benefit from having role models such as openly gay and lesbian teachers, coaches, and administrators. Straight students are offered an alternative to the stereotypes with which they have often been raised. Gay and lesbian students get the chance, often for the first time, to see healthy gay and lesbian adults, which gives them hope for their own future. Schools need to create the conditions necessary for gay and lesbian faculty to feel safe in

"coming out." If no role models are available from within the school community, the school can bring in presenters from a local gay and lesbian speakers bureau or from a college gay and lesbian student association.

4. *Provide Support for Students.* Peer support and acceptance is the key to any student's feelings that he or she "belongs" in the school. "Gay Straight Alliances," groups which welcome membership from any student interested in understanding issues of sexual identity, regardless of sexual orientation, have been the key to creating such an atmosphere in many schools. Counselors must also be specifically trained in the needs of gay and lesbian youth in order to provide the support that students struggling with their sexual identity so desperately need.

5. *Provide Training for Faculty and Staff.* School staff need to be equipped to serve all the students with whom they work, including gay and lesbian ones. Understanding the needs of gay and lesbian youth, and developing the skills to meet those needs, should be expected of all staff members. Schools must provide the ongoing training necessary for the staff to fulfill this expectation. (Figure 1)

6. *Reassess the Curriculum.* Teachers need to incorporate gay and lesbian issues throughout the curriculum—not just in classes such as health education, where students would learn about the continuum of sexual orientation, but in other classes taught in the school. For example, when discussing hate crimes or civil rights issues in a social studies class, include examples related to gays and lesbians. If you would address the fact that Langston Hughes is a Black author because of the impact of his race on his work, then also address the fact that Walt Whitman was a gay author because of the impact of his sexual identity on his work. This identification also provides positive role models from history for our gay and lesbian youth. Teachers can also work to undo the "hidden heterosexism" of the curriculum, such as the exclusive use of opposite-sex couples in math word problems and foreign language exercises.

7. *Provide Appropriate Health Care and Education.* While being gay is not a "health issue" (any more than being heterosexual is), health education on sexuality and sexually transmitted diseases should sensitively address the particular issues of gay and lesbian people.

8. *Diversify Library and Media Holdings.* Often the school or classroom library is the first place students turn to for accurate sexuality information. Yet, too often, few or no works on gay and lesbian issues are found there. It is important that library holdings are up to date, present accurate information about

homosexuality and a positive view of gay and lesbian life, and are catalogued so that students can easily access the materials. (Figure 1)

Conclusion

Although the National Middle School Association took a courageous stance in passing Resolution 93–4 in Portland, NMSA is not promoting homosexuality. It is simply stating that if the middle school's mission is to meet the needs of all young adolescents, then the needs of sexuality minority youth must also be met. There is a great deal we all have to learn in order to meet these needs. NMSA, by adopting this resolution, is simply acknowledging these needs and encouraging us to get started. May we, teacher by teacher and middle school by middle school, have the courage to continue this process "in order to ensure safe and equitable school environments for youth of every sexual orientation."

References

Andrews, J. (1990). Don't pass us by: Keeping lesbian and gay issues on the agenda. *Gender and Education, 2,* 351–355.

Boxer, A. M., Cook, J. A., & Herdt, G., (1989, August). *First homosexual and heterosexual experiences reported by gay and lesbian youth in an urban community.* Paper presented at the Annual Meeting of the American Sociological Association. San Francisco, California.

Boxer, A., Levenson, R., & Peterson, A. C. (1990). Adolescent sexuality. In J. Worrell & F. Danner (Eds.), *The adolescent as decision-maker* (pp. 93–124). New York: Academic Press.

Colorado Department of Health. (1992). *Adolescent health in Colorado: Statistics, implications and strategies for action* (Report and Recommendations of the Advisory Council on Adolescent Health). Denver, CO: Author.

Dennis, D. I., & Harlow, R. E. (1986). Gay youth and the right to education. *Yale Law and Policy Review, 4,* 445–455.

Dunham, K. L. (1989). *Educated to be invisible: The gay and lesbian adolescent.* University of Southern Maine: U.S. Department of Education.

George, P. S., & Alexander, W. M. (1993). *The exemplary middle school* (2nd ed.). Fort Worth, TX: Holt, Rinehart and Winston.

Gibson, P. (1989). *Gay male and lesbian youth suicide.* In Report of the secretary's task force on youth suicide. Volume 3: Preventions and interventions in youth suicide. (DHHS Pub. No. ADM 89–1623). Washington, DC: U.S. Government Printing Office.

Gordon, L. (Ed.). (1983). Homophobia and education (Special double issue). *Interracial Books for Children Bulletin, 14,* (3/4).

The Governor's Commission on Gay and Lesbian Youth. (1993). *Making schools safe for gay and lesbian youth: Breaking the silence in schools and in families.* (Publication No. 17296–60–50-2/93-C. R.). Boston, MA: Author.

Grayson, D. A. (1987). Emerging equity issues related to homosexuality in education. *Peabody Journal of Education. 64,* 132–145.

Harbeck, K. M. (Ed.). (1992). *Coming out of the classroom closet: Gay and lesbian students, teachers, and curricula.* Binghamton, NY: Harrington Park Press.

Herdt, G. (1989). Introduction: Gay and lesbian youth, emergent identities, and cultural scenes at home and abroad. In G. Herdt (Ed.), *Gay and lesbian youth* (pp. 1–42). New York: Harrington Park Press.

Herdt, G., & Boxer, A. (1993). *Children of horizons: How gay and lesbian teens are leading a new way out of the closet.* Boston, MA: Beacon Press.

Hunt, C. Y. (1986). Adolescents at risk: Homosexuality. In C. Y. Hunt, (Ed.). *The tree of life: A response to teen suicide* (pp. 41–46). Wayne, MI: Wayne County Intermediate School District.

Jay, K., & Young, A. (1979). *The gay report: Lesbians and gay men speak out about sexual experiences.* New York: Washington Square Press (Simon & Schuster).

Jennings, K. (1995, January). What you can do: Ten steps toward ending homophobia in your school. (Available from Kevin Jennings, GLSTN, 2124 Broadway, Box 160, New York, NY 10023).

Krysiak, G. J. (1987). A very silent and gay minority. *The School Counselor, 34,* 304–307.

Lenskyj, H. (2990). Beyond plumbing and prevention: Feminist approaches to sex education. *Gender and Education, 2,* 217–230.

National Middle School Association. (1995). *This we believe* (3rd ed.). Columbus, OH: Author.

Powell, R. E. (1987). Homosexual behavior and the school counselor. *The School Counselor, 34,* 202–208.

Ramafedi, G. (1987). Male homosexuality: The adolescent perspective. *Pediatrics, 79,* 326–330.

Remafedi, G., Resnick, M., Blum, R., & Harris, L. (1992). Demography of sexual orientation in adolescents. *Pediatrics, 89*(4), 714–721.

Rofes, E. (1989). Opening up the classroom closet: Responding to the educational needs of gay and lesbian youth. *Harvard Educational Review, 59,* 444–453.

Russell, T. G. (1989). AIDS education, homosexuality, and the counselor's role. *The School Counselor, 36,* 333–337.

Savin-Willimas, R. C. (1990). Gay and lesbian adolescence. In F. W. Bozett & M. B. Sussman (Eds.). *Homosexuality and female relations* (pp. 197–216). New York: Harrington Park Press.

Sears, J. T. (1987). Peering into the well of loneliness: The responsibility of educators to gay and lesbian youth. In A. Molnar (Ed.). *Social issues and education: Challenge and responsibility* (pp. 79–100). Alexandria, VA: Association for Supervision and Curriculum Development.

Sears, J. T. (1989, March). *Personal feelings and professional attitudes of prospective teachers toward homosexuality and homosexual students: Research findings and curriculum recommendations.* Revision of a paper presented at the Annual Meeting of the American Educational research Association, San Francisco, CA.

Sears, J. T. (1991). Helping students understand and accept sexual diversity. *Educational Leadership, 49*(1), 54–56.

Troiden, R. R. (1993). The formation of homosexual identities. In L. D. Garnets & D. C. Kimmel (Eds.). *Psychological perspectives on lesbian and gay male experiences* (pp. 191–217). New York: Columbia University Press.

VanMeter, V. L. (1991). Sensitive materials in U.S. public schools. *School Library Media Quarterly, 29,* 223–227.

Whitlock, K. (1989). *Bridges of respect: Creating support for lesbian and gay youth* (2nd ed.). Philadelphia, PA: American Friends Service Committee.

Men and sex at 20, 30, 40

Why is sex so important to guys? 21 men say the answer changes as they age

JAMES STURZ

James Sturz is a freelance writer living in New York City.

THE FIRST TIME I HAD BONA fide great sex—when I realized what everyone else had been *ooh*ing about—I was 20 years old, and right in the middle I started to laugh. "What's so funny?" my partner asked, bewildered. I told her that I was laughing because I was thrilled. Sexual intercourse was turning out to be so fantastic, and, like a little boy, I was laughing because I knew no better way to express how I felt.

In time, we learn to show our passion in more complex ways—in part because our passion becomes more complex. As we get older, our sexual selves mature and change just as our bodies do. Sex takes on new meanings and its importance in our lives fluctuates.

While we don't all reach life's important stages at precisely the same age, there *are* shifts almost all of us experience along the way. The first serious relationship, the first child, the first mortgage—all these affect a man's sex life more than hormones ever will. There's sex when it's new, sex when it's serious, sex when you're distracted by work, and sex when you're so besotted that you use your whole body to love her because your heart's not enough.

That may sound touchy-feely, but sex is, by definition, a touchy-feely subject. What follows is an honest, introspective overview of male sexual evolution, a chronological exploration of sex from the neck up.

Sex at 20: From ego to intimacy

For a man in his twenties, sex is both a release and relief. We learn to trust our instincts, even as we learn that there's more to sex than instinct alone. We move beyond anxiety toward unbridled enjoyment.

When a body first does things it has only read about or imagined, a healthy dose of self-congratulation attends the act. "The first few years I was having sex, just getting that far was the whole challenge," says Gordon, a 23-year-old musician. "Reaching that point was as gratifying as the intercourse itself. Sex was all about saying, 'Wow, I'm getting laid.'"

The ego boost can be fleeting, however. George, a 24-year-old graphic artist who's single, admits how self-conscious he used to feel during intercourse: "I knew how it should be, how I *wanted* it to be, but everything would always move so fast. Afterward I'd find myself apologizing, 'I'm sorry I did a certain thing,' or asking, 'Did that hurt?' Deep down, I really wanted to ask, 'Was I OK?' Many of those insecurities are still there," he says, "but now I have enough experience to reassure myself, so they bother me less."

By our midtwenties, our obsession with scoring fades, the rules of sports having become less important than the rules of life. Our first adult, long-term relationships help put sex in perspective. "Because I love my girlfriend so much, it's no big deal if occasionally one of us doesn't completely satisfy the other," Gordon says, seeming a little astonished. "I've realized it's only when you don't love someone that performance is everything."

With closeness and confidence comes a chance for honesty. Sex becomes less about impressing, and more about expressing. "Through much of my twenties, I was concerned with demonstrating my ability," says Peter, a 28-year-old fundraiser who's single. "Sex used to be very quiet and serious. Usually I was much too shy to talk. But now that I'm older, I feel I've proved my ability. I can open up and say what I want sexually." The emphasis switches from, Wow, I'm having sex, to, Who am I, sexually? "Sex is a way of exploring and fashioning an identity," says Lee, a 29-year-old graduate student. "At 20, I had to find out, Am I the kind of guy who has sex all night? Am I a great lover? Am I really macho? I'm finally developing a grounded sense of who I am, so sex is more a way of just being me."

Now it's not the physical but the emotional side of sex that seems daunting. "When you fantasize about sex, you don't fantasize any accompanying problems," says Lee, who lives with his girlfriend. "In my midtwenties, I began realizing that sex, like real life, is much more complicated than I'd imagined. I had to learn how to cope with all the jumbled feelings that sex brings out, like jealousy and guilt." We learn that sex can be emotionally daring and reckless, even risky. "When I sleep with a woman, I give part of myself to her," says Ben, a 26-year-old lawyer. "For me, that makes sex both generous and dangerous, irresistible but also intimidating."

When sex satisfies both emotionally and physically, it can be an efficient balm for almost any twentysomething tension. Passionate encounters make setbacks suffered outside the bedroom seem small. "Sex is definitely a quality-of-life thing," Ben continues. "You know it was good when lying there afterward your girlfriend asks, 'How was your day?' and you can't remember."

Looking ahead, Gordon sees his sexuality on a continuum: "I hope it's going to be more controlled as I get older," he says, "I still come too quickly." Daniel, a 27-year-old writer, says, "I've been in love and that's been the best sex so far, but the greatest sex will come with the greatest love." Men in their twenties are supposedly at their sexual peak, biologically speaking, but they all seem to share a confidence that their enjoyment is only bound to increase. They focus on refining their raw sexual energy without ever fearing that pleasure could diminish. "I have to hope sex will become more transcendent, more honest, more powerful. I don't see why it wouldn't—it's been improving up to this point," says Jack, a single, 25-year-old public relations assistant. Gordon agrees: "I'm still saying 'Wow,' not just because I'm having sex but because the sex keeps getting better."

Sex at 30: A sense of purpose

I went to Ted's bachelor party—a weekend-long bacchanal at his mother's lake house—when we were both 27. Saturday night, drunk and bellowing around a fire, Ted swallowed a spit-roasted worm, howled primevally at the starlit sky, threw up and then trudged into the house to try to interest his sleeping fiancée, Emma, in a little action. At that age, you seized the opportunity for intercourse as often as possible, even when your body hurt and your girlfriend was exhausted. "In our twenties we'd stockpile sex," says Ted, "so that if it dried up, you wouldn't be left wishing you'd had more."

Today, Ted and Emma are 31, married and pursuing careers in New York City. As for sex, Ted muses: "I used to love going camping with a girlfriend. For some reason, sex in a tent was the best. But at this stage of my life, a bed-and-breakfast is definitely preferable. I'm fond of pillows." Nowadays, Ted spends so much time in his office walled in by stacks of papers that it's hard to feel primal. "At 20," Ted sighs, "I wanted to get laid. At 30, I just want to get home in time to have dinner with my wife."

When sex is no longer needed for ego gratification, it can serve a more important purpose: helping a man attract and keep a desirable partner. The romantically committed 30-year-old finds that sex is a valuable barometer of a relationship's health. "When I was in my twenties and a month went by without sex, I lost self-esteem," says Brian, 32, an attorney who's been married for three years. "If a month were to pass now, I'd worry about my relationship with my wife, which is the most essential aspect of my life."

Which is not to say that men see sex as the primary bond in long-term or married relationships. Making love keeps already-healthy couples on course, but it won't create a happy connection out of discord. "Sex isn't the be-all and end-all of our relationship, but it definitely keeps us from fighting that day," Brian allows. "It puts us in a good mood. It's an enhancer." Sex also becomes less critical to ego maintenance as other successes come within reach. "In your thirties, it's not how good-looking or athletic or seductive you are that matters," says Judith H. Gurfein, Ph.D., a clinical psychologist and assistant clinical professor at Mount Sinai School of Medicine in New York City. "At this state, career and money equal power, as opposed to sexual prowess. So while a man still has physical desires, they become far less important.

Nonetheless, the single man in his thirties senses that the sexual stakes are higher. As he watches his married friends celebrate anniversaries and births, he realizes that good sex is essential to recruiting a girlfriend, making a commitment, building a life. "None of my friends are married to women I wish *I'd* married," says Russ, 31, a single campaign organizer in Washington, D.C. "But I envy every one of them for being so far along with his life."

Married *or* single, men in their thirties start focusing on family. It turns out that we have our own biological clocks; they emit the same urgent alarms as the female models, even if we do press the snooze button a few more times. I'll share a personal confession: Now that I'm 30, after years of deliberately blocking conception, I have begun to feel my own urge to impregnate my partner. As we make love (armed with the usual precautions), I have found myself thinking the startling mantra, "Be pregnant—be pregnant." It is nothing I would act on—certainly, not without consulting her—but the desire is there.

Once both partners have readied themselves and their nest, starting a family can forever affect the significance of sex. "I was the one pushing to have a baby," says Evan, a 33-year-old expectant father. "My wife and I started talking about children a few years ago, and I held her to the schedule. Making love when we were trying to conceive was the best sex I've had. I felt stronger, more virile. There was an erotic power. Also, when your wife walks around eight months pregnant, everyone knows you had sex. I like that," Evan says, self-satisfied.

The orgasm, for all its spasms and shuddering, is fleeting. Yet my friend Leo, 35, sees that climactic moment differently since his daughter was born.

"At 20, I wanted to get laid. At 30, I just want to get home in time to have dinner with my wife."

"It's more meaningful now," he says. "The idea that a random act that feels so good for such a brief time can lead to something permanent is just incredible."

"You're more completely aware of the power of sex when you use it to conceive," agrees Tim, 33 and a father of two. "The pressure is on. In fact, the only time I've come up soft is when we were trying to get pregnant. The first time it took us about seven months. As each cycle went by, it felt like an eternity." Once his children were born, Tim and his wife, like many couples, found that they couldn't help but scale back the frequency of sex. "I hate to admit that I fit a stereotype," Tim says, cringing, "but I've had significantly less sex since we've had kids. The passion is there; we just have less time and energy. We're more likely to watch the ten o'clock news than get involved in foreplay.

"When we do have sex, we say, 'This is great. We should do this more often,'" he continues. "But loving my wife is something I do all the time, in a lot of ways. We do everything together—cook, clean, laugh, argue, as well as bring kids into the world. As far as I'm concerned, all that is making love too. I don't need to have sex with her to show her."

Single men are less realistic about sex. They allow themselves the luxury of believing they'll be the anomaly, the only married man to maintain inexhaustible sexual interest and activity. In the meantime, their most common sexual fantasy may center around falling in love. "I think there's nothing more erotic than two people honestly and passionately telling each other how much they're in love," says Richard, 32, who has yet to find a long-term partner. Thirtysomething men in committed relationships tend to characterize sex as recreation; single guys nurture the hope that sex, when combined with love, will lead to endless elation.

Sex at 40: A welcome calm

My friend Janice claims to have slept with enough men to qualify as an expert. She says: "At 20, men want to get laid. At 30, they want to get laid. At 40, they want to be held."

"She's absolutely right," says Otis, a 40-year-old sound engineer, who's single. "But I'd add: At 40, they want to get laid and *then* be held. I still have raging hormones, but now they're wiser and

more tender hormones. Sex, for me, has become a more relaxed experience."

With maturity, some men say, the focus of intercourse becomes emotional intimacy, not physical gratification. "I wouldn't say the sex is better now, but it is more enriching," explains Otis. "Satisfying your own selfish sexual desires gets to be so tiresome after a while. Before, it was, 'Sex, sex, sex, more, more, more.' Now sexual energy does not even have to be expressed in sexual ways—we could have great conversation or just cuddle instead. It's more like, 'OK, whatever, it's cool.'"

Alan, a 44-year-old video technician, concurs: "I'll always be a very sexual person, but it's on a more spiritual level now. The sex is all about sharing. I'm relieved—it used to be so time-consuming to figure out how I was going to get laid." It's not that sex becomes any less enjoyable as men age, only that the desire, which once seemed unquenchable, can finally be compartmentalized. For many, it's a welcome calm. As one married father reports: "I envied my virgin roommate in college, because I hated the fact that once I'd discovered sex I couldn't live without it. It's a very satisfying feeling today to know I've got my sex drive under control. The control is as satisfying as the act itself."

Some men, however, maintain their sex drive with grim determination. "I live by a credo," says Walter, 48, a widowed chef who is newly engaged. "You have to have sex every day. Sex is like any other work—say, doing your income tax. You sit down and start sorting those receipts, and once you get into it, you just get it done. You can't slip into the rut of falling asleep on the couch, because at this age, if you stop having sex regularly, you won't start up again." The payoff for all his hard work: "In my forties, sex gives me a sense of security."

For fortysomething men in committed relationships, the "thrill of the chase" sounds as old-fashioned as a foxhunt. It's not that attraction to other women wanes, but the potential repercussions—the loss of a partner or of your own self-respect—drown out the urge to prowl. Men who remain single still relish the pursuit of

someone new, though the excitement changes, depending on the woman's age. "If I hook up with someone young, it's because I want the fire, the thrill of the moment," says Bruce, a 41-year-old banker who's single. "But when I meet a woman closer to my own age, there's the bigger thrill that this might last for more than a moment." What really stirs him now is the prospect of stability, the thought that the woman he's sleeping with is the woman he'll sleep with in a year or in a decade, that they might create something inviolable and unique together.

Many older men say they don't have sex in order to cling to youth, but to embrace the present at its most sublime and robust. "It's funny," says Jacob, a 46-year-old furniture designer who is divorced, "when I have sex with a woman now, what I like isn't that it makes me feel young, but that it makes me feel good about how I am right now."

"I think the sex is better now than at 20 or 30," argues Michael, a 40-year-old physician who married in his midthirties. "When I was younger and single and sex was casual, you'd do this incredibly intimate thing and then feel funny walking around without your shorts on. Now the inhibitions of the past are all gone. There aren't the hang-ups. Very little shocks or worries me, and that's a comfort I really appreciate."

Michael says the thoughts he has during sex with his wife make the epiphanies of his twenties and thirties seem picayune. "I outgrew the joy of conquest a long time ago," he says. "Now there's more the feeling of, This is what I'm supposed to do. It's a heavy realization, almost a philosophical conviction. It's, I'm a guy, this is marriage. And to be grandiose, This is the meaning of life."

When you talk about sex with men whose ages span three decades, only one constant emerges: We always like it. Perhaps it's precisely because men want different things at different times—romance, compassion, distraction, flirtation, unadulterated lust—that sex has the potential to constantly surprise us. The essential elements of satisfying sex rearrange themselves beneath our sheets as we age and change, creating a newly powerful experience at every stage of our lives.

A SPECIAL *AMERICAN HEALTH* SURVEY

THE JOY OF MIDLIFE
SEX

We made love, not war; defied the double standard; and redefined female sexuality. Now the daughters of the sexual revolution are marching through midlife—and changing the way America thinks about what it means to be women of "a certain age." > According to an exclusive new *American Health* survey of 500 women between ages 35 and 55, boomer babes are still sexy after all these years, with the healthiest women reporting the happiest sex lives of all. Among the eye-opening findings from our peek into the bedrooms of women in their prime:

BY DIANNE HALES

HEALTHY ATTITUDES + HEALTHY HABITS = HOT SEX More than half of you say sex is better now than at age 25. Why? "Practice, practice, practice," quips one respondent. But seriously, "you're more comfortable with your body, your sexuality, your partner," says San Francisco psychotherapist Lonnie Barbach, Ph.D., author of *The Pause*. "It's like learning to drive. First you're nervous. Then it becomes second nature."

Your health is also a factor: 54% of you exercise regularly, and 81% watch what you eat, although you don't obsess about every calorie. You also make healthy communication a priority: 55% discuss sexual issues with your partner; 40% talk things over with close women friends.

The payoff? A whopping 30% of you make love three to six times a week. "This frequency absolutely shocked me," says Beverly Whipple, Ph.D., of Newark, NJ, president-elect of the American Association of Sex Education Counselors and

RATING Your Mates

Women whose partners are in good shape are more likely to report that sex is better than it was at age 25. Here's what you said about *his* physique:

14% *EXCELLENT* HE'S THE NEXT JAMES BOND
55% *GOOD* HE COULD GO JOGGING WITH PRESIDENT CLINTON
19% *NOT SO HOT* HARVEY KEITEL HAS NOTHING TO FEAR
4% *LOUSY* HOMER SIMPSON HAS HIM BEAT

From *American Health for Women*, January/February 1997, pp. 78-81. © 1997 Dianne Hales. Reprinted by permission.

Therapists. "It's extremely high compared to past studies." The 44% of you who report having sex three to six times a month is more in line with previous reports. Of those who describe their health as good, 37% make love three to six times a week. By comparison, only 19% of those in poor health have sex three to six times a week.

Yet sometimes even the liveliest sex lives run out of steam. Seven in 10 of you have felt too tired for sex at some time in the past year, while half have felt too stressed.

Unfortunately, help can be hard to find—at least in doctors' offices. When it comes to sex, physicians don't ask and women don't tell. About eight in 10 of you have never discussed sex with your doctors. "It's sad that even though so much has changed from a generation ago, physicians and patients still aren't comfortable talking about sex," says Fran Kaiser, M.D., a specialist in geriatrics, endocrinology and sexuality at St. Louis University.

But this too may change. "The baby boom generation has

GETTING PHYSICAL

44% of those who don't exercise, versus only **30%** of those who work out regularly, report they've felt too fat or undesirable for sex. Among those eating high-fat diets, **69%** have felt that way, vs. just **33%** of healthy eaters.

rector of women's health at Canyon Ranch Health and Fitness Resort in Tucson, AZ. "For the short amount of time that sex takes, we get so much out of it," she says. "We sleep better. We feel better. Loving sex with a trusted partner may be the best thing you can do for your body."

"WHY GIVE UP ON SEX?" SAYS ONE WOMAN. "AS A GOOD BABY BOOMER, I WANT IT ALL."

demanded more for itself all the way through the life cycle, and that's not going to stop now," observes psychologist Michael A. Perelman, Ph.D., acting codirector of the sex therapy program at New York Hospital–Cornell Medical Center in New York City. As an unmarried survey respondent, age 50, puts it, "Why should I give up on sex? As a good baby boomer, I still want it all."

PRIME-TIME SEX

How does what's going on in your bedroom compare to what you see on TV? The ratings look like this:

MAD ABOUT YOU	**65%**	(warm, friendly sex)
SEINFELD	**13%**	(all talk, not much action)
THE SINGLE GUY	**12%**	(sex life? What sex life?)
E.R.	**7%**	(fast-paced, short-lived sex)

SECRETS OF SEXUAL VITALITY Asked to rate your sex lives, 32% of you say things are "smoking!" What accounts for all this sizzle? "It may well be a function of being in better health in mind and body," says Dr. Perelman. About six in 10 of those with X-rated sex lives work out regularly.

"If you're feeling good, you're more aware of your body, and that spills over into sex," says Lana Holstein, M.D., di-

Women in good physical condition are also more comfortable during pelvic exams and Pap smears and less prone to health problems such as high blood pressure, which can sabotage sexual pleasure. But life's fast pace is taking a toll on even the healthiest, wealthiest and wisest (or, at least, best educated) of you. "Fatigue has become the most common cause of sexual problems," says Dr. Perelman. "Busy people put sex last on their priority list, and then they're just too tired to do it." His advice: Make time for dating (each other). "A date can be very romantic. Even if half the time you just have a good time together and don't have sex, your marriage and sex life will definitely improve," he says.

SEXY IS AS SEXY DOES How-to sex manuals and videotapes. Sex-related Websites. Vibrators. Masturbation. A generation ago, middle-aged women might never have acknowledged that such titillating things existed, let alone admitted to trying them. But the veterans of sexual liberation are much more open-minded. "I'm impressed with their self-help efforts," says Dr. Perelman, "and they've tried a lot."

Six in 10 of you dress up in sexy clothes. More than four in 10 (42%) masturbate, while 44% read sex self-help books and 38% surf into sex info Websites or watch sex videos. About 40% use vaginal lubricants or do Kegel exercises to strengthen vaginal muscles; 21% have tried a vibrator.

But some of you still struggle with inhibitions: 23% have felt too fat for sex at some time in the previous year, while

13% have felt physically undesirable for other reasons. "This whole idea of equating feeling pretty or thin with being sexy is one of the few remaining differences between the sexes," notes Dr. Perelman. "Men are much less likely to say, 'Gee, I put on two pounds; I just don't feel like sex tonight.'"

THE SCREEN TEST *Mad About You,* TV's top-rated show about a pair of nicely neurotic New Yorkers, may not seem like the stuff sexual fantasy is made of. But when we asked you to compare your sex life to a sitcom, 65% chose its warm, friendly, lighthearted brand of sex.

"My husband and I are definitely like *Mad About You,* " says a 54-year-old survey respondent married for 25 years. "Sex is a connection we feel all day long. I'll put a note in my husband's lunch—something like 'Think of me when you're eating this.' He'll leave me a sexy message on the answering machine. It's that kind of back-and-forth that makes sex fun."

"The quality of a relationship has a lot more to do with how satisfied women are than with whether their orgasm was a '10' or an '8,' " says psychologist Norma McCoy, Ph.D., a professor of psychology at San Francisco State University. "As women get older, sex remains very, very gratifying even if they do it less, because it's a symbol of the relationship."

In our survey the women with smoking-hot sex lives were likeliest to give credit to a longtime, comfortable relationship with a loving partner. "If they're lucky, couples who've been together awhile move into a phase of lovemaking where they still play around and tease, but where there's also a deeper kind of bonding taking place because they've shared a lot. Most people really treasure this," says Dr. Holstein.

Other factors also contribute to the joys of midlife sex. "In the past there was always the fear of pregnancy," notes a 46-year-old respondent who has been married for 23 years. "The spontaneity wasn't there. Now we're comfortable with each other, and I've come to value not just the sex, but

HEALTHY SEX
62%
of women who describe their health as good say sex has improved with age, and **37%** of them make love three to six times a week. By comparison, just **45%** of those in poor health think sex has gotten better, and only about half as many—**19%**—have sex that often.

having someone to go through life with. That makes everything better as you get older."

HOW MATES RATE Who are the men sharing the beds of the sexiest midlife women? Not baby-faced boy-toys (Cher, take note), but thoroughly grown-up guys. Of the women who rate sex as better now than at 25, two-thirds have partners between 40 and 54. These fellows aren't sexual Olympians either. In the past year 52% of your partners have felt too tired or stressed to have sex, 21% were occasionally impotent and 17% were premature ejaculators. Four percent of you have partners with persistent impotence; after age 45 this percentage doubles.

Most of you (63%) don't worry about a partner's less-than-impressive sexual performance. Dr. Perelman finds that fact encouraging. "Men need reassurance that they are more than their penises," he says, adding that when imperfect sex persists, remedies are available. "Women who feel angry or frustrated because of a partner's sexual difficulties [as do 8% of survey respondents] need to know this."

THE LAST TABOO Sexual dysfunction doesn't discriminate against women. In the past year, 41% of you experienced a temporary loss of interest in sex. Dr. Barbach isn't surprised.

BETTER THAN SEX
(Well, Almost)
Your top five sources of sensual pleasure—outside of intercourse, that is:

1 MASSAGE
2 EXERCISE
3 MASTURBATION
4 CHOCOLATE
5 SHOPPING

CAN WE TALK?
(Maybe). When it comes to confessing your concerns about sex to your doctor, menopause may be the catalyst for more open, honest communication. Twenty-three percent of postmenopausal women, vs. only 12% of premenopausal ones, say they have discussed sexual issues with their physicians.

"For many midlife women, it's difficult just fitting sex into a busy schedule," she says. Twenty-one percent of you have lacked desire for your partner, 15% have a problem with vaginal dryness and 10% have difficulty achieving orgasm. Women who are ages 35 to 44 and who are juggling the demands of little kids and careers are likeliest to feel too stressed or tired for sex, to report other sexual problems and to avoid bringing up sexual concerns with their partners.

And what of the 80% of you who *never* talk about sex with your doctors, regardless of whether the physician is male or female? Why are you far likelier to report an ingrown toenail than a lack of sexual desire? "Those of us who grew up in the '50s and '60s never heard sex discussed," says a married 52-year-old respondent. "We may feel freer and be more sexually active than our parents were—or than we think they were—but that doesn't mean it's easy to talk to our doctors." Like 75% of survey respondents, she'd talk if her doctor asked. But our survey shows that when conversations do take place, women are the instigators 67% of the time. Why don't doctors ask? "Their education doesn't include enough information on sexuality," notes Dr. Whipple. "Health professionals need more than one lecture on sex—which is all they get if they're lucky."

Of the women who did ask about sexual concerns, 28% were told to relax, go home and keep trying. "That is truly unfortunate, because so much more can be done to help," says Dr. Perelman. Dr. Kaiser agrees. "It would be sad for women to think that sexual pain or problems have to be part of aging, because they don't," she says. "A lot can be done so women can continue to enjoy sex throughout their lives."

For many respondents that's exactly what's happening. "Our children may not believe it, but sex goes on," says a 53-year-old who has been married for 30 years. "I had a stroke nine years ago; my husband has had prostate cancer. But we're not dead yet. And the love we have for each other after all we've been through makes sex more beautiful than ever."

"Such feelings aren't unusual," says Dr. Barbach. "Sex truly is wasted on the young. They may have the equipment and the energy, but they don't have the experience. Couples who have a really good, caring relationship over a long period talk about sex in a way that a 25-year-old couldn't begin to understand."

———

Dianne Hales writes extensively on women's issues and is co-author of Caring for the Mind.

Everything you always wanted to know about sex after 50

If the subject of human sexuality has lost much of its old taboos, one major reason is the 1969 publication of *Everything You Always Wanted to Know About Sex (but were afraid to ask),* by David Reuben, M.D. This groundbreaking question-and-answer guide was written in a chatty but informative style, making it "user-friendly" long before the term came into common use. The book eventually racked up worldwide

(BUT WERE AFRAID TO ASK)

sales of 40 million and forever made it acceptable to explore in public our private concerns about sex.

But in spite of all the openness in our attitudes about physical intimacy, misinformation and destructive myths remain—especially in the realm of sexuality in midlife and beyond. With that in mind, *NEW CHOICES* asked Reuben, now in his 60s, to answer your questions. We hope you'll share his responses with a loving partner.
—THE EDITORS ▶

BY DAVID REUBEN, M.D.

From *New Choices: Living Even Better after 50* June 1997, pp. 44-47. © 1997 by Retirement Living Publishing Company, Inc. Reprinted by permission.

Does a person's sex life really change significantly after the age of 50?

It certainly does—fortunately! The complicated business of sex changes constantly throughout a person's life. But the changes that occur after the fifth decade solve a lot of problems that may have caused trouble before.

Do you mean to say that sex gets better with age?

Yes. Take premature ejaculation, for example, a problem for many younger men, and one of the most frustrating of all because both partners suffer. When they are younger, some men may ejaculate in as little as 30 seconds—long before the woman has a chance to reach a climax. But by their 50s, most men's ejaculation reflex has slowed to average or even beyond.

That means the woman has plenty of time for ample stimulation and a far better opportunity to reach her orgasm.

What about women? How does sex improve for them after 50?

By approximately age 50, most women have stopped menstruating and all fear of unwanted pregnancy is gone. That in itself can make sex a lot more spontaneous and relaxed. But there's another big bonus.

fect on her sexual satisfaction can be dramatic. Symptoms usually vanish promptly, and there's one almost immediate sexual bonus: hot flashes disappear. After all, who can enjoy sex in a blast furnace?

So, my bottom line is this: I don't think it makes sense for a woman to start hormone replacement therapy just to improve her sexual satisfaction. But if she has serious symptoms that affect her entire body and she and her doctor agree that replacement therapy is medically indicated, her sex life will get a big boost at the same time.

How about hormone replacement for men?

That turns out to be a more complicated situation. When the subject of hormone replacement therapy for men comes up, it's not a question of hot flashes but rather better erections.

Of course, it's true that at age 50 men don't have erections as hard or as long-lasting as they did at age 25. But taking everything into consideration, sex can be as good—or better—in these later years, even with less aggressive erections. Of course, a mate has a role to play as well. Direct stimulation of the penis by stroking and gentle rubbing can help bring on a firm erection, although it may take a little longer. In addition, it's helpful to make the sexual moments more spontaneous, exciting and emotional.

Sex between loving partners is a tranquilizer, a form of mild exercise and just plain fun

What's that?

We have witnessed tremendous advances in the past 20 years. Medical science now has the answer for almost any problem that can interfere with sexual satisfaction after age 50. For example, women may begin to experience pain with intercourse. Although sex can be a lot of things, it isn't supposed to hurt. Almost invariably, the pain results from thinning of the tissue that lines the vagina. Most of the time, applying a prescription cream that contains estrogen (the female hormone) inside the vagina solves the problem. The estrogen builds up the tissue and eliminates the pain. A small amount of an over-the-counter vaginal moisturizing gel can also make penetration painless.

Should a woman over 50 go on hormone replacement therapy to improve her sexual functioning?

I'll tell you how I feel about that. Even after menopause, some women produce sufficient estrogen in their adrenal glands that they never need replacement hormones. On the other hand, if a woman has severe symptoms of menopause—hot flashes, dry skin, depressed mood, insomnia and the like—she should consult her doctor. If, between them, they agree that hormone replacement therapy is a good idea, the ef-

Further, an erection doesn't have to be rock hard to work; even a slightly soft erection can do the job. If the penis is just stiff enough to enter the vagina, often thrusting during intercourse will help an erection build.

Why not just let a man take male hormones?

Because you don't want to take the chance of causing prostate problems. The prostate sits astride the urethra and produces a milky fluid that's mixed with seminal fluid during ejaculation. During puberty, the prostate enlarges to the size of a walnut in response to male hormones. Then, at about age 45, it generally begins to grow again at a substantial rate and can eventually reach the size of a small peach. The resulting pressure on the urethra can make urination difficult. Prostate enlargement is related both to male hormones and to age. Testosterone, a male hormone given in replacement therapy, undoubtedly puts more punch into an erection, but it also makes the prostate grow. And an erection isn't much good if you can't pass urine. But there's a bigger problem.

What's that?

If a man has cancer of the prostate (and after age 50 that becomes a real possibility), testosterone can increase the rate of its growth. Obviously, no one wants to feed a cancer. So, at the very least, testosterone replacement for men should raise a yellow caution flag.

Supplemental testosterone can improve a man's erections and sexual performance. But it comes with a risk of increasing the size of the prostate and accelerating any prostate cancer. The best solution is to talk with your doctor about the benefits and drawbacks for *you*. That way, you and your partner can be confident that you're not sacrificing your long-term health to give a boost to your sex life.

What about sex and heart disease?
You're probably referring to those cases where men supposedly have a heart attack during sexual intercourse. But those cases are few and far between.

Of course, for all men—and women—sexual intercourse may be too stressful during the period of recovery immediately after a heart attack. But after that, there's no reason not to enjoy the pleasures of sex. This same concept applies to many chronic diseases. High blood pressure, arthritis and a whole host of illnesses can now be managed well enough for sex to continue to play a satisfying part in a person's life. Naturally, that doesn't mean indulging in acrobatics or trying to set new endurance records. But easy-going, relaxed sex can be a real mental and physical boost to men and women recovering from any illness.

It sounds as if you're saying sex has medical benefits. Are you?
Yes, I am. Sex between loving partners is a tranquilizer, a form of mild exercise, a release of physical and mental tension, and just plain fun. That's about as much health benefit as you can get from any activity. That's why it's so important for men and women to do their very best to continue to make sexual activity an important part of their lives.

What about people over 50 who are told they're too old for sex?
Who made that rule? Is sex supposed to be only for beauty queens in tiny bikinis and 20-something muscular weight lifters? Human sexuality doesn't check the calendar. The drive for sex is built into every human being—and the appreciation of sex can grow with each passing year.

And so what if someone in your family criticizes you for enjoying sex? Think of it this way. One of the advantages of getting older is that by the time you're in your 50s, you don't care so much about winning the approval of everyone around you. If a son and daughter-in-law, for instance, suggest that you're "too old for things like that," ask them how they became sex experts so young and so fast. Sex is good for you, and the older you get the more benefits it offers.

Assuming people are in good health, how often should they have sex if they're over 50?
As often as they want and as often as they can. There are no rules about what happens between men and women as long as they're both involved in the decision and both derive satisfaction from the relationship.

What's your final word about sex after 50?
We can't ignore the most important sexual organ of them all—the brain. The emotional bonds that are built up over the years are far more important to sexuality than physical appearance. A warm, loving relationship is the best aphrodisiac we have.

DAVID REUBEN, M.D., has written seven books in addition to EVERYTHING YOU ALWAYS WANTED TO KNOW ABOUT SEX (BUT WERE AFRAID TO ASK). His most recent book is DR. DAVID REUBEN'S QUICK WEIGHT-GAIN PROGRAM (Crown).

Old/New
Sexual Concerns

Sexual Abuse and Harassment (Articles 40–43)
Legal and Ethical Issues Related to Sex (Articles 44 and 45)
Focus: The Future of Sex (Articles 46–49)

This final unit deals with several topics that are of interest or concern for different reasons. Also, as the title suggests, it combines "old" or ongoing topics and concerns with "new" or emerging ones. In one respect, however, these topics have a common denominator—they have all taken positions of prominence in the public's awareness as social issues.

Tragically, sexual abuse and violence are long-standing occurrences in society and in some relationships. For centuries, a strong code of silence surrounded these occurrences and, many now agree, increased not only the likelihood of sexual abuse and violence, but the harm to victims of these acts. Beginning in the middle of this century, two societal movements helped to begin eroding this code of silence. The child welfare/child rights movement was in the process of exposing child abuse and mistreatment and sought to improve the lives of children and families. Soon after, and to a large extent fueled by the emerging women's movement, primarily "grass-roots" organizations that became known as "rape crisis" groups or centers became catalysts for altering the way we looked at (or avoided looking at) rape and sexual abuse.

Research today suggests that these movements have accomplished many of their initial goals and brought about significant social change. The existence and prevalence of rape and other sexual abuse is much more accurately known. Many of the myths previously believed (rapists are strangers that jump out of bushes, sexual abuse only occurs in poor families, all rapists are male and all victims are female, and so on) have been replaced with more accurate information. The code of silence has been recognized for the harm it can cause; and millions of friends, parents, teachers, counselors, and others have learned how to be approachable, supportive listeners to victims disclosing their abuse experiences. Finally, we have come to recognize the role that power, especially unequal power, plays in rape, sexual abuse, sexual violence, and, a term coined more recently, sexual harassment.

The articles in the first subsection, *Sexual Abuse and Harassment*, seek to highlight several ongoing and emerging issues with respect to sexual abuse, violence, and harassment. Despite some progress, such abuse still occurs, and the damage to victims can be compounded when they are not be-

lieved or, worse yet, are blamed. The profound sense of violation, the loss of feeling safe, the erosion of esteem and, especially when the abuser is someone in authority or known to the victim, the resultant inability to trust are illustrated in the initial articles. At the same time, these and the remaining articles identify emerging complexities surrounding sexual abuse, and in turn, all sexual behavior. As we as a society have sought to expose and reduce abusive sex, it has become increasingly clear that all of society and each of us as individuals/potential partners must grapple with the broader issue of what constitutes consent: What is nonabusive sexual interaction? How can people communicate interest, arousal, desire and/or propose sexual interaction when remnants of unequal power, ignorance, misinformation, fear, adversarial sex roles, and inadequate communication skills still exist?

The second subsection, *Legal and Ethical Issues Related to Sex*, delves into some current legal and ethical dilemmas associated with sexuality and sexual behavior. All societies have struggled with the apparent dichotomy of freedom versus protection when it comes to enacting laws about human behavior. In addition, the pace of technological advances (infertility treatment, AIDS, and cloning, to name just a few) has far outstripped society's attempts to grapple with the legal, ethical, and moral issues involved. At the present time, a variety of laws about sexual behaviors exist. Some are outdated, apparently in conflict with evolving social norms, even majority behaviors. Some laws are permissive, seeking to protect individual freedoms. Others are restrictive, seeking to protect society and allowing the intrusion of legal representatives into the private, even consensual, sexual behaviors of otherwise law-abiding citizens. The two articles in this subsection explore legal dilemmas as they relate to the issues of sex in the military and how to handle the AIDS epidemic without jeopardizing civil rights. They are handled informatively, but with many thought-provoking, even sometimes troubling, perspectives illustrating the far-reaching nature of today's legal-ethical controversies.

The final subsection, *Focus: The Future of Sex* asks a question central to both the how-far-have-we-come and the where-are-we (or should-we-be)-going query. Histori-

Talk about AIDS before it hits home.

"I really don't have to tell Linda about AIDS. They're teaching about it in school."

"Why discuss AIDS with my Johnny? He isn't gay."

"If I talk to them about AIDS, they'll think it's okay to have sex."

If you're thinking any of these thoughts, you're not doing all you should to protect your teenager from AIDS.

So put your embarrassment and your fear of encouraging sex aside.

Just sit down and tell them the facts.

Tell them that you just can't be sure who's infected with the AIDS virus. Sometimes it can be carried for years without any symptoms.

Tell them that since they can't possibly know who's infected they must use precautions to protect themselves.

Tell them if they're having sex, they must always use a condom. And not having sex is still the best protection.

Tell them that AIDS is incurable, there's no vaccine, and once you get it you'll likely die.

Then tell them it's preventable.

Tell them everything you can about AIDS. But make sure you tell them now.

AIDS Because by the time you think they're old enough to know, it might be too late.

cally, western culture has been very limiting with respect to sex, restricting it to sex within marriage and forbidding sex other than for procreation. Over time, these limits were challenged—especially the double standard, the marital restriction, and what constituted appropriate styles and purposes of sexual activity—with a resultant increase in individual sexual freedoms. Today, some people point to such sociosexual problems as the incidence of AIDS and other STDs, unmarried parenthood, concerns about early teenage sexual activity, multiple partners, "casual" sex, and increasing acceptance of "alternative" sexual activities as negative outcomes of the collapse of traditional limits on sex. Should we be nostalgic for sexual limitations? The old ones were often not followed and the double standard and other components contributed to hypocrisy and victimization. Yet has sexual freedom increased our capacity for healthy, fulfilling,

joyful sex? Even though many see freedom of sexual expression as their right, must sexual license be separated from sexual responsibility? Is there a balance between complete sexual freedom for the individual and subjugation and homogenization of individuals' sexuality to the common good? The articles selected for this section are ones that will confront and challenge today's issues and trends and help readers conceptualize their views on desired future directions.

Looking Ahead: Challenge Questions

What does your college or community do about date or acquaintance rape or child sexual abuse? Are there any education or prevention efforts? What do you think of them?

Have you overheard or participated in formal or informal discussions about potential or real sexual harassment at your job or school? How do you, your classmates, or coworkers feel about it? How would you rate your school or employer regarding awareness, prevention programming, and response to complaints?

How do you feel about laws restricting sexual behaviors (for example, age limits or marital requirements for engaging in sex or laws making specific sexual behaviors illegal)?

Where do you believe "personal freedom" or "choice" about sexually related behaviors begins to collide with the "greater good" of society?

What is your response to radio or television talk shows on sexual topics? Be honest: Do you watch them? Why? Do you think the media should report on the sexual activities of public figures? Why or why not?

Have you surfed or would you surf the Internet for information about a sexual topic or sexually explicit materials? Which of the following two statements do you most closely agree with and why? (1) Available online networks provide an important, private way to obtain accurate, discreet information and materials that can enhance intimate relationships. (2) Sex online is simply pornography, which is clearly harmful to society, people, and healthy intimate relationships.

THE TOWN THAT CLOSED ITS EYES

Four high-school football heroes were charged with raping a mentally retarded girl as their companions watched. How could the pride of Glen Ridge High commit such a shocking crime?
By Bernard Lefkowitz

 s her seventeen-year-old daughter Leslie* ran down the steps in her sweats to shoot some baskets, Rosalind Faber* felt a familiar anxiety. It was never easy to let her daughter go out alone. Leslie Faber was retarded. With an IQ of 49, she fell in the bottom 1 percent of the population. Still, it comforted Ros to know that they lived in the sort of tranquil, protected place where the strong didn't prey on the weak. The Fabers had never regretted their move from New York City to the suburb of Glen Ridge, New Jersey (population 7,800), in 1964.

Glen Ridge was just the sort of peaceful community many Americans dream about but few can afford. Neat, spacious houses bordered immaculate cobblestone streets; the schools were good and the values of the community were solidly planted in family, country and free enterprise.

Opposite the basketball court in Cartaret Park where Leslie practiced her shots, Glen Ridge's championship baseball team was having an unsupervised preseason practice session. The stars of the high school's wrestling and football teams were also there, checking out the scene.

Leslie had known most of these guys all her life, but they had followed separate paths through childhood and adolescence—Leslie, friendless and alone; the boys, clustered in the most envied teenage clique in town. No matter how friendly she was, how desperately she yearned for recognition from her heroes, Leslie Faber could never break through the wall that separated her from the cool kids. She couldn't imagine being invited to one of the legendary parties given by the Scherzer twins—Kyle and Kevin, co-captains of the football team. If you got invited, it showed that you belonged. You counted.

About half an hour after Leslie began practicing, five or six of the boys, with Christopher Archer in the lead, made their way toward the basketball court. Leslie knew Chris and his brother, Paul, well. She really liked Paul—he had a kind smile, and he always treated her just like any other girl. Chris, a year younger than Paul, had cold eyes and a sly grin, but it was important to her to please him: Chris might say something nice about her to Paul.

After chatting Leslie up for a while, Chris invites her for an impromptu party in the Scherzers' rec room. Leslie can't imagine why they would want her there—they've always called her retarded—but Chris tells her that Paul will be there and that he wants to go out with her.

The guys enter the Scherzer home, and Chris takes Leslie inside. On the way downstairs, she sees Kevin and Kyle's grandmother bustling about in the kitchen, which reassures Leslie. Chris leads her into the rec room and puts her on the sofa next to Bryant Grober. Leslie doesn't know him as well,

Name has been changed.

but he is popular with the guys and the girls think he is really cute.

At first there is a hum of plesantries, then, suddenly, an expectant silence. Thirteen young men are gathered around the sofa, some seated on folding chairs they have just set up. Chris leans over and whispers something to Leslie, and Bryant pulls off his pants and his underpants. A sophomore boy, who sees confusion in Leslie's eyes, turns to a friend and says, "Let's get out of here." In all, six young men eventually follow suit. Seven—Kyle and Kevin Scherzer, Bryant Grober, Paul and Chris Archer, and two of their friends and teammates, Peter Quigley and Richard Corcoran, Jr.—remain in the basement.

Leslie later remembers feeling a hand on her head, pushing her mouth down onto a penis. One boy calls her a whore. One boy reaches for a broom with a bright red handle. Another fishes through a pile of sports equipment and pulls out a bat. A voice says, "Stop. You're hurting her." Another voice says, "Do it more." "Everyone was laughing," Leslie remembers, "but I had tears coming out of my eyes." The boys tell her, "This has to be our secret. If you talk, you'll get kicked out of your school, and we'll tell your mother."

Nevertheless, Leslie waits outside the Scherzer house for Paul Archer, her dream date, to show up. He never does.

When Glen Ridge Detective Sheila Byron walked into the squad room on Monday, March 27, 1989, after a week's vacation, she could feel the tension. She was handed a slim file that began with the day Charles Figueroa, a high-school senior, told school officials that he had overheard students talking about a sexual encounter between several athletes and Leslie Faber, a

a buttonhole. Activities the other kids enjoyed didn't interest her. But she was unflaggingly cheerful, and she never cried for her mother. Give it time, said the pediatrician. But in kindergarten, the teacher suggested she be tested.

The results were imprecise. The Glen Ridge school system's Child Study Team chose to inform the Fabers that their daughter was neurologically impaired, a diagnosis that suggested at least a possibility of progress. They did not mention that she met all the criteria for the classification of mental retardation. In 1976, when Leslie entered the Glen Ridge school system, mainstreaming the disabled was the new approach, so Leslie was placed in a class with the other children.

But the other kids knew Leslie was different, and they exploited her. One afternoon, when five-year-old Leslie was looking for someone to play with, a few boys—including the Scherzer twins—called her over. "Got something special for you, Les," one boy said, "something really nice." It was a ballpoint pen, the tip coated with a dark substance that the boys told her was chocolate. Taste it, they urged. When Leslie picked up the pen and caught the smell, she hesitated; she knew this wasn't candy. She didn't want to eat dog feces, but if that's what her friends wanted, she'd do it. She'd do anything for her friends.

As Leslie licked the pen, her eight-year-old sister, Carol*, happened by. Quivering with rage, she pulled Leslie into the house and told their mother what had happened. Ros's first instinct was to call the boys' parents, but she felt you shouldn't complain unless you had witnessed the incident. Also, complaining would only draw attention to Leslie's special condition. So instead she told Leslie not to play with these boys. "But, Mommy," Leslie replied, "they're my friends. They like me."

The boys are all laughing. One calls Leslie a whore. When they are finished, they tell her, "This has to be a secret."

retarded girl. Sheila was shocked, not only by what had occurred but by the names of those involved. They were popular, the best athletes in school. They came from good families: Their parents were the cream of Glen Ridge, active in church, social and civic circuits.

Sheila had never backed away from a challenging investigation. What exactly happened in the basement? Did Leslie say no? Did she even have the capacity to say no? The latter question was answered for Sheila later that afternoon when she interviewed Leslie. "Les," Sheila said, "do you want me to make these boys stop bothering you?" Not missing a beat, Leslie replied, "Yes. Please call their mothers and tell them they're bad boys."

With that answer, all the surface layers fell away, leaving at the core a mentally retarded, emotionally unguarded child. That's a child talking, Sheila thought. A first-grader.

at ten months old, Leslie Faber couldn't sit up. At four years, she couldn't manage to get a button into

A few weeks later, neighborhood boys molded mud into the shape of a candy bar and told Leslie they would be her best friend if she ate it. She did.

Another evening her father asked about the huge red welts all over Leslie's arm.

"The boys were pinching me," she answered.

"Well, why didn't you tell them to stop?"

Head hanging, "I don't know," was all she could say.

In middle school, it was the same story. Leslie was the odd kid out, the butt of all the jokes, the one who always sat alone. In 1985, Leslie entered a special-education class at Columbia High School, functioning at a second-grade level. When she had not progressed by 1987, she was retested: The diagnosis was now unavoidable, and Leslie was reclassified as "educable mentally retarded" and enrolled at West Orange High School, which had an all-day, self-contained class for retarded students. The school psychologist noted that she "may be easily influenced by peers and may not be fully aware of the consequences of her behavior." School officials put it more bluntly: "We're concerned about her being the victim of a sexual attack."

the behavior of the jocks in the Scherzer basement was hardly an anomaly. In junior high and in high school, they had wrecked the home of a classmate at an out-of-control party, trashed the country club, bought liquor illegally and stolen some $600 from handbags at the fancy-dress Candy Cane Ball. None of this was a secret to police, parents or townspeople. As early as the eighth grade, teachers were describing Kevin Scherzer's behavior as "compulsive, rude, disrespectful." Yet his difficulties were generally perceived as normal growing pains. Kyle had similar problems. Paul, an average student with flashes of above-average intelligence, was described as a "follower." Paul's younger brother, Chris, displayed "a tendency to hyperactivity." Many of these boys had academic problems, too. But the unstated policy at Glen Ridge was, as one teacher put it, "Keep the bad kids moving and get them out of your hair."

The jocks quickly became veterans of the Glen Ridge party scene, the essential components of which were alcohol, a house with no adults present, and girls. By junior year, jock parties followed a familiar pattern: While the young women chatted, the boys retreated to another room to watch a porn video. But the ultimate team experience went beyond looking at videos. It wasn't enough for a jock to get what he wanted from one of the girls he considered a sex toy. It was fun only if you could tell your teammates about it, and better still if you could pass her on to them. Some nights one of the jocks would go upstairs with a girl and come down a little while later to declare loudly to his buddies, "I just got a blow job." Then he'd nod toward the stairs as if to say, "You're next in line if you want it." Other times a couple would go upstairs, and some of the guys would follow them, stand outside a door left partly ajar and watch them. They also liked to hide in shower stalls or outside windows where they could watch the girls using the bathroom.

Monday mornings in physical education, the guys would recount their sexual activities and voyeurism over the weekend. "I'd hear it every week," the teacher said. "Their asides to each other were loud enough so everyone could hear. You'd hear them, but as a teacher, what do you do?"

Students at Glen Ridge High have to maintain at least a C-minus average to remain eligible for sports, but none of the jocks had ever been threatened with disqualification because of misbehavior.

Yet Kevin was notorious. One student remarked that as soon as the teacher's back was turned, Kevin would start in: "He'd unzip his pants, expose himself, and then try to get the girls in the front to turn around and look." One girl remembered that when the lights went on after a class film, she saw Kevin smiling as his hands moved under his sweatpants. The teacher merely said in a mocking tone, "There's Kevin, with his hands down his pants."

When a teacher did report such behavior to the vice principal, the boy was brought to the nurse with the expla-nation, "This kid might have crab lice. Call his mother."

It apparently didn't occur to school officials that this aberrant conduct might signal a need for psychological intervention. When Kevin and Kyle were selected as co-captains of the football team and Kyle was made captain of the baseball team, no administrator openly questioned whether they had the character to hold these positions.

by mid-March 1989, a number of people had heard about what happened in the Scherzers' basement. These included Leslie's parents (Leslie staunchly maintained to them that a boy had put his hand down her pants—nothing more); the swimming coach, a classroom teacher, the social worker and the principal at West Orange, where Leslie attended school; the social worker at Glen Ridge High School; and thirty or more Glen Ridge High athletes, male and female, and their friends.

The issue that would trouble educators, parents and students for years to come was this: Why did it take more than three weeks before anyone reported Leslie's experience to the police?

Technically, neither school was legally required to report the incident, because it occurred outside of school, after school hours. But the silence was finally broken when Charles Figueroa, a prominent football player and wrestler, told his special-ed teacher, Ariel Riviera, what he had heard. At a meeting of the Child Study Team on March 22—which included a social worker, several special-education teachers, a guidance counselor, a social psychologist and a specialist in learning disabilities—Riviera spoke up.

it was almost a year before the grand jury returned indictments on Kyle and Kevin Scherzer, Peter Quigley, and Richard Corcoran, Jr. After a protracted battle, an appellate court approved a request to try Paul and Chris Archer and Bryant Grober as adults. By the time the case came to trial, in October 1992, the defendants numbered four: Chris Archer, Kyle and Kevin Scherzer, and Bryant Grober. (Paul Archer and Peter Quigley pled guilty to a misdemeanor charge of endangering the welfare of a mental "defective." Corcoran was to be tried separately, but charges against him were later dropped.)

The trial itself—as Sheila Byron had speculated—focused on Leslie's ability to say no. Experts testified that Leslie felt obligated to go along with whatever a friend asked, even if the "friendship" had begun five minutes ago. Family and acquaintances supported this: Leslie might look disgusted when she had to eat dog feces, she might cry when kids ridiculed her, but she had *never* walked away, responded in anger or even tried to avoid her tormentors.

This very quality, however, made Leslie a less-than-ideal witness: She was easily manipulated by the defense attorneys' pretending to be on her side, and appeared willing to change her testimony to make everyone happy. The defense's strategy was to try to prove that Leslie was a wily seductress with an insatiable sexual appetite.

As the trial progressed, it became clear that Leslie did not

One of the jocks' pastimes was to hide in the shower stalls and watch the girls.

grasp the fact that she could have refused to participate in what happened that day. Asked frequently why she complied, she replied, "I had to" or "because they told me to" or "I didn't want to hurt their feelings."

After a five-month trial, on March 16, 1993, the jury convicted Chris Archer and Kevin Scherzer of two counts of first-degree aggravated sexual assault (in New Jersey, virtually synonymous with rape) and second-degree conspiracy; Kyle Scherzer, of one count of first-degree aggravated sexual assault, one count of second-degree attempted aggravated sexual assault, and second-degree conspiracy; and Bryant Grober, of third-degree conspiracy—but Grober was acquitted of the most serious charges of aggravated sexual assault.

Judge R. Benjamin Cohen sentenced Chris, Kevin and Kyle to a maximum of fifteen years; as first offenders, they would probably serve two. In an even more controversial ruling, considering the gravity of the crime, Cohen permitted them to go free until their appeals were decided—perhaps four years hence. Grober was given three years' probation and two hundred hours of community service.

Five days after the trial, a *New York Times* editorial noted that when it comes to crime, "it seems there's still nothing like being white, middle-class, and suburban to get the benefit of the doubt." But it wasn't only their race and class that got these young men a deal. The nature of their crime also had a lot to do with it.

What happened to Leslie was an act of singular cruelty, but she was not the only one to be abused in Glen Ridge's aggressive culture. The indifference in the community to how girls were being treated by young men robbed many of them of their innocence and their self-esteem.

What happened to Leslie Faber is important because it reveals the extreme outcome of the behavior of young men who are made to feel omnipotent. If a culture is measured by how it treats its weakest members, the Glen Ridge case revealed American culture at its basest.

Editor's note: On May 20, 1997, the New Jersey appellate court overturned one count of the rape conviction of Kevin and Kyle Scherzer and Chris Archer, which charged that the three former athletes had used force or coercion against Leslie Faber. However, the court upheld the charge that they had raped Leslie when they knew, or should have known, that she was mentally retarded.

The sentences of Chris Archer and Kevin Scherzer are not likely to change. Kyle Scherzer's second-degree rape conviction stood, but his sentence will very likely drop to a maximum of seven years, making him eligible for parole after only one and a half years in prison. As LHJ went to press, the judge ordered the three convicted defendants to surrender on June 30, 1997. At that time it is likely they will be sentenced and finally sent to prison, eight years after they raped Leslie Faber.

SEXUAL

VIOLENCE IN THE

BLACK

According to a 1992 study by the National Victim Center, of Arlington, Va., 84 percent of rape survivors do not report their rape and, consequently, many do not get the professional help that can aid in the healing process. Sexual assault is a serious problem in the African–American community. Though Black women are 7 percent of the population, they are 27 percent of rape victims, according to federal statistics. Two African–American counselors discussed the consequences of rape and how it can be overcome.

Rhonda Brinkley–Kennedy is the clinical director of the Rosa Parks Sexual Assault Crisis Center in South Central Los Angeles. Brinkley–Kennedy, 41, received her master's degree in clinical psychology in 1986 from Pepperdine University and her doctorate of psychology from the California School of Professional Psychology in 1992. She has been counseling victims of sexual assault for more than 10 years and continues to train future psychologists on the issue of sexual assault in the African–American community.

Andrea Thompson Adam, 44, is the Crisis Intervention Direct Services Volunteer Coordinator at the Los Angeles Commission on Assaults Against Women. She earned her bachelor's of arts degree in theater in 1975 from Fontbonne College in St. Louis, with a minor in sociology and psychology. Adam has been counseling sexual assault victims for more than six years.

EMERGE: According to the U.S. Department of Justice, a woman is raped every two minutes. Why do some men rape?

THOMPSON ADAM: The first thing about rape is that it's not about sex.

COMMUNITY Healing the SCARS PRODUCES TRAUMA

THAT TEARS AT

BY LOTTIE L. JOINER

Rape is actually about power and control. And people who perpetrate this kind of crime have issues of their own that are driving them to do these things. It's all about having some loss of control within their own lives. This is another way for them to get this control, to dominate someone else in this manner...and compensate for what they don't have in their own lives.

EMERGE: Give me a clear distinction between consensual sex and rape and do most men understand the difference between the two?

BRINKLEY–KENNEDY: Consensual sex means that two adults have agreed to engage in a mutual encounter that's pleasurable to both people. I think men and women are often confused in that understanding. People do not understand the difference between sex, love, consent, power. Our society, in general, doesn't teach us these things. So there lies part of our dilemma.

SELF-WORTH, FAMILY

THOMPSON ADAM: In terms of the way law enforcement looks at it and the judicial system looks at it, rape is, as is stated in most of the penal codes, the act of sex forced on another person without their consent. There

AND GENDER ISSUES

has to be an actual yes given, and if there is no yes given, her not saying yes...leaves room for them to prosecute on a rape charge.

I think there are men who really don't understand what rape is. I mean really don't understand that forcing your wife to have sex, forcing their girlfriend to have sex, forcing somebody that they meet...they don't understand that that is wrong. They don't understand that because society has allowed people to get away with this without any repercussions. So it's been an allowed tradition that a man can take what he wants and a woman simply must deal with that.

When a person says no, regardless of what you may think that person feels about you, the answer is no.

EMERGE: Why is it important for a woman who has been raped to get counseling?

BRINKLEY–KENNEDY: The reason people, especially African–Americans, need to deal with the trauma of sexual assault in one's history is because it does not go away. It will impact your children. It will impact all relationships. It will impact how you see the world and especially how you see yourself.

We have women who are walking around, especially African–American women, with so much pain they don't even know they have because we have carried the weight of the world for so long that our attitude is "get over it." The women come in and they feel ashamed for feeling pain. We don't know how to say, "I hurt."

this is an objective third party who has nothing vested except your well-being.

EMERGE: You don't hear much about male rape, but it does occur. What does rape do to a man's psychological and emotional well–being and how does he deal with this?

BRINKLEY–KENNEDY: We really have increased our male–client population, believe it or not. I understand that this whole issue is often a childhood issue and the boys are taught not to talk about these things. All I have to do is go into the drug treatment facility and ask the right question about when a big brother or big uncle did the wrong thing or did the thing that wasn't quite right. They didn't know what to do with it at the time and never dealt with it. We have so many men now from our recovery system who are knocking at our doors. Men are now understanding that if they're going to move forward in their lives, they have to deal with the traumas in their lives. They're very cautious. They just don't call up and say, "I was sexually assaulted." ...They do handle it differently.

One of those ways is...feeling out of control. If you ask the rapist, they are going to tell you that they come from a history of sexual assault, the majority of them. One way is to act out against another [person]. Another way is substance abuse. Another way is to mistreat others in different kinds of ways, maybe, that might be to abandon their own children, and then do some other things. So

Rape will impact all relationships. It will impact how you see the world and especially how you see yourself.

We don't know how to say, "You hurt me." We know how to say, "You piss me off," which is just a mask for pain anyway. But we do not know how to say, "I'm hurting." And we have been hurting for a long time.

THOMPSON ADAM: And one of the things that we also have to address is the fact that for so many of us, talking about things that happened that are considered personal is so taboo. You don't go outside the family. You don't go outside and tell people your business. You don't share this kind of information.... Trying to get our people into counseling is a major struggle. It's a major struggle because they can't feel the freedom to unburden themselves to somebody that they don't know. Being a professional doesn't make any difference. You can have the 26–letter alphabet behind your name and have all the credentials and schooling in the world, but if that person cannot relate to you on a very personal level, the chance of your doing any type of treatment with them is out the door.

Another thing that we have to address within our own communities is the fact that sometimes the best person to tell is not somebody in your family. Sometimes the best person to talk to about

yes, men do have that history. Yes, they must come to terms with it if we are going to ever feel safe. We must help men deal with that history and let them know that it's okay to talk about these issues.

EMERGE: When a high–profile person in the community is accused of rape, how does that affect gender relationships? What about the sense of loyalty to race?

BRINKLEY–KENNEDY: We would be happy to support all of our men if they were all doing right. But you know what? Black, White, Latino, Asian, there is no race where they're all doing right or they're all doing wrong. So we have to take each one of them on individual merit. What we have to do is be willing to look at the fact that some of these people are not the saints we want them to be. On the issue of these young girls making accusations against these men and people saying, "Well why was she doing this, and why was she doing that?" I'm sorry, but regardless of what she did, she may be guilty of making a stupid choice, she may be guilty of dressing inappropriately, that does not mean that she deserves to have whatever happens happen to her. We have got to get away from that [mindset].

EMERGE: What is more common in the African–American community, rape by a stranger or someone that the victim knows?

THOMPSON ADAM: It doesn't make any difference whether it's an African–American community or any community. The majority of rapes occur with people who you either know or are acquainted with or even have a passing relationship with. Most of the time, the people who rape are people who have watched you for a day or two, a week, or something. They know something about your behavior, something about your habits, because what happens is that a lot of these petty people pick prey and they acquaint themselves with behavior. So it's almost like they're stalking their prey before they commit the act. There is a very small percentage of people who are raped by onetime strangers who absolutely have no connection to them whatsoever.

EMERGE: What are some of the ways the African–American community handles rape?

BRINKLEY–KENNEDY: Well, first of all, we want to say it doesn't happen. That's the first problem and I think that's one of our biggest denial issues. The other issue is that the majority of rapes happen by someone you know, and to add to that, in the home. Also, the rapist picks people who they feel they can overpower, because it's about power and control. That's why men don't rape men unless they are gang–raping men, because the issue is I don't pick someone that I think I'm going to lose to. They take the woman who looks confused, who looks distracted, the vulnerable. But the biggest piece we have in our community is denial. In the Black community, and I think all communities, they assume that rapists have these neon lights on that say, "I am a rapist." When rapists are people who are living next door to you. This is a scary thought for us. We want to feel safe. So we have the myth that it has to be somebody that is somewhere else. And the other thing, too, with the Black community is that we don't understand the impact, even if we believed it happened. We also believe that it's not a big deal. We do not understand the connections between something — someone assaulting you today — having an impact in your life tomorrow. So part of it is just even if I can say, "yes it happened, I'm sorry it happened," we still don't understand the importance. But because we don't see blood, we just sweep it under the rug and say, "Okay, you know, get over it, you're going to be okay," and that's part of the problem.

EMERGE: Why do some men who may spend a large amount of money on their dates assume that the woman is obligated to have sex with them?

BRINKLEY–KENNEDY: Our society has taught them that. They're grown up on thinking that, first of all, they should be able to have sex on demand, period. They've also been taught that that's all women think about and that's all they really want but they're saying no because they have to play coy. It's like an "I do this for you so you're going to do this for me" kind of belief system. Unfortunately, women believe it, too.

It's really the way we raise our children. It's the way we pretty much are as a society.

EMERGE: What are some safety measures that women should practice to avoid or prevent being raped?

THOMPSON ADAM: For our organization, when we talk about self-defense, we don't talk about women simply learning how to do physical exercises and defense movements to protect themselves. We talk about a woman using her mind... all of her senses to take care of herself. You want to be aware. You want to be alert. You want to think before you put yourself in any situation. So we have to be cognizant of every little thing. That's part of what our self-defense program teaches women. It's not all about getting in there and learning how to kick butt. This is a good thing, but that's not enough. We have to be aware on all levels and no one is saying that you can't make mistakes, that's fine, just learn from whatever mistakes you do make. It's going to take a lot of time and energy to make women believe that they have the right to say no.

EMERGE: Justice Department figures indicate that a large number of rapes occur among children. Is that true for African-Americans and how do we protect our children?

BRINKLEY–KENNEDY: Yes, it is true, and there are many ways we can protect our children. One is to be more involved with our children. Two is to understand what the signs might be of any kind of abuse going on. Sometimes we don't look at our children when their behavior changes and so we don't know what the signs are. Teachers don't know what the signs are. We don't know the impact of it so, therefore, we're not even looking for it, we're not even understanding that it could possibly happen. So yes it's higher for our children, and it's really clear to me when I talk to women.

EMERGE: What can we teach our children to combat the problem of rape?

THOMPSON ADAM: One of the things is we not only have to educate our children, we have to educate the parents. But the other thing, too, is that we can't just do this with women. We have to do this with the men. The men have to take as active a part as the women. Because who are the people who rape? And how can a woman make a man understand it?

You have to be willing to teach your boys and girls the same thing. You have to be able — be willing — to teach your son, just as you would teach your daughter, what it is to respect another human being. If you do not touch that child and love that child and hug that child, then that child is not going to know to touch, hug, or love anybody else. That's where it comes from. One of the most important things is that we have got to make our children understand that they are worth something. They are worth something, and you can't put a dollar figure on it.

BRINKLEY–KENNEDY: We have to sensitize ourselves to dealing with this issue. It's a hard thing because it means a shift for everybody, not just for women or just for the people dealing with this, but for everybody, for an entire community.

Lock Up Your Sons! This Is the Sexual Revolution

Young women of the 1990s are having sex far earlier and have many more premarital partners than any previous generation of women. And they don't give a damn if he stays the night.

Kate Fillion

Sarah is twenty-four but still has the improbably large eyes and coltish grace of adolescence, so it's easy to imagine her as she was ten years ago, flushed with the sweet arrogance of the baby of the family. She had won a scholarship to a ballet school far from home and she was going to be a star, just like her mama always said.

The ambience at the school was heady, particularly for a girl from a small town where everybody knew everybody else's business and where, if you were daring enough to sneak down to the quarry looking for trouble, your parents somehow heard about it within the hour. At the school, so long as you could dance until your calves knotted up and then keep on dancing through the pain, no-one seemed to care what else you got up to. Sarah and her friends tiptoed around the dorm at night, listening, wide-eyed, outside the doors of the older girls—impossibly glamorous creatures who said "f . . ." and drank cheap jug wine and climbed out the windows looking for adventure. "It was probably not the healthiest atmosphere," she reflects, " living with a bunch of sixteen- and seventeen-year olds who were basically running wild."

When Sarah herself turned sixteen, she was ready to do more than just eavesdrop. She was bored, she was restless, and she had come to a conclusion: "I was never going to be Gelsey Kirkland." Her Achilles tendons were too short and her breasts—the breasts she had once prayed for—were too large, at least by the minimalist standards of ballet. Overcoming these physical limitations would have required a desire so fierce that just thinking about it made her tired She didn't care if she never saw a pair of pointe shoes again. Life was passing her by.

She stopped daydreaming about curtain calls and started painting her nails blood-red and scaling down the side of the residence with the other girls who were lucky enough not to have braces or pimples or a flat-chested inability to pretend they were a day older than sixteen. They headed off to the local college bars with fake IDs they were never even asked to produce, ordered drinks with what they hoped was a jaded

air, and set their sights on the big-game trophies: college men, so worldly and sophisticated.

After a few of these excursions, Sarah found a boyfriend and did not draw the line where she had previously drawn it, at everything-but. She went all the way with Mark, who was twenty-three (the number had such a weighty, pleasing ring that she found a way to work it into every conversation), but he didn't have to talk her into it. There was no talking her out of it. Yes, she had the usual fears – sex would hurt, she would be bad at it – and the physicality of the enterprise struck her as so preposterous that she couldn't imagine much ecstasy in it. But she was sixteen, *practically all grown up*, so she got the Pill and hurled herself into sex as though it were a test of courage.

After the first few times, she was surprised to find that she was rather enjoying herself. "Let's do it again," she'd prod Mark, wanting an instant replay of that moment when he flung his head back and moaned her name. He was so old, so wise, so good-looking – she stumbled dreamily through her classes counting the minutes until she would see him again, not caring that she was falling behind. School was so trivial compared to the wrenching violence of her feelings.

She didn't take Mark seriously at first when he announced, after only a few months, that he was tired of dating a sixteen-year-old. She was so accustomed to getting her own way that she assumed he must be joking. "My mother instilled confidence in me, and going to the school gave me even more confidence. What I didn't have was an ability to accept failure," Sarah says now. "My reaction to failure was to quit. If I couldn't have exactly what I wanted and if I couldn't be the best at something, I just gave up."

Quitting, in this instance, meant giving up on the whole idea of love. What was the point, if love meant letting someone get close enough to hurt you so deeply? Then, after a few days of steeping in her own misery, she had another question: how *dare* he? She would show Mark, make him see what a fool he'd been to dump her. She could have any guy she wanted.

"I'd finally realized that I could *make* guys notice me, *make* them trail around after me, *make* them come to my room at night. It was like, 'Gee, these guys are so dumb!'" Sarah says. "I slept with a very long string of guys from my school and the college on the day I met them. At first, I was a textbook case of equating love with sex, but when they didn't fall in love with me on the spot, my attitude was, 'To hell with you, I never want to see you again.' I was completely screwed up, drinking a lot, and after a while it just turned into a big power trip. I went a little bit crazy, drawing guys in and basically using them."

Many of her classmates were doing the same thing, drinking and sleeping around and not thinking much about anyone aside from themselves. "It's weird because this was the late eighties and dancers were dropping like flies, dying of AIDS, but none of us connected that to our own behaviour," she says. "We must have been the most deluded people on the planet."

In her clique, the coolest thing of all was to sleep with someone and then brush past the next day as though nothing had happened. For Sarah, this wasn't much of a stretch. "Even while I was having a one-night stand, I was already targeting who the next person would be," she remembers. "I just wanted to get as many guys as possible."

She liked best the moments before any physical contact, sitting in her room babbling away and pretending not to notice that the guy could barely concentrate, his brain was so clouded with desire. The air was charged and she felt the thrill of complete mastery: *his fate is in my hands.*

"After the first kiss, I got very little out of it," she recalls. "But I felt like I had to go ahead – not because they pressured me, but be-

was and how the men didn't know what they were doing," Sarah says. But, she insists, "They weren't using me. I was using *them.*"

Many social scientists hypothesize that girls like Sarah suffer from low self-esteem: *promiscuous girls are insecure and desperate for affection, not sex.* Some feminists would add that part of Sarah's problem was false consciousness: *a young woman who gets off by turning men on has merely eroticized her own oppression.* Pop psychologists who theorize that men are from one planet and women from another would diagnose her as seriously deluded: *a promiscuous girl can't use boys, since she's only giving them what they want – no-strings sex.* Conservatives might claim her behaviour proves that the sexual revolution and the breakdown of the traditional family have hurt women: *she was infected by the virus of immorality.* Liberals might contend that Sarah's in denial: *her innocence was exploited – the boys were older, after all, and didn't use condoms.*

Thirty years after the sexual revolution and the modern women's movement began, female sexuality is still presumed to be reactive rather than active, cuddly rather than carnal, and essentially romantic rather than purely physical – in short, the opposite of male sexuality. In the public discourse, girls want love, not sex (presumably, no teenager in her right mind has sex for its own sake), and female sexual agency is discussed in speculative, maybe-some-day-in-the-distant-future tones. Although boys who sleep around are considered sexual agents, in control of and accountable for their own behaviour, girls who behave the same way tend to be pathol-

Most women

responded to a man's reluctance to have sex with a range of classically "masculine" tactics: telling them how enjoyable sex would be, sulking, and claiming they were too aroused to stop.

cause I pressured myself." Being a tease did not fit in with her new image of herself as an erotic champion. About the sex itself, the best she can say, after lengthy consideration, is, "Well, it wasn't *horrible.* I got off on the idea that they'd remember this night with me for the rest of their lives, but I didn't get a million orgasms, that's for sure. Basically I just faked it, pretending they were pleasing me and I was wildly turned on, when really, they weren't doing a thing for me."

But telling a man how to please her seemed to defeat the whole purpose of these conquests. It would be an admission of need and, besides, she didn't want to lose control, the way she had with Mark. Watching a man give himself over to pleasure, while she simulated ardour and remained unmoved, seemed a form of radical sovereignty.

Her emotional detachment was, in fact, a source of pride. "Once it was over," she reports, "I always kicked them out. I would go through the typically male thing: how soon would it be polite to ask them to leave? I never let them spend the night."

She relished recounting these exploits to her friends, dwelling on the men's buffoonery and ineptitude, how easy they'd been to fool and how surprised they'd been afterwards, when she displayed no interest in seeing them again. "When I think of locker-room conversations, I think of men talking about how they scored and how great it was, and women talking about how disappointing it

ogized as victims. Girls are supposed to be morally superior to boys, and thus we tend to ignore evidence of female agency unless it happens to involve a happy ending.

But self-determination, sexual or otherwise, has nothing to do with morality, and it's never been a guarantee of happy endings. Agency merely consists of the power to make choices, which can, in practice, simply mean the power to make mistakes.

Sarah, for one, insists that she did have this power. "I don't blame anyone but myself," she says of her "experiments," and offers a fairly simple explanation for them: "I was young and dumb." For her, sex had little to do with love and even less to do with subjugation. Sometimes it was just another weird thing that happened when she was blasted, sometimes she viewed it as a sporting event, and sometimes it seemed like a good way to have an intense connection with a boy while keeping him at a safe emotional distance. Taking the Pill and seeking out partners instead of waiting to be chosen – and then dumping them unceremoniously after they had fulfilled the purpose of feeding her ego – made her feel powerful and cool.

If she had it to do all over again, she wouldn't. Yet Sarah still frames her adolescent adventures positively, as learning experiences. "I certainly wouldn't recommend promiscuity, because I think you're probably doing it for the wrong reasons. I mean, I can't imagine why anyone would want to sleep with that many people," she explains. "But the bottom line is that if I hadn't slept around, I'd always wonder what it would be like."

Most young women don't simply wonder any more. For one thing, they don't have to: traditional societal restrictions on women's sexuality have been undermined by new norms of equality, new educational and professional opportunities, the availability of reliable contraception and legal abortion, and the permissiveness ushered in by the sexual revolution. For another thing, most girls don't want to wonder; they want to find out for themselves what all the fuss is about.

Female sexual attitudes and conduct have changed – dramatically – over the past thirty years, and continue to change. In fact, the behaviour of a young woman in the late 1960s or early 1970s, when the rallying cry was "Make love, not war," was quite unlike that of a young woman in the 1990s. Young women today are *far* more adventurous: they start having sex at a younger age and have many more premarital partners than any previous generation of women.

The reality is that, by a number of measures, young women today act more like men of any age than like their mothers and older sisters. Consider the findings of the National Health and Social Life Survey (NHSLS), popularly known as the "Sex in America" study, which was published in 1994 and touted as the "definitive" and "most comprehensive" sex survey ever conducted. Unlike the Kinsey and Hite reports, which relied on the responses of volunteers, the NHSLS was based on exhaustive face-to-face interviews with Americans who were selected at random and then approached by the researchers. About eighty per cent – 3,432 men and women aged eighteen to fifty-nine – agreed to participate. The more random the sample and the higher the response rate, the more representative and scientifically accurate a study is considered to be.

The NHSLS, then, was big news, and was widely reported as providing conclusive proof that the sexual revolution was over. *Time* magazine's cover story was typical: "There may have been a sexual revolution... but the revolution turned out to have a beginning, a middle and an end." According to *Time*, Americans were having much less sex than anyone dreamed, and the roles of the traditional sexual script had not been recast: "Over a lifetime, a typical man has six partners; a woman, two."

But the media missed the real scoop, failing even to mention one of the survey's most striking findings: there is an enormous generation gap in women's sexual behaviour. Relatively speaking, the conduct of men has changed only modestly over time. For women, however, the story is very different. The youngest women in the NHSLS, those born between 1963 and 1974, were almost twice as likely as women born just ten years earlier – and six times as likely as those born thirty years earlier – to have had multiple sex partners before the age of eighteen. A minority were virgins when they turned eighteen; twenty-three per cent had already had one sex partner, twenty-five per cent had had two to four partners, and ten per cent had had five or more. Furthermore, the gender gap in terms of sexual experience, which had been substantial for previous generations, was far smaller among the youngest group. Only eight per cent more men than women had had multiple partners before they turned eighteen, and the difference was concentrated at the top of the scale, with more men than women reporting five or more partners.

By the age of twenty, three-quarters of the youngest group of women had had multiple sex partners; one-third had had four

or more. In short, most twenty-year-olds have already had at least as many sexual partners as *Time*'s "typical American woman" has in her whole lifetime. In fact, the youngest women in the NHSLS behaved more like the "typical man." Again, the only statistically significant difference between men and women born after 1960 was at the high end: roughly equal numbers had had between one and nine partners, but more men than women had had ten or more partners by the age of twenty.

Unfortunately, because of the way the NHSLS data are presented, it's impossible to tell how many sexual partners in total the youngest women have had since the age of twenty. But statistics on their behaviour in the twelve months before the survey provide solid evidence that unmarried women continue the pattern established in their teens. Sixty per cent of those under the age of thirty were single when the survey was conducted; twenty-five per cent of them reported having had two to four partners, and an additional six per cent had had five partners or more, *in the previous twelve months.*

Other studies amplify the unheeded message of the NHSLS: far from being over, the sexual revolution is actually picking up speed. In 1992, according to the Centers for Disease Control and Prevention, fully one-third of fifteen-year-old American girls had intercourse—an astonishing 100-per-cent increase over 1980 and a 560-per-cent increase over 1970.

Equally rapid change is being charted in terms of traditional gender differences. For instance, after studying more than 400 heterosexual college students, sociologist Ilsa Lottes reported in the academic journal *Sex Roles* in 1993 that "there were no significant gender differences in age of first intercourse, frequency of intercourse, oral sex participation, prevalence of coitus, oral and anal sex, rating of how often their partner satisfied their sex needs and desires, and reactions to recent intercourse."

On average, the women in her study were twenty years old, happy with their sex lives, and experienced: one-half had had four or more sex partners. They were also "beginning to assume roles once thought to be only appropriate for men": the vast majority had asked men out and paid for dates, and virtually all had split the bill on a date. This is a remarkable change from just ten years ago, when researchers reported that only a minority of women were sharing date expenses, much less shouldering them entirely or asking men out.

Furthermore, three-quarters of the women – and equal numbers of men – told Lottes that men and women should be equally responsible for initiating sex. Again, this is a significant change. In a similar study of university students published in 1985, seventy-eight per cent of men but only fifty-nine per cent of women believed that both genders should initiate sex equally; forty-one per cent of the women but only eighteen per cent of the men thought men should be primarily responsible for initiation.

The women in Lottes's study were talking not just about initiating sex in established relationships, but about making the first moves in new relationships. More than one-third said they had initiated sexual involvement with new partners; more than two-thirds of the men reported experiences in which women made the first moves. This too is a major shift: throughout the 1970s and early 1980s, researchers consistently reported that men almost always led the charge to the bedroom.

Numerous other researchers report that another type of behaviour once considered uniquely masculine – pressuring a reluctant partner into sex – is, in fact, practised by young women, too. For instance, in studies conducted by psychologist Charlene Muehlenhard, an ardent feminist and leading expert on sexual coercion, more young men than women reported that they had had unwanted sex: sixty-three per cent versus forty-six per cent. The reason isn't simply that young men don't feel entitled to say No, but that young women are determined suitors and, like men, sometimes misread their partners' signals.

For example, psychologists Lucia O'Sullivan and E. Sandra Byers asked 201 men and women aged eighteen to twenty-nine

like young men, yet continue to think like "good girls"; they have sex, then try to convince themselves and anyone who will listen that they did it because they were swept away by love.

Currently, large numbers of young women are paying lip service to "feminine" roles they're not even following. For instance, ninety-two per cent of the female undergraduates in Ilsa Lottes's study declared that emotional involvement is necessary for sex "most of the time or always"; forty-four per cent of them also said that they

Young women

act like young men but continue to think like "good girls": they have sex and then try to convince themselves they were swept away by love.

whether they had experienced "disagreements in which a woman attempted to influence a reluctant man to engage in sex" within the past year. As they reported in the prestigious *Journal of Sex Research* in 1993, more men than women said yes: sixty-four per cent compared to forty-nine per cent, which suggests that some women are unaware of the extent to which they attempt to influence partners to have sex.

Most women responded to a man's reluctance with a range of classically "masculine" tactics: touching, flattering, pouting, sulking, talking about their "real feelings" towards their partners, telling them how enjoyable sex would be, and claiming that they were too aroused to stop. Conversely, the men's perceptions seem downright "feminine": two-thirds said they were reluctant to have sex because it was too early in the relationship or the relationship was "inappropriate."

But despite all the evidence that the gender gap in sexual behaviour is narrowing, traditional stereotypes continue to be repackaged, recycled, and reinforced in best-sellers and box-office hits, greeting cards and academic treatises, sitcoms and everyday conversation. Women speak one language, we're told, and men speak another; women want love, men just want to get off. Loving saints and lusting rakes, blushing maidens and brutish villains – oppositional ideas still attract, not least because they hold out the promise of resolving the messy complexities and ambiguities of real life.

Understandably, given the doubt, guilt, fear, shame, anxiety, high expectations, and confusion attached to sex in our society, a script that tells us what sex is supposed to mean and how we should play our roles will have mass appeal. And in the prevailing script, with its good girls and bad boys, there's something for everyone: men are reassured of their power, and women are reassured of their moral superiority.

Although most young women and men aren't actually following this old-fashioned script, it may very well still guide their thinking. "We expect our lives to follow certain scripts, and we make an effort to follow them, too," explain sexologists Judith Long Laws and Pepper Schwartz. Thus, for instance, large numbers of young men have unwanted sex because they fear seeming unmasculine and because they figure that they *ought* to want it.

"We also try to make our experiences accord with these scripts, sometimes even reinterpreting reality so as to make it fit them better," Laws and Schwartz add. In other words, even when we deviate from the sexual script, we usually refer back to it to explain what we've done. So, for example, many young women act quite a bit

had had casual sex. Since half had already had four or more sexual partners, they either possessed an extraordinary talent for falling in love or they were breaking their own rules on a fairly regular basis.

Desire, apparently, is still a dirty word to many young women. This isn't terribly surprising given that they learn defensive sexuality – how to say No, how to react to boys who want sex – but aren't taught to think of themselves as sexual agents. Consequently, many are confused by and ashamed of their own sexual stirrings, and don't have a clue about what it means to own their sexuality. Instead, they continue to subscribe to the tidal-wave theory, in which women are compelled to have sex by forces of nature they are powerless to control: romantic love and/or the male sex drive.

Being swept away is, among other things, an excellent first-line defence against guilt. Moreover, girls who invoke tidal waves can plead modesty – *I didn't really want it, I wasn't in control, I don't have those kinds of appetites* – while boasting: he really wanted to, he was so turned on by me. Every young woman gets to be the star of her own drama, the irresistible erotic lure who drives men wild, but also gets to be the good girl, the one so well bred that she never aches to be touched, never actively seeks sex, and never feels the surge of raw, carnal desire.

Ironically, girls often seem to wind up making bad decisions precisely because they are trying so hard to persuade others – and themselves – that they aren't actively making choices. Each year, more than a million North American teenagers become pregnant, and it's the same old story: large numbers tell researchers that they didn't keep contraception on hand because doing so would have indicated that they expected and wanted to have sex. Far too many girls still seem to believe that it's more shameful and more harmful to admit to desire than it is to become pregnant or risk exposure to sexually transmitted diseases.

Clearly, sex education isn't working with this group. Nor is it effective to appeal to them on the grounds that they have a responsibility to their bodies. After all, many torture their hair, experiment with drugs and alcohol, race around without helmets on bicycles and without seat belts in cars, stay up late and subsist on candy bars, or starve themselves until they faint in history class. Telling them that sex may make victims of them doesn't work when the other option seems to be eternal love; tossing condoms their way doesn't do much good when they're frightened to admit that they even want sex – they don't use them.

What girls desperately need are some positive images of women desiring, women as sexual subjects, women taking charge – and taking responsibility. Currently, many don't even have a realistic idea of what female sexual pleasure looks like. Instead, they have some half-baked notions from Hollywood films in which there is zero foreplay and women are portrayed as ecstatic enthusiasts of intercourse.

Frankly, if girls were taught that the minimum requirement for getting into bed with someone is being able to articulate one's own sexual desires, many would wait a whole lot longer to have sex – and more would use birth control. Even adults who are long past the acute self-consciousness of adolescence find it difficult to say "I want" or "Touch me here" or "This is how I like it." You have to trust your partner to make those kinds of requests; you also have to honour your own sexuality and take some responsibility for your own pleasure.

Girls need new messages about sexual pleasure, namely, that they are absolutely entitled to it and are most unlikely to get it if they feel they have to pretend they don't have desires – and if they're so terrified of being judged that they won't even take basic contraceptive precautions. So long as girls learn that the female role is to attract, some, like Sarah, will think that it's cool to rack up conquests, even joyless ones. If, however, she had learned that sex without pleasure is totally uncool and immature, it wouldn't have taken her so long (or so many partners) to figure out what she now believes: a steady sexual partner has a far better idea of what she likes and a far bigger investment in pleasing her than a man she's just met and is only planning to sleep with once.

If we want teenage girls to make good choices, we have to start acknowledging just how many choices they have and move away from the simplistic notion that sex has only two meanings for women: love or subjugation. We need to encourage them to think of themselves not as members of the "same" sex, all of whom share a unitary sexuality, but as individuals who have the right to define for themselves what sex means. The truth of the matter is that gender does not necessarily dictate what one does, when, where, why, with whom, and how one feels about it before, during, and after. In fact, sex stubbornly resists easy cate-gorization precisely because motives, behaviour, and responses are so strongly influenced by socialization, past experience, external stimuli, and deeply personal idiosyncrasies, emotions, fantasies, desires, and sensations.

Even for a person who has only one partner in his or her lifetime, sexuality is not a fixed trait like height or eye colour. It varies depending on one's mood, appetite, health, feelings about one's body, and feelings towards the other person. Just as most of us exhibit a wide range of behaviour throughout our lives – aggressive with the boss who steals credit, passive with the critical father – we also exhibit a range of sexual behaviours and experience a spectrum of sexual feelings and responses.

Sex can be motivated by excitement or boredom, physical need or affection, desire or duty, loneliness or complacency. It can be a bid for power or an egalitarian exchange, a purely mechanical release of tension or a highly emotional fusion, a way to wear oneself out for sleep or a way to revitalize oneself. Sex can be granted as a reward or inducement, an altruistic offering or a favour; it can also be an act of selfishness, insecurity, or narcissism. Sex can express almost anything and mean almost anything – to men and women.

If we want girls to behave responsibly, we have to honour the individual complexity of their sexuality, educate them about their sexual choices, and acknowledge that equal rights entail equal responsibilities. Girls don't need a sexual script. Rather, they need a gender-blind standard of accountability, in which agency is defined not in terms of happy endings but in terms of having the power to make choices – including bad ones.

If women want sexual self-determination, we have to resist, strenuously, the temptation to flee from responsibility because equality does not look the way we thought it would and power is not as glamorous as we'd hoped. Most important, we must reject entirely the myth of female moral superiority. It is, in the end, a lie that costs us nothing less than everything: our power to choose a new kind of future for ourselves, one in which we are more than victims and less than saints, fully human, and the equals of any man.

Cyndi Potete's Fire and Rain

Cyndi Potete came to Fargo to build a new life. Instead, she became the first North Dakotan ever charged with attempted murder by HIV. Amid this spring's devastating floods, she talks about the firestorm that nearly ended her life.

BY NANCY EDMONDS-HANSON

The ground shivers beneath the pounding convoy of heavy equipment. Under Fargo's steel-gray April sky, an army of volunteers shoulders the muddy muscle of the Red River of the North back between its slippery banks. Truckloads of men and women—outfitted in duck-hunting waders, in jeans and college sweats, in National Guard green camo—are fighting side by side to construct a wall of sandbags and clay to shelter their community from the punishing floodwater that surges against its front door.

Scarcely a hundred yards from the flood-fighters' beachhead, Cyndi Potete looks away, biting back tears. She's talking about another time, another torrent—the rush of mud and shame that invaded the safe, small-town haven she'd fashioned for herself and her two children.

"It ruined everything... everything good in my life," she says.

Two years ago, during a cloudy April not so different from today, Cyndi Potete unwittingly made history. Swept away on an ill-fated alcoholic binge, she became the first person ever in the taciturn, rock-steady state of North Dakota to be accused of attempted murder with a singular and controversial weapon: HIV. Amid a firestorm of newspaper headlines and television newscasts, she stood accused of not informing a sex partner she had AIDS.

No matter that she had grappled for years to turn back her own torrent of demons—childhood abuse, a shame-shadowed decade on the street, half a lifetime of dependency, first on drugs, then alcohol.

No matter that shortly before the accusation that would damage her forever, Cyndi was finally tapping a wellspring of inner strength that seemed ready to draw her into life's sun-dappled shallows. Her courageous campaign of rural AIDS education—christened Positive Voices—was winning her friendship and respect. Only a week before, she and colleague Cody Rogahn had accepted the J. C. Penney Company's prestigious Golden Rule Award for outstanding volunteer service. She had received a commendation from President Clinton a few months earlier: "You stand as an inspiration for people everywhere who desire to improve our world."

To no avail. Cyndi's hard-won gains were washed downstream on that lost weekend. What had begun badly enough with falling off the wagon after nearly a year of sobriety quickly turned into outright disaster. Arrested for the alleged "crime" of having unprotected sex with an old acquaintance she met in a bar, Cyndi was charged with attempted murder under an untested and ill-conceived six-year-old state statute intended to control transmission of HIV.

Suddenly—in a small-town setting where everybody knows everybody else's business—the 40-year-old divorced mother of three was dragged into the spotlight. Though the charge was later dropped for lack of evidence, the damage was swift and seemed irreversible.

But Cyndi Potete is a survivor. Against the odds, she had created the kind of life that eluded her for much of her youth.

From *POZ* magazine, August 1997, pp. 58-61, 80, 81. © 1997 by POZ Publishing, L.L.C. Reprinted by permission.

Here, in a conservative Midwestern community that seems the mirror- opposite of the hard road she had known. The flood of publicity threatened to sweep her away. But when it ebbed, she was still standing, sturdy and determined as the sun broke through.

Today, curled up in a booth at the Fryin' Pan Restaurant, this cheerful mother of three—warm, witty, achingly direct—draws strength from an unending confrontation with a foe she has not faced alone. HIV positive for nine years, a PWA for seven, she still struggles against her brush with notoriety—perhaps the most devastating blow of all.

She has brought friends to offer moral support as she plunges deep into dark memories. Cody and his partner, Jon Yarbrough, are there as a touchstone, for they know who she really is: A brave woman, survivor of a brutal past, generous in sharing both pain and hope. Together they give AIDS a face among rural people who rarely recognize that HIV is as much a part of the flat-as-a-tabletop North Dakota landscape as the normally lethargic river now roaring its fury.

Ironically, AIDS is the foundation on which Cyndi has built the strong family of friends that gathers around her. Facing up to her illness provided the impetus for turning her life around—for raising her younger son and bringing her daughter home for good, for settling down and tending close friendships, for mending some family fences and especially for finding a larger purpose in her life in AIDS support and education.

"If I could take any one thing out of my life, it wouldn't be AIDS. I didn't really have a life before AIDS," Cyndi reflects. "What I'd take away would be the alcohol. Sober, I don't do crazy things. I'm really a very nice person. The whole court thing would have never, ever happened—unless I was drunk."

Until the incident in 1995, in fact, Cyndi Potete was well known throughout the area. Her name was becoming almost synonymous with responsible, enlightened understanding of AIDS. Billing themselves Positive Voices, she and Cody— along with their friend Gary Stevenson, who died of AIDS in 1994—had carried that message to almost 25,000 young North Dakotans and Minnesotans.

Small-town school superintendents and college professors had invited them to share their message at more than 70 high schools, at least 15 colleges and universities, and in community and parent forums. They brought AIDS awareness to towns ranging from tiny Flasher (pop. 317) to Wahpeton (nearly 9,000) in North Dakota to Moorhead, Minnesota (almost urban at 30,000).

Their twofold message: AIDS is very real and walks among us, even here on the sparsely populated plains, and the only surefire protection is abstinence. Part of their credibility rests on Cody's personal background of 19 years as a rural school superintendent, part on their certification by the American Red Cross as HIV/AIDS educators. Most of all, they are welcomed. Frank but nonthreatening, authoritative but sincere, they're pre-paring the youth of remote mid-America to cope with risks that neither distance nor ignorance can keep at bay.

Cyndi and Cody's visibility in telling others how to stay safe gives Cyndi's story the tang of irony, ultimately tinged with hope: How the AIDS educator was caught in currents she teaches teens to avoid—and how her pain became instructive, opening discussion of a topic rarely touched in places like North Dakota.

The number of North Dakotans with AIDS is minute. Just 200 cases have been reported to the State Health Department from 1985 through the first quarter of this year. Fewer than 10 percent are women.

Cyndi became the first, in 1988.

Only days before getting the news, Cyndi had arrived in North Dakota at the lowest ebb of her life. Thirty-three years old, she stepped off the flight from Illinois having already logged several lifetimes' worth of urban pain. The nearly treeless Red River Valley offered unexpected refuge. With nowhere to hide, Cyndi at last could confront her demons and build the stable life she sought.

She was emerging from a brutal past. Kicked out of her home by a father who had long abused her, Cyndi had lived on the streets since her teens. She had worked as a prostitute, losing custody of her first child to her stepmother, who adopted and raised him.

Cyndi had married and then divorced a drug-addicted pimp who beat her, and had given birth to a daughter, Tarsi. Her daughter, too, eventually wound up in relatives' care. Along the way, Cyndi got hooked on heroin and cocaine. She served time in the Illinois State Penitentiary for felony theft, becoming pregnant with her youngest child, J.J. (known as Duke), while out on work release.

Paroled, she slipped back into life on the edge—the only life she knew. Within a few months, she was homeless and wasted, mother of a newborn, looking forward to nothing. No shelter. No hope.

Estranged from most of her family, still she turned to them for help. Her stepmother, several sisters and brother lived in a tiny farming town half an hour north of Fargo. There Cyndi called Tracy, the sister to whom she's closest, and begged her to talk the family into letting her come home.

"At first Tray said no," she remembers. She pauses, then sighs: "I do understand why. Can you imagine the fallout they'd have to deal with—having someone like me in a quiet, conservative place like North Dakota?"

Reluctant at first, Tracy at last persuaded the family to relent. They were there at Hector International Airport in Fargo to meet Cyndi as she stepped off the plane. They hugged her, hustled her into the car and drove her . . . not home but straight west to Jamestown, North Dakota, where they committed her to the state hospital to receive treatment for chemical dependency.

"I was wild. Believe it or not, I'd never been in treatment before," Cyndi says. "I was having withdrawal real bad when

I got there. But after a couple of weeks, I could tell I was getting better. I was feeling good, beginning to see that light at the end of the tunnel. Turns out, it's a train headed straight at me."

Among the papers she'd signed upon admittance was consent to be tested for HIV. She didn't remember signing it, and so was stunned when a counselor delivered the news: She was HIV positive. She was making history: The first HIV positive woman in North Dakota.

Not only that—her tiny son was at risk of becoming the state's first infant HIV statistic.

"This was nine years ago, remember, and no one knew much about AIDS," Cyndi says. "I was just speechless. I remember it so clearly: Where we were sitting, how the counselor looked, how he was trying to reassure me—y'know how it is when they know you're going to croak. I prayed to God down on my hands and knees that my baby would be OK. But God doesn't always answer prayers the way you want." Duke tested positive for antibodies to the virus.

Cyndi could only think of running—from her family, from the tatters that were left of her life. "But I thought, if this was what I'd done to my innocent little baby, the least I could do was be there when he died."

So this time, she didn't run. She faced her problems head-on with a determination that amazed the new friends she was gathering around her. She completed treatment, then moved with her son into a YWCA shelter in Fargo. Two months later, she had rented her own apartment, was holding down two jobs, had enrolled in college and had gotten the very best news of her life: Her son no longer tested positive for HIV. Babies are born with their mother's antibodies, and the last traces of Cyndi's had cleared. Without HIV antibodies of his own, this meant Duke never actually had the virus at all.

Duke was then nine months old. And a new Cyndi had grown strong enough to raise him, regaining daughter Tarsi along the way.

Life was coming together. Cyndi had given up illegal drugs for good, though she still struggled with alcohol. Duke's father had come to Fargo to live with them—a "good-hearted man and a good father," she says, though they no longer live together. Despite developing full-blown AIDS in 1990, she was working toward an associate degree as an administrative legal secretary. She had friends, a job, a life and a mission. Through Positive Voices, she was making a real difference.

Then a disease breached the defenses she'd built against her past. Not AIDS—alcoholism.

The weekend that changed everything began with one bad choice. She should never have gone to the Bismarck Tavern, a semi-tough bar on the north edge of Fargo's six-block downtown district. She should never have sat down with Tim Martin, a heavy-drinking ex-boss she hadn's seen in years. She shouldn's have had one beer, or the next, or any of those that followed—especially since even the first beer violated conditions of her five-year probation.

Days later, she awoke sick, naked and alone in the back of Martin's pickup camper. Ashamed. Embarrassed. About to be charged with attempted murder.

During their binge, the two had stayed at the apartment of a mutual friend—a drifter whom Cyndi had met and befriended at the HIV support group. He reported her drinking to her probation officer. Still blurry on what had happened, she was taken into custody for that violation, while police arrested her companion for DUI.

A Fargo police detective interviewed Cyndi at the local detox center. Her blood alcohol level was .17, almost twice the legal standard for intoxication. "I remember how uncomfortable he looked. He loosened his tie, squirmed around and finally blurted out, 'I've never had to do this before,'" Cyndi recounts. "Then he informed me that it's illegal in North Dakota to have unprotected sex if you're HIV positive and don't tell the other person.

"I told him that Tim and I hadn't had sex, at least as far as I could remember—it's all sort of a blur to me, even now."

But the erstwhile friend who'd turned her in carried another, far more graphic tale. He told police he'd watched them have unprotected sex—defined as attempted murder under a 1989 state law that had never before been tested. (The state's governor signed in April a new law that goes even further: It allows judges to jail people and *then* test them for HIV if they are suspected of exposing others to the virus.)

Was the friend's story true? Cyndi denied it from the first. Others' stories vary: Some witnesses recalled Martin's boozy boasts, back at the bar, about the naked woman in his pickup camper. They say he invited his buddies to use her. A very different version came from a female witness, who remembered seeing Cyndi fending off Martin's attempts to have sex.

Cyndi was sent back to the state hospital's chemical dependency unit. While there, her counselor broke the worst possible news: Not only was she in trouble for drinking while on probation, she was being accused of attempted murder.

Cyndi fingers the front-page newspaper story that brought the tale scathing public attention in her adopted hometown. We're in the living room of her duplex on a pleasant, tree-lined street on the south side of Fargo. Three eight-week-old kittens scramble for the door as daughter Tarsi, 18, arrives home from school and heads for the kitchen.

Her mother is still deep in dark memories of two years ago. "Now, if I was so out of it in the back of his camper—if the sex ever did happen—what is that?" she questions. "Was I raped? I sure was in no shape to give my consent. We were both totally wasted. Am I more responsible than the guy who may have raped me?"

Yet the state's attorney never asked her if she wanted to file charges. Nor was Martin himself tested for HIV.

The most unbelievable part of the charge, given Cyndi's commitment to education, was the allegation that she had hidden her condition from the man. "After all, I'm a Red Cross-certified HIV/AIDS educator," she points out with a wry grin. "I'm a lot more likely to stand on a table and shout it out in front of *everyone*."

But the nightmare was real. Reporters from around the country would soon be dogging her steps from the Cass County Jail to the courthouse. As friends, including the stalwart Cody, struggled to shield her, members of the national media lined the corridors. Bookers for TV talk shows jockeyed for her attention. Writers called her in her jail cell. A photographer for a metropolitan daily captured her distress in a color photo that ran on the front page: Blue eyes wide with anguish, the well-known AIDS activist is peering out from behind bars.

"It was awful, just awful," reports Cody, who stood beside her throughout her public ordeal. "Cyndi was just shattered. And her poor children!"

Public reaction formed two camps—one predictable, the other a more heartening measure of the growing understanding of AIDS. While some clearly shunned her, friends and strangers alike spoke up on her behalf. People whom she'd never met wrote letters to the editor of the local daily newspaper, castigating the state attorney's decision to pursue his tenuous case. The potential penalty of 20 years in prison, they said, amounted to a life sentence for a woman with AIDS. A spokeswoman for the North Dakota State Health Department opined that the whole incident was being handled inappropriately. Behind the scenes, ACT UP/Minnesota organized a letter-writing campaign pressuring the prosecutor to drop the case.

At school, Tarsi (whose last name, unlike Duke's, is Potete) received the support of several concerned teachers and her good friends. A few less-benign classmates did slyly ask her to spell her last name, wondering if the woman in the news was her mother. "The name Potete is real out-there," Tarsi volunteers. "Around here everybody is a Johnson or an Olson."

"So what did you tell them?" Cyndi asks curiously.

The lovely 18-year-old gives her mother a typical teen-age look of exasperation: "That you didn't do it, of *course.*"

Her confidence, it turns out, was well-placed. The legal drama quickly turned to farce when it reached the courtroom. Martin—who has a criminal record of his own—denied that they'd had sex; when he'd told the story to police, he said, he'd just been bragging. He added, "Cyndi's a nice person. I've known her a long time. She used to baby-sit my kid." He turned toward her and apologized: "I didn't want to be here, Cyndi. They made me." (Martin in fact had to be subpoenaed to appear.)

Next, the so-called "witness" who'd turned Cyndi in to probation recanted his story. He'd been, he claimed, misunderstood.

Faced with his star witnesses' failure to support his case, the state attorney dropped charges. The attempted murder case was dismissed. But the probation violation was more problematic. Cyndi was sentenced to a year and a day in the North Dakota State Penitentiary. She served six months, followed by three more at a Fargo halfway house.

Though the legal nightmare was over, the damage had been done. Cyndi Potete had become, for the moment, a seeming parody of the responsible behavior she had worked so hard to inspire. She's learning to hold her head up again: "I made a mistake. I paid for it. It's not who I really am."

She adds: "The paper made it sound like I was out there trying to pick up this fine, outstanding citizen and give him AIDS. That's not like it was at all, in any way. Yet this is like being accused of child abuse. Even if you're innocent, people always sort of think you did it. And Fargo people are real reserved. They're too polite to ask. I wish they would, so I could answer them. You always wonder what they're thinking."

Cody believes that even in her pain, Cyndi was sharing a gift with the community. "Despite the terrible price Cyndi paid and what she suffered, the incident has probably had a positive effect overall on awareness of HIV and AIDS in North Dakota," he says. "There was very little discussion of the disease in the local news media before all this happened. A lot of information was made available, and anyone who honestly went looking for knowledge now has a much better understanding."

Of battles fought across the landscape of her life, Cyndi's plunge into North Dakota's legal system may have been the most bitter—facing her apocalypse just when she had something to lose.

But as sure as April's floods turn to mud in May, as sure as warmth and sun dry tears, the resilient AIDS activist has begun to re-emerge on the other side. Buoyed by her own strength and caring friends, she is recovering her confidence and firmly keeping her demons at bay.

She is desperately determined to avoid alcohol. Recently she convinced her physician to prescribe Antabuse, which produces a sensitivity to alcohol so violent that even one swig of a beer results in copious vomiting, dizziness and other reactions. "He was worried about what Antabuse would do to me—you know, with AIDS and all," she says. "I told him that alcohol could kill me long before AIDS gets the chance." For once, luck was on her side: Unknown to her or her doctor at the time, Antabuse is now being studied for its anti-HIV effect.

Cyndi is back: Reaching for hope, resurrecting her mission, taking pleasure in the self-respect and accomplishments she has fought to preserve against long odds.

She holds no grudge against the state. She is comfortable in Fargo, where she holds to the high ground, and where her story (the whole story) cannot drown her buoyant spirit.

"I like the community. I like the neighborhood. I like having my kids go to schools without guards standing at the door," she says. "You might find some ignorance here, but it's nothing that can't be cured with education."

North Dakota is the only place she's ever lived with AIDS. It's where she has carved out a home, forged friendships, fought against the darkness and found hope she shares with those who know her well. "To survive AIDS, I need people around me who care. I have that. I have wonderful friends. I want to be an individual . . . to be somebody . . . to do good things," says Cyndi Potete, who's waded through deep water to reach the firm ground beneath her feet. "I'm not just a number here. In North Dakota, despite everything, I know I still can make a difference."

S e x   i n   t h e   M i l i t a r y

WINGS OF DESIRE

The Air Force's star female pilot finds herself enmeshed in a tale full of passion and lies

By NANCY GIBBS

THE MILITARY DEMANDS FROM ITS SOLDIERS an old-fashioned marriage, a vow to love, honor and obey. Love, full of sacrifice and hardship, to the point of risking your life and taking other people's lives in your hands, in the belly of your bomber. Honor, through every large and small token of respect: keep your hair short, press your shirt, shine your shoes, salute your superior. And above all, obey without question even the rules that break your heart.

The strange tale of First Lieut. Kelly Flinn has been packaged as a passion play about the man she loved and the job she lost as a result. She has been cast as a victim by a culture that exalts love first and then negotiates honor and obedience. But the military inverts the scale and ranks duty above all else, a marriage under crossed swords. The Flinn case is less a struggle between two people than a conflict between two codes of conduct. The facts weren't much in dispute, only what to make of them.

From *Time*, June 2, 1997, pp. 28-34. © 1997 by Time Inc. Magazine Company. Reprinted by permission.

From a distance, Flinn's story, of a luminous Air Force star who committed adultery, lied about it and disobeyed orders to stop, offers everyone something to believe in and rail against. Those who believe that a sexist Pentagon is holding women to a different standard than it has held generations of men before them were glad to see someone take the system on. Those who believe that the public and especially the press don't understand the unique nature of military culture were grateful that the Air Force wouldn't

Morning America "to convey our story." The family had built a Website to solicit contributions for her legal-defense fund and invite readers to E-mail Congress or Kelly with their support. The letters, phone calls and editorials were running heavily in her favor; politicians from both sides of the aisle were blasting the Air Force for conducting a witch-hunt. Senate majority leader Trent Lott, no softy on matters military, declared the previous day that the Pentagon was clueless. "I mean, get real: You're still deal-

solid. That morning a defiant Air Force Chief of Staff, General Ronald R. Fogleman, had thrown down the gauntlet before a Senate committee in a statement that Spinner claimed poisoned any chance of a fair military trial. "This is not an issue of adultery," Fogleman said. "This is an issue about an officer, entrusted to fly nuclear weapons, who lied. That's what this is about."

The Air Force case doesn't suggest the story of a girl who lost her heart to a cad; its account is of an officer and a vixen. The setting is made for mischief—the cold prairie city of Minot, where all winter long the blizzards howl maddeningly across the frozen North Dakota plains. More people moved out of North Dakota than any other state in the country, according to a survey by Allied Van Lines last year. It's so cold in the winter that the funeral homes stockpile bodies in special warehouses and wait until the earth thaws to dig the graves. Other places welcome spring by dancing around a Maypole. In North Dakota they have lots of burials.

"This is an issue about an officer, entrusted to fly nuclear weapons, who lied. That's what this is about."
—General Ronald R. Fogleman

bend the rules for someone entrusted with a plane carrying 70,000 lbs. of nuclear bombs. Everyone can identify because up close, no one involved—not Flinn, her lover, the Air Force, her unusual array of supporters—is without some merit or without some blame. And so last week it made sense to both sides to just call the whole thing off.

THE TURNING POINT CAME IN A MEETING last Wednesday night. Flinn's lawyer, Frank Spinner, was in his room at the Best Western Safari Inn in Minot, N.D., when the call came from Washington: no way was Air Force Secretary Sheila Widnall about to let Flinn resign with an honorable discharge. So several hours after dinner, Spinner sat down with Kelly and her family to look at her choices. He knew what Kelly would say: she would want to fight. She thought she had been abused, not just by the con man she claims lied to her but also by the Air Force. Her crime, she had explained in a letter sent to Widnall a few days earlier, was to fall for the wrong guy. "I truly fell deeply in love with a man who led me down this path of self-destruction and career destruction. . . . I only want to serve my country and be forgiven for my human faults."

Flinn, 26, maintained that she was being made an example; that was nothing new, though until now it had always worked in her favor. After graduating as most distinguished in her training class, she became the Air Force "showgirl," as she put it, the first woman ever to pilot a B-52, the one picked to fly the Air Force Secretary around on her visit to the base. Known as BUFF, for Big Ugly Flying Fellow (or a more colorful variant), the B-52 is the largest bomber in the Air Force, 488,000 lbs. of titanium, aluminum and steel, rigged with eight Pratt & Whitney engines and a 35-ton payload.

Flinn had learned to be a good pilot and a good fighter, and once she came under fire from her chain of command, she wasn't about to crash. That Wednesday, her mother Mary and brother Don had done the *Today* show, and her Uncle John had gone on *Good*

ing with human beings. I think it's unfair." Flinn was being "badly abused," Lott said, and at the very least deserved an honorable discharge.

But Secretary Widnall said no, and that night, as the family gathered once more in the Holiday Inn, it was Spinner's job to unravel their optimism. "You have to think about jail," he said to Flinn. If found guilty on all charges, she could face as much as 9-½ years in prison. "The closer you get to the courthouse steps, the more the reality sets in," Spinner told TIME later. "And in a criminal trial, the closer you are to the courthouse steps, the closer you are to the jailhouse."

The p.r. battle had taken a bad turn that day as well. Just when the whole affair was looking like a victimless crime, out stepped Gayla Zigo, deceived ex-wife, who alone among the contestants had played the game by the rules. Her letter to Secretary Widnall about her husband's affair with Flinn had leaked that morning; it gave the story a new twist. Gayla wrote that when she discovered Flinn's love letters to Marc, she complained to her supervising sergeant. When the affair continued, she felt outmaneuvered and overwhelmed. "How could I compete with her?" the wife wrote. "She had power, both as an officer and academy graduate. She also had special status as the first female B-52 pilot." Clearly frustrated, Gayla continued, "I am tired of Lieut. Flinn acting as if she is the victim, when she is the one who committed the crimes." Flinn last weekend had a response. She told TIME, "Airman Zigo is not a victim of me, but she is a victim of Marc."

The prosecutors were planning a bare-knuckle attack. They planned to drop the adultery and fraternization charges, the focus of all the public outrage, in order to deny Flinn the high ground in the media wars. Instead, they would go after her on the counts of lying to investigators about her affair with Zigo, disobeying a direct order to stop seeing him, and conduct unbecoming an officer—charges the Air Force believed were rock

There's not much to do on a Saturday night in Minot. Flinn wouldn't date fellow officers, she said; it wouldn't be professional. And anyway, there are few places to go. The drive down to Bismarck for crab legs at the Red Lobster takes an hour and a half. Minot offers darts or billiards at the local taverns and a bowling tournament every Friday night. Flinn's favorite bar was a college and Air Force hangout called Peyton Place.

THE AIR FORCE VERSION OF EVENTS starts not with Zigo but with a wine-tasting party Flinn gave last June for her soccer team. According to a prosecution report made available to TIME, among the guests was Senior Airman Colin Thompson, whom Flinn had met a few months before. During the party, the report alleges, Flinn and Thompson had sex on the lawn of her residence; then Thompson spent the night. According to the report, Thompson claimed that Flinn, his superior in rank, told him that she knew what they did was wrong but that no one would ever find out about it. It was this encounter that gave rise to the fraternization charge against her.

Just days after that party, Airman Gayla Zigo arrived at the Minot Air Force Base with her husband Marc, who was hired as the base youth sports director. Marc and Flinn met when he too joined a soccer team. Gayla says she and Marc had dinner with Flinn and Thompson and another couple after a soccer game on June 30. She recalls Flinn and Thompson flirting, joking about marriage. "She said, 'Where's my ring?' and held out her hand," Gayla remembers. Thompson fashioned a paper ring out of a napkin, and he put it on Flinn's hand. Gayla says Thompson had drunk too much to drive home, so after dinner Flinn drove him.

Flinn's mother says Kelly had dated a lot but had never really fallen in love. That all changed with Zigo. On July 3, about three days after Marc and Kelly met, the report alleges, Marc and Gayla had an argument. Marc telephoned Flinn, who invited him to her house. "Less than a week after we arrived to the base," charges Gayla, "Lieut. Flinn was in bed with my husband having sex." Flinn insists the relationship was not "consummated" until August. But Gayla's fears were magnified when she found a letter alluding to that July day. "I want to spend the rest of my life beside you, walking through life hand in hand," Kelly wrote to Marc. She even enclosed a picture taken the next morning, July 4. "You have my heart, soul, mind and body . . . you are my soul mate. You make me whole." Flinn explains that the love notes were a signal of her affection for Marc—a signal that he demanded in exchange for his own sentiments.

A week later, Flinn helped the Zigos move into their new home. In the weeks that followed, Gayla says, she often came home to find Kelly there. "I began to wonder if she ever went to work because she was always there," Gayla says. On July 11, she says, Marc came home drunk from a bar, and they got into a fight. Marc called Flinn, who offered to come pick him up. While she sat crying on her stoop, Gayla says, the bomber pilot drove up in her Honda Accord and whisked Marc Zigo away.

man, told a superior that an officer was trying to steal her husband, the Air Force had to go on alert.

The affair boiled over in November, when another officer, First Lieut. Brian Mudery, was brought up on charges of sexual misconduct and assault, and proceeded to point the finger at other officers for similar misdeeds. None of his accusations panned out—until investigators got to Flinn. She made a pact with Zigo to deny their affair and gave base police several sworn statements that she and Marc had no sexual relationship. She didn't know that Marc was busy making a statement of his own.

By the time Marc was done, he had given investigators the full tour of Flinn's privacy, a map of where and how and how often they had had sex. Four days later, on Dec. 1, he tried to kill himself by taking sleeping pills and stuffing a rag in the exhaust of his car. But he left the garage door open and called Gayla from the car phone. In the hospital, he finally admitted the affair to her, and she announced that she was through with him. When Kelly went to see him, says Ann Dell Duncan, a clinical psychologist who evaluated Kelly later in February, Marc told Kelly, "If you leave me, I'll hurt you and I'll kill myself." When Zigo left the hospital, Flinn took him in. She bought a new car—the Jeep he'd always wanted. He was living in her house on Dec. 13 when Flinn's commander, Lieut. Colonel Theodore LaPlante, ordered

when she heard about the court-martial. "She was devastated," Duncan says, especially because the Air Force p.r. officer had apparently released the information without advising Flinn first. "She hadn't thought the Air Force would treat her that way." Duncan viewed Flinn as "competent, careful, capable of handling external emergencies and unequipped from her training in the Air Force Academy to deal with personal emergencies. I think the academy prepares pilots and military personnel. What they don't do is prepare people," says Duncan, who designed family-advocacy centers for the Air Force in the 1980s.

Once the case became public, it was the Air Force and its rules that went on trial first. Even though Flinn had been given several chances to extricate herself from the whole business if only she would stop seeing Marc, the case soon became one of sex discrimination in the service. Connecticut Republican Representative Nancy Johnson complained in a May 19 letter to Widnall, "It is disgraceful that Lieut. Flinn's career as a [bomber] pilot will be over simply because overzealous prosecutors targeted her case over numerous others with more egregious circumstances." New York Democratic Representative Carolyn Maloney wondered "if an equally accomplished male pilot had made the same mistakes, how many high-ranking Air Force members would have looked the other way?"

For Widnall, 58, the first woman to be Secretary of the Air Force, the case was a nightmare. She canceled a trip to Greenland and England to work almost full time to defuse the time bomb. Defense Secretary William Cohen was silent on the issue, fearing that if he made so much as a peep, he'd be drawn into it by appeals from Flinn's lawyers. As for the White House, former Clinton adviser Dick Morris says, "If you're going to talk about adultery on the one hand and the military on the other, those are two reasons [the President] should stay out."

On Monday, Flinn and her lawyers submitted a request to resign in lieu of a court-martial on the condition that it be an honorable discharge. The petition was rushed up the Air Force chain of command in three days, lightning speed in the military bureaucracy for such a request. On Tuesday, Widnall put the Flinn court-martial on hold while she considered the request. An honorable discharge was out of the question; there would be practically a mutiny in the senior officer corps if she allowed such blatant favoritism for an officer charged with these offenses. In private with Widnall, Air Force General Fogleman was even blunter than he had been before the Senate. This was an issue of integrity, he told the Secretary. Forget adultery. The Air Force's core values were at stake. Officers don't lie.

So it was that Pentagon lawyers phoned Spinner Wednesday night with word that the

Kelly realized that the career she wanted so badly was over

After Gayla found one of Kelly's love letters to Marc in his car, she felt she had to act. She took the letter, along with others (one of which had come with a key to Flinn's apartment attached), to her supervisor, First Sgt. Kathleen Blackley. It was at this stage that Flinn was offered her first escape hatch. Blackley confronted Flinn with the evidence and warned her that if she didn't break off the affair, Blackley would report it to Flinn's commanding officer. Prosecutors claim that Flinn told Blackley she knew she was in the wrong and promised to "cease contact" with Marc. Blackley decided to let the matter drop.

Had that been the last of it, the affair might have ended like most adultery cases, privately, discreetly, without official sanction. Of the 67 Air Force court-martial cases in 1996 that involved adultery, only one did not include other counts, like sexual assault or disobeying orders. When an affair involves an officer messing around with a civilian marriage, officials tend to look the other way. If Marc and Gayla had been separated—as Marc had convinced Kelly they were—there would probably have been little intervention. But once Gayla, an enlisted air-

her to have no further contact with Marc. Flinn signed a statement acknowledging she understood the order. A week later, Kelly took him to Georgia for Christmas to meet her parents.

It was not until the end of January that Flinn finally learned how much Marc had told the investigators. She learned a lot more about him too. It turned out that four months after he married Gayla, he was charged with beating her, in a case that never went to trial. He had lied about where and when he was born, his life, his career, nearly everything.

Flinn threw Marc out of the house and found herself a lawyer. Lieut. General Phillip J. Ford, commander of the Eighth Air Force at Barksdale Air Force Base in Louisiana, approved a recommendation that she be court-martialed. Ford could have slapped her with a "nonjudicial," or administrative, punishment, such as a reprimand or reduction in rank, which is what senior Air Force officials in the Pentagon now wish he had done. Instead, on Feb. 25, Flinn was ordered to stand trial.

Flinn was in the middle of a three-day psychological evaluation with Duncan, which was recommended by her lawyer,

request was rejected. By 11 p.m., Kelly and her family had gathered with Spinner at their hotel and were arguing that she should quit the fight and pray that the Air Force would agree to give her a general discharge, not an other than honorable one. "Kelly being a fighter, her first inclination was to fight all the way," says her father Don of the session. "But we said it was pretty much that if she won the fight she might lose the war."

Kelly left the hotel about 1 a.m. Half an hour later, her two brothers drove to her house to remonstrate, reminding her that she was "dealing with a force that did not have a face and that we do not have control over." One of her chief concerns was the fate of the next person to face an ordeal like hers if she didn't carry the fight all the way. "She was frustrated," says brother Don. "And yes, there were tears." Finally, at 3 a.m., she seemed to cave in quite suddenly. She would take the general discharge.

And at last everyone went to bed.

"Kelly is prepared to sign," brother Don told Spinner the next morning. Widnall, meanwhile, was at the Pentagon, where she worked out with weights, then pedaled furiously on her exercise bike to think through the final decision she would make. By 5:30 p.m. she went before the cameras to announce the resolution. "Although it is the adultery charge that has received the greatest public focus," Widnall said, "it is the allega-

tions of lack of integrity and disobedience to order that have been of principal concern to the Air Force. It is primarily those allegations that have made an honorable discharge unacceptable."

Flinn leaves the service with a stigma on her service record. By military definition, a general discharge is given to someone whose "service has been honest and faithful," according to military regulations, but when "significant negative aspects of the member's conduct or performance of duty outweigh positive aspects of the member's military record." Since she is resigning so soon after graduation, Flinn will have to repay about 20% of the cost of her Air Force Academy education, or about $19,000.

For all the anguish, Spinner was elated after the deal was sealed Thursday. He told Kelly that in all his adultery or fraternization cases, none of his clients had got off so lightly. As he and the Flinn family lashed out at the Air Force in the press room Thursday afternoon, about 15 Air Force men and women stood silent in the back, looking stern, sad and angry. "This goes against everything I learned in basic training," said a young enlisted man as he left the room.

Minutes later, Marc Zigo, who had returned to Minot to testify against his former lover, called a press conference of his own, which Kelly's parents attended. "Don't worry," Kelly's mother Mary told an anxious

Air Force spokesman. "Our dignity is not worth sacrificing for this man. We just want to hear what he has to say." And so they stood outside behind the wall of cameras and microphones, as the man who helped wreck their daughter's career belligerently declared that Flinn was no abused victim. "At no time was a gun to Lieut. Flinn's head," he said. He admitted that he had lied about his life and offered apologies to his family and his former wife; he had not a word of remorse for Kelly.

Gayla Zigo is on her own. To supplement her pay, she took a second job—working the front desk at the Holiday Inn, where the Flinns have been staying. Meanwhile, Peyton Place has become a sort of informal clearinghouse for Kelly's civilian-job offers, which have been pouring in from all around the country. On Friday, the Air Force ordered her to relinquish the locker containing her survival gear. Flinn ended the week deluged with book and movie inquiries, and certain she has a story that bears retelling. Or that is too much to bear. "I just want to get in my Jeep and go," she told TIME. "I'll probably throw some outdoor gear in the Jeep, put the top down, get myself a dog and go."

—Reported by John F. Dickerson and Kevin Fedarko/Minot Air Force Base, Julie Grace/Chicago and Douglas Waller/Washington

THE

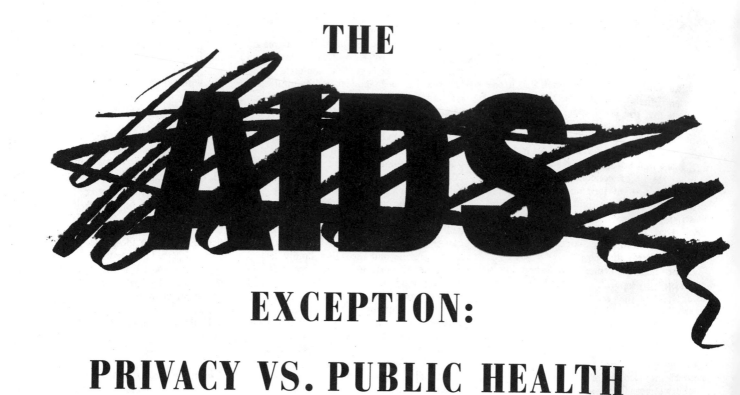

EXCEPTION:

PRIVACY VS. PUBLIC HEALTH

by CHANDLER BURR

EPIDEMIOLOGY, which encompasses both the systematic study of infectious disease and the implementation of the means to contain it, is something of a medical oddity. As dependent on statisticians and politicians as it is on medical-care providers, and often used at times of desperation, by practitioners who have been accorded police and in certain cases military powers, epidemiology has sometimes had to strike a balance between the harshness that may be required to control infectious diseases and the civil liberties of people whose rights may be subject to abridgment.

Since the turn of the century, with the introduction in this country of bacteriological testing and the establishment of boards of health, standard public-health measures have been deployed against infectious diseases. These measures, leaving aside the extreme step of holding people in quarantine, have typically included at least some of the following: *routine test-*

> *It's time to stop granting "civil rights" to HIV— and to confront AIDS with more of the traditional tools of public health*

ing for infection, often undertaken without explicit patient consent; *reporting* to local health authorities of the names of those who test positive for infection; *contact tracing*, or the identification of any people who may have been exposed to infection; and *notification* of these possibly infected people that they may have been exposed. Some combination of these four practices has been commonly applied against outbreaks of infectious diseases, including typhoid, diphtheria, and tuberculosis, and against upsurges in sexually transmitted diseases. It would be surprising if, out of all the viruses and bacteria that can do us significant harm, one was exempted from the scope of these measures. It would be even more surprising if the one chosen pathogen was responsible for an epidemic that today constitutes the leading cause of death among all Americans aged twenty-five to forty-four.

This very thing has, of course, happened, largely in order to accommodate civil-rights concerns. The practice of traditional public health has been to a great degree suspended for acquired immune deficiency syndrome and for human immunodeficiency virus, the virus that causes it. Although various traditional public-health steps are being taken against AIDS and HIV, in differing combinations from state to state, the result is a chaotic patchwork—one that is inadequate, a growing number of critics say, to the task of containing and eradicating AIDS.

"We have convinced ourselves," Ralph Frerichs, a prominent epidemiologist at the University of California at Los Angeles, wrote in a recent issue of the journal *Epidemiology*, "that the fight for survival can be waged in a way that is socially acceptable but not always biologically credible." Many public-health officials, he contended, "have remained steadfast in their commitment to programs and approaches that have hidden the identity of HIV carriers but have failed to halt viral transmission"—a commitment that is in the end bound to prove self-defeating, "making winners of the virus but losers of people."

THE PRICE
OF COOPERATION

WHAT is known in the field of public health as AIDS exceptionalism has been maintained in legally and programmatically direct ways and also in complex and subtle ways. Its origins are not difficult to ascertain.

When AIDS first surfaced, in the early 1980s, it was indisputably a disease of urban male homosexuals (and, to a far lesser extent, of intravenous-drug users). Public-health authorities, faced with a fatal, communicable disease whose method of transmission they did not understand, desperately needed the cooperation of the infected—as they would in any epidemic. In the case of AIDS, however, the infected eventually became disinclined to cooperate. "In the first months and years of the epidemic," the journalist Elinor Burkett, the author of *The Gravest Show on Earth* (1995), recalled not long ago, "people with AIDS died in the hallways of hospitals, where nurses wouldn't touch them. They were kicked out of their apartments. Insurance companies canceled their policies. Their bosses fired them. They had no idea how to get Social Security disability payments or Medicaid."

The discovery of HIV, and the development of a test that could detect it, brought matters to a head. In the aftermath of anti-gay persecution and even violence, the price exacted by a terrified gay community for cooperation in even a rudimentary public-health effort was ironclad anonymity. In 1985, shortly before the federal government was to announce the licensing of the first test for detecting HIV, the National Gay Task Force and the gay civil-rights group Lambda Legal Defense and Education Fund filed a petition in federal court to delay this action, pending a legal guarantee that the test would not lead to widespread screening aimed at gay men. They then

DOES AN ABSENCE OF ROUTINE TESTING, REPORTING, AND NOTIFICATION MEAN THAT A LOT OF UNDISCOVERED AIDS AND HIV CASES ARE FESTERING IN THE LARGER SOCIETY? YES.

put pressure on the Food and Drug Administration, which along with the federal Centers for Disease Control (now the Centers for Disease Control and Prevention, and henceforward referred to as the CDC) had been made aware of eager queries from school districts hoping to use the HIV test to identify and fire gay teachers. The FDA quickly acceded to the demand that the HIV test be used not to screen and identify people for HIV infection in systematic campaigns but only to screen the blood in blood banks.

Out of the threat that the HIV test posed to privacy grew a rigid resistance to almost all HIV testing without consent—and a public-health approach to combating AIDS characterized by considerable delicacy. The FDA's agreement to restrict how the HIV test could be used resolved, temporarily, a political problem. Left unanswered, as Randy Shilts, in his book *And the Band Played On* (1987), observed, was "the broader public health question of how you can control a disease if you decline to find out who is infected." Shilts went on, "In this poisoned atmosphere, the nuances of long-term consequences for control of the infection fell low on the list of gay concerns."

The result, ultimately, was the effective suspension of traditional public-health procedures for AIDS, which is to say, there would be no routine testing for HIV; the reporting of the names of the HIV-infected would be required only in some places, and would miss the epidemic's hotspots; and contact tracing and notification would as a result be greatly handicapped, and in many places pursued in desultory fashion if at all, often in the face of opposition. All efforts were to be voluntary—dependent on educational outreach and persuasion rather than on systematic procedures. "U.S. officials had no alternative but to negotiate the course of AIDS policy with representatives of a well-organized gay community and their allies in the medical and political establishments," Ronald Bayer, a professor at the Columbia University School of Public Health, wrote in a critical retrospective some years ago. "In this process, many of the traditional practices of public health that might have been brought to bear were dismissed as inappropriate."

A NUMBER of opportunities present themselves for the routine testing of people for various diseases by public institutions, routine testing being defined as testing that can be performed without a person's explicit consent. Pregnant mothers are routinely tested for tuberculosis, hepatitis B, and syphilis; testing for chlamydia and group-B streptococcus is also common under certain circumstances. Newborn babies are routinely tested, without the mothers' permission, for phenylketonuria and hypothyroidism. Patients admitted to hospitals may undergo a variety of blood tests, depending on their symptoms, the tests being performed as a matter of course, without necessarily informing the patient or asking explicit permission. Although a patient can at any time refuse to undergo a routine test, he or she does not have to be specially notified that the test is being done or given a specific opportunity to refuse.

HIV testing, in contrast, is almost always voluntary—which means it is done either at an anonymous-testing site or with a person's explicit permission (and which usually means also that the person being tested must sign a release). At the federal level HIV testing is required only of immigrants entering the country, foreign-service and military personnel, and federal-prison inmates. At the state level routine testing is prohibited everywhere except under narrowly defined circumstances. Marcia Angell, the executive editor of *The New England Journal of Medicine*, and a proponent of routine testing in some form, says, "Having to ask specifically has a huge effect, and it is a clear difference between AIDS and many other diseases."

Making even certain subpopulations the target of routine testing would turn up large numbers of infected people who currently escape detection. In a 1992 *New England Journal of Medicine* article Robert Janssen and his colleagues at the Division of HIV/AIDS at the National Center for Infectious Diseases recommended voluntary targeted testing for HIV in certain hospitals, a policy well short of routine testing and yet one that has been implemented virtually nowhere. They wrote,

> We estimate that about 225,000 HIV-positive persons were hospitalized in 1990, of whom only one third were admitted for symptomatic HIV infection or AIDS. Routine, voluntary HIV testing of patients 15 to 54 years old in hospitals with 1 or more patients with newly diagnosed AIDS per 1,000 discharges per year could potentially have identified as many as 110,000 patients with HIV infection that was previously unrecognized.

Testing that is merely voluntary may also miss populations that disproportionately need to be reached. The people least likely to have the virus are the most likely to say yes to a test, and the people most likely to have it are the most likely to say no. In one study infection rates were 5.3 times as high among people who refused HIV testing as among people who consented to it.

One might ask, How could a study give the infection rate of those who refused the HIV test? The answer demonstrates the methods that researchers—in this case, at the New Mexico Health and Environment Department—must employ in order to obtain data without violating personal rights as protected by law. Voluntary, anonymous HIV tests were offered over a three-month period to all patients visiting a sexually-transmitted-disease clinic. Eighty-two percent of the patients consented to being tested for HIV. To determine the rate of HIV infection among those who did not consent to testing, researchers located serum that had been taken from these patients for syphilis testing, removed all identifying information, and then tested the serum for HIV.

Exceptionalists argue that routine testing will "drive AIDS underground"—make people avoid the health-care system altogether. There is no empirical proof that this will or won't occur to a greater extent than it already does, under a voluntary regime. Ultimately one must ask whether people who would go underground because of perceived self-interest should dictate policy—and also whether such people would cooperate in disease-prevention efforts under any circumstances.

W HY does testing matter? The most basic epidemiology holds that early knowledge of where a virus is moving—into which populations—is essential to slowing its spread. Even if a disease cannot be cured, knowing who the infected people are may help prevent the transmission of the disease to other people. Geneviève Clavreul, a California-based consultant to the International Cancer and AIDS Research Foundation, says that because of testing and reporting restrictions the California Department of Public Health is in essence "flying blind" in its epidemiological tracking. By law or regulation, cases of certain sexually transmitted diseases and of many other infectious diseases must be reported to state departments of health, and the names of the infected are in most cases provided and are always held in confidence. HIV is the exception. Although the disease called AIDS must be reported by name in all fifty states, infection with HIV, the virus that causes AIDS, need not be: only twenty-six states mandate the (confidential) reporting by name of positive test results for HIV, and these states tend to be ones with modest caseloads. Twelve states—including California and New York, by far the two worst-afflicted states—have no broad reporting requirements for HIV.

KNOWING WHO IS INFECTED WITH AIDS AND HIV IS ESSENTIAL IN HELPING TO PREVENT NEW INFECTIONS, EVEN IF THE INFECTED PEOPLE THEMSELVES CANNOT BE HELPED.

Requiring the reporting of AIDS but not HIV seems equivalent to requiring, say, that full-blown cases of hepatitis B be reported but not any newly detected infections with the hepatitis virus. Actually, it is worse. The incubation period for hepatitis B is usually two or three months, whereas the period between infection with HIV and a diagnosis of AIDS is often longer than ten years. This means that during all this time HIV-positive people can be both infectious and outside the public-health system. The disease is further privatized by the HIV home-testing kits now on the market, which to yet one more degree put testing and reporting into the hands of individuals.

As noted, state public-health practices mandate that certain sexually transmitted diseases be reported; in part to avoid reporting HIV some states have decided not to classify HIV as a sexually transmitted disease—even though the primary mode of HIV infection is, of course, sexual. As of 1995 only twelve states had classified AIDS and HIV infection as sexually transmitted diseases. Only sixteen states had even classified them as communicable diseases. Treating AIDS and HIV infection as exceptions, twenty-three states, including New York and California, had classified them as a separate category of disease. A report prepared for the CDC by Georgetown University and Johns Hopkins University's Program on Law and Public Health observes of this situation: "Disease-specific legislation may thwart public health goals by generating separate policies, programs, and procedures for diseases that may share common behavioral risk factors and require a unified approach for treatment and prevention."

BEYOND issues of testing and reporting lies the issue of partner notification. "Partner notification" is the term used by the CDC to describe a spectrum of outreach efforts. One such effort is contact tracing, also called "provider referral," in which doctors or public-health officials locate partners of infected people (if the infected people are willing or able to provide names) and notify them of possible infection; the name of the known infected person is always kept confidential. At a further remove on the spectrum is "patient referral," in which infected people locate and notify partners on their own. Only thirty-three states have laws that explicitly allow doctors or public-health officials to notify the sex or needle-sharing partners of those with AIDS or infected with HIV. Only four states (Arkansas, North Carolina, South Carolina, and Oregon) have statutes requiring notification.

All states technically have something that they can point to as a "partner-notification program," having such a program being a prerequisite for obtaining certain federal funds. But the effectiveness of partner-notification programs varies widely, for reasons relating as much to how the programs are implemented as to what specific steps they call for: the real difference is between states, such as Colorado and North Carolina, that actively strive to find and notify partners primarily through provider referral, and states, such as New York and California, that tend to rely on patient referral, deferring the responsibility of notification to the infected.

As one would expect, there seems to be a marked contrast between the effectiveness of well-established partner-notification programs in which provider-referral services are made available, and that of programs in which infected people themselves do the notifying if they are so inclined. One study found that active partner-notification programs offering provider-referral services get 30 to 90 percent (depending on the city or state) of people who have tested positive to cooperate in contacting those they may have infected. Ninety percent or more of those contacted agree to be tested. However, programs in which notification is left up to the infected achieve a cooperation rate of less than 10 percent. It should be noted also that by virtue of the fact that trained public-health personnel in most instances make the notifications in provider-referral cases, testing information and counseling are made readily available to possibly infected contacts. Programs that notify primarily through provider referral find a larger proportion of other infected people, and find them earlier. The sooner a person knows of his or her infection and begins treatment, and the higher that person's T-cell count when treatment begins, the better the prognosis. In a recent study conducted at a Los Angeles AIDS clinic the average T-cell count in HIV-positive women who entered the clinic through active provider-referral partner notification was found to be 411; the average for all other women entering the clinic was 157. ("T-cell count" refers to the number of Thelper cells, a kind of white-blood cell that is essential to the proper functioning of the cellular immune system; HIV attacks and kills these cells. The T-cell count is closer to 1,000 in a healthy person, though the healthy range is subject to considerable variability. A T-cell count under 200 is one of the criteria for a diagnosis of AIDS.)

Does an absence of routine testing, reporting, and notification mean that a lot of undiscovered AIDS and HIV cases are festering in the larger society? Yes. According to the CDC, the number of Americans infected with HIV is as high as 900,000; of these, the CDC estimates, perhaps half are unaware of their infection. At least a quarter of all people in whom AIDS was diagnosed from 1990 to 1995 in Los Angeles County first became aware of their infection when they came to hospitals or clinics with advanced symptoms, having never previously been tested for HIV. In all likelihood such people had been HIV-positive for years. Most cancer, diabetes, or high-blood-pressure patients have been tested for these medical problems, know their status, and have begun treatment well before admission to a hospital with advanced symptoms. The situation with AIDS means, as one Los Angeles AIDS clinic director observed during a recent interview, that "something is really wrong." Because the lifetime cost of treating HIV is so high (estimated in 1993 to be $119,000 per patient), the CDC has concluded that AIDS and HIV notification programs pay for themselves if only one in eighty notifications prevents a new HIV infection by indicating to the notified person that a change in behavior is warranted.

AIDS has been so thoroughly exempted from traditional public-health approaches that civil libertarians have defeated in court attempts by health authorities to notify the spouses of people who have died of AIDS that their husbands or wives were HIV-infected. During the first years of the disease, legislation urged by civil libertarians prohibited physicians and public-health officials from notifying even the spouses of living people who had tested positive for HIV, some of whom continued to have unprotected sex with their partners. In some states laws have been enacted making partner notification by a physician at best discretionary under tightly defined circumstances.

National legislation on spousal notification, passed last year, mandates that states make a "good-faith effort" to notify at-risk spouses. However, in effect the law applies only to states that already require the names of infected people to be reported. And in any event, the matter of partner notification when the partners are (or were) married addresses, of course, only a small part of the AIDS problem.

WRONGHEADED RATIONALES

HOW has AIDS exceptionalism been justified? In the mid-1980s four arguments were regularly heard for exempting AIDS from standard public-health prac-

tices. 1) There had never before been a disease that seemed to constitute a de facto marker for homosexuality, with all the social stigma that this label carries. 2) The confidentiality of testing would inevitably be violated, precisely because AIDS is more stigmatized than any other disease. 3) Given the large number of sex partners of many of those who have become HIV-infected, contact tracing would be ineffectual. 4) Because there is no cure for AIDS, and no treatment to render the infected uninfectious, it was pointless to report HIV infection as is done for other infections.

However legitimate the civil-liberties issues it sought to address may have been more than a decade ago, the exceptionalist orthodoxy is now fundamentally wrongheaded as a matter of good public health and medicine.

The argument that AIDS is a unique marker for homosexuality is incorrect, and always was so. Rectal gonorrhea in men has been almost exclusively a disease of the gay population, and is a more reliable marker for homosexuality, if anyone were looking for such a marker, than AIDS ever was. And yet cases of rectal gonorrhea have appeared for decades, by name and date, in confidential case reports sent to state public-health departments.

The argument that confidentiality will inevitably be violated has met a serious counter-argument in the form of reality: the experience of Minnesota and Colorado, which have since 1985 mandated the confidential reporting by name of both HIV and AIDS cases. As of the end of last year, for example, Colorado health authorities had received the names of 5,723 people with AIDS and of 5,137 additional people infected with HIV. There have been no breaches of confidentiality. As noted, twenty-six states now require confidential reporting of all HIV cases by name. A single intentional breach of confidentiality in the CDC's AIDS surveillance system is known to have occurred (in Florida).

As for discrimination, the federal Americans with Disabilities Act (ADA), passed in 1990, a decade after the beginning of the AIDS epidemic, prohibits discrimination based on HIV status. In addition, the federal Vocational Rehabilitation Act of 1973, state discrimination laws, and state constitutions have all been interpreted by courts as protecting people from exactly the sort of discrimination that AIDS exceptionalists claim is inevitable. And courts have in most cases ruled that being infected with HIV constitutes a disability according to the legal definition of the term, even when the infected person is asymptomatic. "We've done more or less everything that can be done on the legislative front to protect people from discrimination on the basis of HIV status," says Chai Feldblum, an associate professor at Georgetown University Law School and one of the principal architects of the ADA. "The laws are there."

The argument that contact tracing will prove to be ineffectual because many of those infected with HIV have had a large number of sex partners ignores the fact that many of those infected with syphilis and gonorrhea, other diseases for which gay men are at increased risk, have also had a large number of sex partners, and yet contact tracing has been standard procedure for these diseases for decades.

The argument that name reporting is pointless because there is no treatment has always been open to question on a number of grounds. Yes, the statement may have a certain logic from the perspective of a given infected individual concerned only about his or her fate. But if infected people can be identified, education and counseling may at the very least prompt changes in their behavior which will diminish the risk that they go on to infect others; contact tracing, in turn, extends the possibility of risk-diminishing behavioral change even more widely. Knowing who is infected is essential in helping to prevent new infections, even if the infected person himself cannot be helped.

In any event, evidence shows that new medical treatments are making HIV less infectious than ever. The latest treatments are astonishingly promising for at least some of the infected population.

Some 15 to 30 percent of HIV-infected pregnant women pass the virus on to their infants. Early treatment with zidovudine, or AZT, for the woman during pregnancy and for the infant after birth, can cut the proportion to eight percent. A new class of drugs called protease inhibitors is likely to cut the rate even further, if the drugs are used early. The key word is "early"—which means testing pregnant mothers, not just newborn babies. The American Medical Association now recommends that HIV testing be made mandatory for pregnant women. Gay and AIDS activists have denounced this recommendation.

Protease inhibitors, which in some cases have reduced the level of HIV in the bloodstreams of the infected to undetectable levels, have revolutionized care for many patients. "I think we already have the capability to make HIV infection a chronic, manageable disease like diabetes in patients who can afford the therapy and who can take it with one-hundred-percent compliance," says Joel Gallant, the director of the Moore HIV Clinic at the Johns Hopkins University School of Medicine. Protease inhibitors have provoked debate as to their long-term effectiveness, their ability to withstand viral resistance, and their price (the protease inhibitor Invirase costs approximately $7,000 for a year's supply), and also, as Gallant has noted, because of the fastidiousness required for effective administration. But the fact remains that the exceptionalist argument that no treatment is possible is losing whatever force it had.

The benefits of knowing who is infected are still more compelling today than they were in 1992, when the CDC AIDS laboratory chief Donald Francis, writing in the *Journal of the American Medical Association* in favor of more-aggressive testing and the channeling of the infected into prevention and counseling programs, brought up "the ability to deliver important new products produced by scientific research." He wrote,

Should the day come when a vaccine or therapeutic drug becomes available, a system for immediate delivery to those in greatest need would be required. There is no system by which to do that now. But if all infected persons were being followed up in an early intervention program, delivery would be straightforward. In my opinion, early intervention should be given the highest national priority.

The fact that AIDS is not easily transmissible (it is a hundred times less infectious than hepatitis B, and incomparably less contagious than an airborne disease like tuberculosis) provides further impetus to discover who is and is not HIV-infected. The knowledge that a given person is infected, if it means that the person takes any preventive measures at all, is much more valuable in the case of AIDS than it is for other diseases.

REMEDY-RESISTANT POLITICS?

DESPITE such developments, attempts to alter the public-health approach to AIDS, though on occasion successful, have met with fierce opposition. A case in point occurred in the spring of 1995, when Gary Ackerman, a liberal Democratic congressman from New York, introduced a bill with 220 co-sponsors to "unblind" a national infant-testing program for HIV run by the CDC as a way of monitoring HIV-infection rates in women. Since 1988 the CDC had been "blind-testing" infants for HIV in forty-five states—using blood samples, collected at birth, from which all identifying tags had been removed. Testing for HIV in this way meant that the CDC knew how many infants carried their mother's HIV antibodies but not who they or their infected mothers were. Mothers, therefore, were being sent home without being informed that they and in some cases their children were infected with a fatal virus. The CDC had no choice in the matter, being legally prevented from testing without informed consent. Under the Ackerman bill mechanisms were to be instituted so that if an infant tested positive, those doing the testing would have a way of knowing who that infant was, and its mother could be informed.

The response to this proposed legislation was immediate. Virtually every gay and AIDS group, including Gay Men's Health Crisis, the AIDS Action Council, and the National Association of People With AIDS, along with the ACLU and prominent public-health experts at leading universities, opposed the bill, largely on the grounds that unblinding the tests would do nothing to help prevent HIV transmission from mothers to their infants and would violate the privacy inherent in such an anonymous surveillance study, potentially scaring pregnant women away from seeking proper prenatal care. The intensity of feeling with which such measures have been opposed should not be underestimated. Ackerman's bill was modeled on a bill introduced in the New York State Assembly by the Democratic legislator Nettie Mayersohn to unblind the anonymous infant-testing program in New York. Mayersohn, a pro-choice, feminist old-line liberal who in 1989 had been named Legislator of the Year by the New York State chapter of the National Organization for Women, was labeled a "fascist" by individuals associated with the AIDS lobby. (Last June, three years after Mayersohn introduced her original legislation, the New York legislature passed a bill allowing the state to institute mandatory HIV testing of newborns and to notify parents of the test results. Newborn testing began last February.)

In the matter of the Ackerman legislation, the head of the CDC informed Ackerman that if the bill were not withdrawn, the CDC would suspend the infant-testing program altogether. Ackerman gave no credence to this threat by a public-health agency, because the infant-testing program was demonstrably useful in tracking the prevalence and trajectory of heterosexual AIDS. But the CDC program was indeed suspended. Public-health authorities thus lost even this imperfect means of monitoring one aspect of the epidemic.

In response to the CDC's suspension of testing, Ackerman joined forces with Tom Coburn, a Republican congressman and a Christian conservative from Oklahoma, to draft new legislation that has become known as the "Baby AIDS Compromise." The legislation was enacted last May as part of a larger bill, the Ryan White CARE Reauthorization Act. The compromise requires state health-care workers to offer counseling and voluntary HIV testing to pregnant women who have not previously been tested for HIV. States that by March of 2000 do not meet certain goals with respect to the voluntary HIV testing of pregnant women or to HIV incidence among newborns will have to implement a mandatory infant-testing program or lose some federal AIDS funding.

THE ultimate question for AIDS exceptionalism is this: Do the disease-containment and disease-prevention measures of traditional public health—the measures from whose full force AIDS has been significantly shielded—work? The answer given to this question by AIDS exceptionalists as well as traditionalists seems to be yes. Joel Gallant, for example, opposes routine involuntary testing for HIV and aggressive partner notification, but not on medical grounds; rather, he fears the potential for employment and insurance discrimination, domestic abuse, and breaches of confidentiality. He maintains that he would otherwise favor traditional public-health procedures for the fight against AIDS, particularly routine testing.

Lee Reichman, the executive director of the National Tuberculosis Center and a physician on the staff of the New Jersey Medical School who cares for AIDS patients, cautions that given the course that the evolution and politics of the disease have taken, traditional public-health measures by themselves may no longer be feasible, in part because of the possibility

that they will drive the infected underground. As noted, this is an exceptionalist article of faith. But Reichman goes on: "Traditional public health is absolutely effective at controlling infectious disease. It should have been applied to AIDS from the start, and it wasn't. Long before there was AIDS, there were other sexually transmitted diseases, and you had partner notification and testing and reporting. This was routine public health at its finest, and this is the way STDs were controlled."

In the months ahead a national debate may well be joined over rescinding the exceptional public-health status of AIDS, owing in part to a bill introduced by Tom Coburn, the Oklahoma congressman. Coburn's bill, the HIV Prevention Act of 1997, would establish confidential HIV reporting nationwide. It would require states to inform anyone who has been exposed to HIV. It would require that all people accused of sexual offenses be tested for HIV. And it would allow health-care providers to test a patient for HIV before performing a risky invasive medical procedure. The Coburn bill contains a number of other provisions and also two nonbinding "sense of the Congress" resolutions, one urging states to criminalize the intentional transmission of HIV, the other affirming the principle that strict confidentiality must be observed in carrying out the bill's provisions. (A companion bill has been introduced in the Senate.) "The fact is that epidemiology works," Coburn says, "and public-health policies work to control disease, and they work by identifying vectors of infectious disease, and you notify people at risk. If you don't do that, you can't control the disease. And that's what we've not done with HIV."

> A TRADITIONALIST APPROACH TO AIDS WILL COST MONEY, AND THOSE WHO ADVOCATE SUCH AN APPROACH SHOULD BE MAKING THE CASE THAT MORE MONEY IS NEEDED.

The AIDS Action Council—a group "dedicated solely to shaping fair and effective AIDS policy," in the words of its literature—has denounced the Coburn bill as "an attempt to federalize policies that do nothing but stigmatize and punish people living with HIV/AIDS." The act, in the view of the council, "replaces education and personal responsibility with 'Big Brother' intrusion and control." In previous statements the council has characterized measures like the ones now proposed as "failed policies that do nothing to prevent any more Americans from becoming infected with HIV."

It is hard to see how traditionalist policies can be said to have "failed" with AIDS, since they have not been systematically tried. Be that as it may, some skepticism toward legislation like Coburn's is warranted. Conservatives representing themselves as public-health advocates are certainly vulnerable to a charge of hypocrisy. Coburn's bill does not address one of the exceptionalists' central criticisms: that although traditional procedures will identify more infected people, conservatives are not prepared to offer any plan for helping those infected people (many of whom have no health insurance and little education, and many of whom are homeless) after they have been identified. The Coburn bill offers no new funds for the state public-health departments that would be obliged to carry out its testing and reporting provisions. A traditionalist approach to AIDS will cost money, and those who advocate such an approach should be making the case that more money is needed.

Exceptionalists also point out, correctly and bitterly, that the hatred directed against homosexuals, and the discrimination they experience at the hands of anti-gay conservatives, among others, are responsible in the first place for the very exceptionalist policies that conservatives like Coburn now so strongly oppose. Coburn's own outlook gives one pause. It was Coburn who elicited condemnation and ridicule when he criticized the airing on network television last winter of *Schindler's List*, complaining about the depiction of violence and frontal nudity.

As noted, epidemiology has sometimes had to weigh the issue of civil rights against the issue of effective disease control. The time has come to consider anew how these factors should tip the scales. We do not, of course, have an absolute guarantee that traditional epidemiology applied to AIDS and HIV would markedly bolster the success of public-health efforts. But such a guarantee is hardly required. Marcia Angell, of *The New England Journal of Medicine*, observes, "Nobody can document or prove that traditional methods of control would work better at containing AIDS, because nobody has done what would be necessary to get such proof—studying two populations, one in which traditional methods are applied and one in which they aren't. The reason no one has done this is that it is impossible. It is impossible because it's unethical and logically unworkable. So, as in many things in life, the default position is common sense. And I have no doubt, given the track record of these methods in controlling other diseases, that if, for example, we screened all expectant mothers, we could prevent AIDS in many cases. And if we traced partners, we would prevent AIDS in many cases. And if we routinely tested in hospitals, we would prevent AIDS in many cases."

Ralph Frerichs, of UCLA, framed the matter like this in the course of an interview: "Historically, public health has always transcended the legal system, much like the military. When you have an outside threat, you can suspend the normal rules of society. Traditionally, we epidemiologists have been granted full responsibility, but society has eroded that, and we now talk about respecting the rights of human individuals who have disease-causing viruses, bacteria, and so on, which makes it increasingly difficult to stop the spread of these diseases. This is society's choice. But this is de facto granting rights to the viruses and to the bacteria. And when epidemics are presented this way, as a matter of rights, the public has a harder time distinguishing the infection from the infected. The virus is our enemy, not the person with the virus, but at the same time that person harbors the virus, and we need to take a series of steps to prevent that virus from moving to another person.

"In AIDS, as in all epidemics, there is a tradeoff between emphasizing detection of the virus and the civil-rights violations that detection engenders. Given that we have not pushed for aggressive testing, reporting, and partner notification, it appears that our society is willing to accept a higher amount of HIV infection to avoid interfering with the rights of HIV-infected people."

Earlier this year the Centers for Disease Control and Prevention reported that largely because of gains in life expectancy among the infected, annual deaths from AIDS had registered a significant decline for the first time since the onset of the epidemic. That they have done so is hardly grounds for complacency. It is evidence, however, that medical interventions make a palpable difference—and is all the more reason to start subjecting AIDS, from a public-health perspective, to more-systematic procedures.

In the end AIDS would be unlikely to prove resistant to good basic public-health policies. It may survive if it can circumvent good sense.

DO ASK, DO TELL

THE AMERICAN PROSPECT
Joshua Gamson

TV talk shows may be crass and voyeuristic, but they give a voice to those who have been silenced

Joshua Gamson is assistant professor of sociology at Yale University and the author of Claims to Fame: Celebrity in Contemporary America *(University of California Press, 1994).*

At the end of his 22 years, when Pedro Zamora lost his capacity to speak, all sorts of people stepped into the silence created by the AIDS-related brain disease that shut him up. MTV began running a marathon of *The Real World*, its seven-kids-in-an-apartment-with-the-cameras-running show on which Pedro Zamora starred as Pedro Zamora, a version of himself: openly gay, Miami Cuban, HIV-positive, youth activist. MTV offered the marathon as a tribute to Zamora, which it was, and as a way to raise funds, especially crucial since Zamora, like so many people with HIV, did not have private insurance. Yet, of course, MTV was also paying tribute to itself, capitalizing on Pedro's death without quite seeming as monstrous as all that.

President Clinton and Florida governor Lawton Chiles made public statements and publicized phone calls to the hospital room, praising Zamora as a heroic point of light rather than as a routinely outspoken critic of their own HIV and AIDS policies. The Clinton administration, in the midst of its clampdown on Cuban immigration, even granted visas to Zamora's three brothers and a sister in Cuba—a kindly if cynical act, given the realities of people with AIDS awaiting visas and health care in Guantánamo Bay.

Thus, according to *People* magazine, did Zamora reach a bittersweet ending. He was unable to see, hear, or speak, yet with his family reunited, "his dream had come true." Behind the scenes, one who was there for Zamora's last weeks told me, the family actually separated Zamora from his boyfriend—quite out of keeping with the "dreams" of Pedro's life. When Pedro had his own voice, he had spoken powerfully of how anti-gay ideology and policy, typically framed as "pro-family," contributed to teen suicides and the spread of HIV; when he died, those who spoke for him emphasized individual heroism and the triumph of the heterosexual family.

That others appropriated Zamora on his deathbed hardly tarnishes his accomplishment. As an MTV star, he had probably reduced suffering among lesbian and gay teenagers more, and affected their thinking more deeply, than a zillion social service programs. He spoke publicly to millions in his own words and with the backing of a reputable media institution, and he did not just tell them to wear condoms, or that AIDS is an equal-opportunity destroyer. Nor did he simply fill in the sexual blanks left by prudish government prevention campaigns. He also told them and showed them: Here is me loving my boyfriend; here is what a self-possessed gay man looks like hanging out with his roommates; here is what my Cuban family might have to say about my bringing home a black man; here is me at an AIDS demonstration, getting medical news, exchanging love vows.

To speak for and about yourself as a gay man or a lesbian on television, to break silences that are systematically and ubiquitously enforced in public life, is profoundly political. "Don't tell" is more than a U.S. military policy; it remains U.S. public policy, formally and informally, on sex and gender nonconformity. Sex and gender outsiders—gay men, transsexuals, lesbians, bisexuals—are constantly invited to lose their voices, or suffer the consequences (job loss, baseball bats) of using them. Outside of the occasional opening on MTV or sporadic coverage of a demonstration or a parade, if one is not Melissa Etheridge or David Geffen, opportunities to speak as a nonheterosexual, or to listen to one, are few and far between. Even if the cameras soon turn elsewhere, these moments are big breakthroughs, and they are irresistible, giddy moments for the shut up.

Yet, in a media culture, holding the microphone and the spotlight is a complicated sort of power, not just because people grab them back from you but because they are never really yours. If you speak, you must be prepared to be used. The voice that comes out is not quite

---

To speak for and about yourself as a gay man or a lesbian on television, to break silences that are systematically and ubiquitously enforced in public life, is profoundly political.

---

yours: It is like listening to yourself on tape (a bit deeper, or more clipped) or to a version dubbed by your twin. It is you and it is not you. Zamora's trick, until his voice was taken, was to walk the line between talking and being dubbed. The troubling question, for the silenced and the heard alike, is whether the line is indeed walkable. Perhaps the best place to turn for answers is the main public space in which the edict to shut up is reversed: daytime television talk shows.

For lesbians, gay men, bisexuals, drag queens, transsexuals—and combinations thereof—watching daytime television has got to be spooky. Suddenly, there are renditions of you, chattering away in a system that otherwise ignores or steals your voice at every turn. Sally Jessy Raphael wants to know what it's like to pass as a different sex, Phil Donahue wants to support you in your battle against gay bashing, Ricki Lake wants to get you a date, Oprah Winfrey wants you to love without lying. Most of all, they all want you to talk about it publicly, just at a time when everyone else wants you not to. They are interested, if not precisely in "reality," at least not in fictional accounts. For people whose desires and identities go against the norm, this is the only spot in mainstream media culture to speak on their own terms or to hear others speaking for themselves. The fact that talk shows are so much maligned, and for so many good reasons, does not close the case.

The other day, I happened to tune into the *Ricki Lake Show*, the fastest-rising talk show ever. The topic: "I don't want gays around my kids." I caught the last 20 minutes of what amounted to a pro-gay screamfest. Ricki and her audience explicitly attacked a large woman who was denying visitation rights to her gay ex-husband ("I had to explain to a 9-year-old what 'gay' means"; "My child started having nightmares after he visited his father").

And they went at a young couple who believed in keeping children away from gay people on the grounds that the Bible says "homosexuals should die." The gay guests and their supporters had the last word, brought on to argue, to much audience whooping, that loving gays are a positive influence and hateful heterosexuals should stay away from children. The anti-gay guests were denounced on any number of grounds, by host, other guests, and numerous audience members: They are denying children loving influences, they are bigots, they are misinformed, they read the Bible incorrectly, they sound like Mormons, they are resentful that they have put on more weight than their exes. One suburban-looking audience member angrily addressed each "child protector" in turn, along the way coming up with a possible new pageant theme: "And as for you, Miss Homophobia . . ."

The show was a typical mess, with guests yelling and audiences hooting at the best one-liners about bigotry or body weight, but the virulence with which homophobia was attacked is both typical of these shows and stunning. When Lake cut off a long-sideburned man's argument that "it's a fact that the easiest way to get AIDS is by homosexual sex" ("That is not a fact, sir, that is not correct"), I found myself ready to start the chant of "Go, Ricki! Go, Ricki!" that apparently wraps each taping. Even such elementary corrections, and even such a weird form of visibility and support, stands out sharply. Here, the homophobe is the deviant, the freak.

Lake's show is among the new breed of rowdy youth-oriented programs, celebrated as "rock and roll television" by veteran Geraldo Rivera and denigrated as "exploitalk" by cultural critic Neal Gabler. Their sibling shows, the older, tamer "service" programs such as *Oprah* and *Donahue*, support "alternative" sexualities and genders in quieter, but not weaker, ways. Peruse last year's *Donahue*: two teenage lesbian lovers ("Young, courageous people like yourself are blazing the way for other people," says Donahue), a gay construction worker suing his gay boss for harassment ("There's only eight states that protect sexual persuasion," his attorney reports), a bisexual minister, a black lesbian activist, and two members of the African-American theater group Pomo Afro Homos ("We're about trying to build a black gay community," says one), the stars of the gender-crossing *Priscilla, Queen of the Desert* ("I have a lot of friends that are transsexuals," declares an audience member, "and they're the neatest people"), heterosexuals whose best friends are gay, lesbians starting families, gay teens, gay cops, gay men reuniting with their high school sweethearts, a gay talk show. This is a more diverse, self-possessed, and politically outspoken group of nonheterosexuals than I might find, say, at the gay bar around the corner. I can only imagine what this means for people experiencing sexual difference where none is locally visible.

Certainly *Donahue* makes moves to counter its "liberal" reputation, inviting right-wing black preachers and the widely discredited "psychologist" Paul Cameron, who argues that cross-dressing preceded the fall of Rome, that people with AIDS should be quarantined, and that sexuality "is going to get us." But more often than not, Donahue himself is making statements about how "homophobia is global" and "respects no nation," how "we're beating up homosexual people, calling them names, throwing them out of apartments, jobs." The "we" being asserted is an "intolerant" population that needs to get over itself. We are, he says at times, "medieval." In fact, Donahue regularly asserts that "for an advanced, so-called industrialized nation, I think we're the worst."

Oprah Winfrey, the industry leader, is less concerned with the political treatment of difference; she is overwhelmingly oriented toward "honesty" and "openness," especially in interpersonal relationships. As on Lake's show, lesbians and gays are routinely included without incident in more general themes (meeting people through personal ads, fools for love, sons and daughters you never knew), and bigotry is routinely attacked. But Winfrey's distinctive mark is an attack on lies, and thus the closet comes under attack—especially the gay male closet—not just for the damage it does to those in it, but for the betrayals of women it engenders.

On a recent program in which a man revealed his "orientation" after 19 years of marriage, for example, both Winfrey and her audience were concerned not that Steve is gay, but that he was not honest with his wife. As Winfrey put it, "For me, always the issue is how you can be more truthful in your life." One of Steve's two supportive sons echoes Winfrey ("I want people to be able to be who they are"), as does his ex-wife, whose anger is widely supported by the audience ("It makes me feel like

---

The shows are about talk; the more silence there has been on a subject, the more not-telling, the better a talk topic it is.

---

my life has been a sham"), and the requisite psychologist ("The main thing underneath all of this is the importance of loving ourselves and being honest and authentic and real in our lives"). Being truthful, revealing secrets, learning to love oneself: These are the staples of Winfrey-style talk shows. Gay and bisexual guests find a place to speak as gays and bisexuals, and the pathology becomes not sexual "deviance" but the socially imposed closet.

All of this, however, should not be mistaken for dedicated friendship. Even when ideological commitments to truth and freedom are at work, the primary commitment of talk shows is, of course, to money. What makes these such inviting spots for nonconforming sex and gender identities has mostly to do with the niche talk shows have carved out for ratings. The shows are about talk; the more silence there has been on a subject, the more not-telling, the better a talk topic it is. On talk shows, as media scholar Wayne Munson points out in his book *All*

Talk (Temple University Press, 1993), "differences are no longer repressed" but "become the talk show's emphasis," as the shows confront "boredom and channel clutter with constant, intensified novelty and 'reality.'" Indeed, according to Munson, Richard Mincer, *Donahue*'s executive producer, encourages prospective guests "to be especially unique or different, to take advantage of rather than repress difference."

While they highlight different sex and gender identities, expressions, and practices, the talk shows can be a dangerous place to speak and a difficult place to get heard. With around 20 syndicated talk shows competing for audiences, shows that trade in confrontation and surprise (*Ricki Lake, Jenny Jones, Jerry Springer*) are edging out the milder, topical programs (*Oprah, Donahue*).

As a former *Jane Whitney Show* producer told *TV Guide*, "When you're booking guests, you're thinking, 'How much confrontation can this person provide me?' The more confrontation, the better. You want people just this side of a fistfight."

For members of groups already subject to violence, the visibility of television can prompt more than just a fistfight, as last year's *Jenny Jones* murder underlined. In March, when Scott Amedure appeared on a "secret admirer" episode of the *Jenny Jones Show*, the admired Jon Schmitz was apparently expecting a female admirer. Schmitz, not warming to Amedure's fantasy of tying him up in a hammock and spraying whipped cream and champagne on his body, declared himself "100 percent heterosexual." Later, back in Michigan, he punctuated this claim by shooting Amedure with a 12-gauge shotgun, telling police that the embarrassment from the program had "eaten away" at him. Or, as he reportedly put it in his 911 call, Amedure "fucked me on national TV."

Critics were quick to point out that programming that creates conflict tends to exacerbate it. "The producers made professions of regret," Neal Gabler wrote in the *Los Angeles Times* after the Amedure murder, "but one suspects what they really regretted was the killer's indecency of not having pulled out his rifle and committed the crime before their cameras." In the wake of the murder, talk show producers were likened over and over to drug dealers: Publicist Ken Maley told the *San Francisco Chronicle* that "they've got people strung out on an adrenaline rush," and "they keep raising the dosage"; sociologist Vicki Abt told *People* that "TV allows us to mainline deviance"; Michelangelo Signorile argued in *Out* that some talk show producers "are like crack dealers scouring trailer park America." True enough. Entering the unruly talk show world, one is apt to become, at best, a source of adrenaline rush, and at worst a target of violence.

What most reporting tended to ignore, however, was that most anti-gay violence does not require a talk show "ambush" to trigger it. Like the Oakland County, Michi-

The vicious voice—shouting that we gay people can be as mean, or petty, or just plain loud, as anybody else—is the first voice talk shows promote. It is one price of entry into mainstream public visibility.

gan, prosecutor who argued that "*Jenny Jones*'s producers' cynical pursuit of ratings and total insensitivity to what could occur here left one person dead and Mr. Schmitz now facing life in prison," many critics focused on the "humiliating" surprise attack on Schmitz with the news that he was desired by another man. As in the image of the "straight" soldier being ogled in the shower, in this logic the revelation of same-sex desire is treated as the danger, and the desired as a victim. The talk show critics thus played to the same "don't tell" logic that makes talk shows such a necessary, if uncomfortable, refuge for some of us.

Although producers' pursuit of ratings is indeed, unsurprisingly, cynical and insensitive, the talk show environment is one of the very few in which the declaration of same-sex desire (and, to a lesser degree, atypical gender identity) is common, heartily defended, and often even incidental. Although they overlook this in their haste to hate trash, the critics of exploitative talk shows help illuminate the odd sort of opportunity these cacophonous settings provide. Same-sex desires become "normal" on these programs not so much because different sorts of lives become clearly visible, but because they get sucked into the spectacular whirlpool of relationship conflicts. They offer a particular kind of visibility and voice. On a recent *Ricki Lake*, it was the voice of an aggressive, screechy gay man who continually reminded viewers, between laughs at his own nasty comments, that he was a regular guy. On other days, it's the take-your-hands-off-my-woman lesbian, or the I'm-more-of-a-woman-than-you'll-ever-be transsexual. The vicious voice—shouting that we gay people can be as mean, or petty, or just plain loud, as anybody else—is the first voice talk shows promote. It's one price of entry into mainstream pubic visibility.

The guests on the talk shows seem to march in what psychologist Jeanne Heaton, co-author of *Tuning in Trouble* (Jossey-Bass, 1995), calls a "parade of pathology." Many talk shows have more than a passing resemblance to freak shows. Neal Gabler, for example, argues that guests are invited to exhibit "their deformities for attention" in a "ritual of debasement" aimed primarily at reassuring the audience of its superiority. Indeed, the evidence of dehumanization is all over the place, especially when it comes to gender crossing, as in the

titles of various recent *Geraldo* programs; the calls of sideshow barkers echo in "Star-Crossed Cross-Dressers: Bizarre Stories of Transvestites and Their Lovers" and "Outrageous Impersonators and Flamboyant Drag Queens" and "When Your Husband Wears the Dress in the Family." As long as talk shows make their bids by being, in Gabler's words, "a psychological freak show," sex and gender outsiders arguably reinforce perceptions of themselves as freaks by entering a discourse in which they may be portrayed as bizarre, outrageous, flamboyant curiosities. (Often, for example, they must relinquish their right to defend themselves to the ubiquitous talk show "experts.")

Talk shows do indeed trade on voyeurism, and it is no secret that those who break with sex and gender norms and fight with each other on camera help the shows win higher ratings. But there is more to the picture: the place where "freaks" talk back. It is a place where Conrad, born and living in a female body, can assert against Sally Jessy Raphael's claims that he "used and betrayed" women in order to have sex with them that women fall in love with him as a man because he considers himself a man; where months later, in a program on "our most outrageous former guests" (all gender crossers), Conrad can reappear, declare himself to have started hormone treatment, and report that the woman he allegedly "used and betrayed" has stood by him. This is a narrow opening, but an opening nonetheless, for the second voice promoted by the talk show: the proud voice of the "freak," even if the freak refuses that term. The fact that talk shows are exploitative spectacles does not negate the fact that they are also opportunities; as Munson points out, they are both spectacle and conversation. They give voice to the systematically silenced, albeit under conditions out of the speaker's control, and in tones that come out tinny, scratched, distant.

These voices, even when they are discounted, sometimes do more than just assert themselves. Whatever their motivations, people sometimes wind up doing more than just pulling up a chair at a noisy, crowded table. Every so often they wind up messing with sexual categories in a way that goes beyond a simple expansion of them. In addition to affirming both homosexuality and heterosexuality as normal and natural, talk show producers often make entertainment by mining the in-between: finding guests who are interesting exactly because they don't fit existing notions of "gay" and "straight" and "man" and "woman," raising the provocative suggestion that the categories are not quite working.

The last time I visited the *Maury Povich Show*, for instance, I found myself distracted by Jason and Tiffanie. Jason, a large 18-year-old from a small town in Ohio, was in love with Calvin. Calvin was having an affair with Jamie (Jason's twin sister, also the mother of a three-month-old), who was interested in Scott, who had sex with, as I recall, both Calvin and Tiffanie. Tiffanie, who walked on stage holding Jamie's hand, had pretty much had sex with everyone except Jamie. During group sex, Tiffanie explained, she and Jamie did not touch each other. "We're not lesbians," she loudly asserted, against the noisy protestations of some audience members.

The studio audience, in fact, was quick to condemn the kids, who were living together in a one-bedroom apartment with Jamie's baby. Their response was predictably accusatory: You are freaks, some people said; immoral, said others; pathetically bored and in need of a hobby, others asserted. Still other aspects of the "discussion" assumed the validity and normality of homosexuality. Jason, who had recently attempted suicide, was told he needed therapy to help him come to terms with his sexuality, and the other boys were told they too needed to "figure themselves out." Yet much talk also struggled to attach sexual labels to an array of partnerships anarchic enough to throw all labels into disarray. "If you are not lesbians, why were you holding hands?" one woman asked Tiffanie. "If you are not gay," another audience member asked Calvin, "how is it you came to have oral sex with two young men?"

This mix was typically contradictory: condemnation of "immoral sex" but not so much of homosexuality per se, openly gay and bisexual teenagers speaking for themselves while their partners in homosexual activities declare heterosexual identities, a situation in which sexual categories are both assumed and up for grabs. I expect the young guests were mainly in it for the free trip to New York, and the studio audience was mainly in it for the brush with television. Yet the discussion they created, the unsettling of categorical assumptions about genders and desires, if only for a few moments in the midst of judgment and laughter, is found almost nowhere else this side of fiction.

The importance of these conversations, both for those who for safety must shut up about their sexual and gender identities and for those who never think about them, is certainly underestimated. The level of exploitation is certainly not. Like Pedro Zamora, one can keep one's voice for a little while, one finger on the commercial megaphone, until others inevitably step in to claim it for their own purposes. Or one can talk for show, as freak, or expert, or rowdy—limits set by the production strategies within the talk show genre.

Those limits, not the talk shows themselves, are really the point. The story here is not about commercial exploitation, but about just how effective the prohibition on asking and telling is in the United States, how stiff the penalties are, how unsafe this place is for people of atypical sexual and gender identities. You know you're in trouble when Sally Jessy Raphael (strained smile and forced tear behind red glasses) seems like your best bet for being heard, understood, respected, and protected. That for some of us the loopy, hollow light of talk shows seems a safe haven should give us all pause.

THE PORNING OF AMERICA

In our rush to break taboos, we've made pornography as ho-hum as sitcoms. Big-name actresses strip for "credibility," Larry Flynt is deified, and lap dancing is more common than tap dancing. Shouldn't private parts—from Demi Moore's to Howard Stern's—remain private? Is nothing dirty anymore?

BY LUCY KAYLIN

In the 1967 classic *The Graduate,* Benjamin Braddock, finding himself fixed up with his lover's daughter, has to make sure the date goes badly. So he takes her to what is clearly the most shocking, most transgressive venue he can think of: a strip club. Predictably, she's appalled. The scene ends with the unforgettable shot of Elaine Robinson's chaste and trembling face framed by a pair of large, tasseled breasts jiggling and spinning like flesh pinwheels behind her.

Smash-cut to the dwindling final years of the millennium, when it's as common to see naked breasts ajiggle as it is geeks on cell phones. Apparently, there's nothing tawdry or shameful anymore about visiting strip clubs—quite the opposite, what with Hollywood's young bucks and various Jets, Mets and Yankees garnering automatic, jaunty mentions in the gossip columns every time they drop by Scores, one of the nation's many upscale tittie taverns. Although Scores has hosted countless bachelor

The Legitimization of Porn: A Time Line

c. 470 B.C.	First century A.D.	c. 1390	1524
Etruscan potters emboss vases with tasteful representations of fornicating human beings.	Vātsyāyana pens the Kama Sutra, the first sex manual.	Geoffrey Chaucer's "The Miller's Tale" features a randy young college student having sex with his host's comely wife, establishing the precedent for at least 90 percent of all *Penthouse* "Forum" letters.	On the heels of the invention of the printing press, Italian writer Pietro Aretino publishes *Postures,* a popular how-to sex guide with illustrations.

Ever since the *Mayflower* lumbered ashore, our culture's had a twisted take on sex—a whipsawing blend of revulsion and obsession.

parties over the years, a *book* party was actually held there last February—a party which found such esteemed guests as a *New York Times* editor paying for and enjoying the services of lap dancers.

Meanwhile, down at the never more odious Cineplex, suburbanites have been taking in sunny biopics on sleaze legends Larry Flynt and Howard Stern; soon the queue will be forming for *Boogie Nights*, a film featuring Mark Wahlberg as an enormously endowed porn star. All this on the marabou-trimmed heels of *Showgirls* and *Striptease*, most notable for the goose-bumps all that bare flesh failed to raise. Elaine Robinson would come across as a hopeless ninny in such a climate, where it's hip to be blase' and pornography, unbelievably, is all of a sudden kitsch.

When exactly did we stop flinching at the sight of other people's privates? When did we lose the reflex to blush? At some point when we weren't looking, porn slithered into the mainstream, and now we find ourselves awash in skank.

Not that we haven't played a role in our own degradation. Ever since the *Mayflower* lumbered ashore, our culture's had a twisted take on sex—a whipsawing blend of revulsion and obsession. The trick, of course, has been to maintain a puritanical pose while secretly reveling in salaciousness. So you have tabloid headlines professing shock and disgust at the details and photos of deviance that are chockablock inside, while Jenny Jones and Jerry Springer tsk-tsk grimly at the panels they have painstakingly stocked with prostitutes and pedophiles.

But now all of that is changing. Thanks to a panicky fin de siècle fitfulness, people find themselves in one of two modes: Either they're on a last-ditch search for meaning and answers—getting religion and buying books about angels and mystical ancient texts—or they're partying like it's 1999, on the conga line to Armageddon. It's this latter crowd that most of us fall into, having traded in that prissy, puritanical disdain for an equally noxious, all-purpose irony. Condemnation meets Condom Nation: With irony as our cover, we can deflect, ignore, transform the horror of anything; armed with irony, we can turn the daily gusher of perverse sexual images and ideas—on cable, on the Internet, in movies, even on sitcoms—into a breezy joke.

Which isn't to suggest that porn itself is such a bad thing. We all need a release, an occasional stroll on the wild side, a chance to nose around in the forbidden zone. At its best, porn has no pride; it lets us run our fantasies in a place that's both boundless and safe. But the power of porn is in the illicit rush. Now that it's being reduced to kooky Zeitgeist fodder and we're having at it like looters during a blackout, porn can't possibly deliver the frisson it was designed to. Where porn is concerned, one can definitely get too much of a good thing.

In a culture that has an enormous economic incentive to exploit, the crusade for some sort of personal responsibility and moderation is a losing battle; it's what makes hand-wringing, antiporn feminists like Catharine MacKinnon and Andrea Dworkin come off as hysterics. (These days the last word in hip comes courtesy of *proporn* feminists, like Sallie Tisdale, Susie Bright and Laura Kipnis.) In our current mad rush to embrace our darker nature, once daring positions become instant party line; anything with the slightest potential to shock is seized

---

1749
English writer John Cleland publishes the ribald *Fanny Hill*, which is initially banned but subsequently republished after its infamy wins it new popularity.

1896
Eleven months after the first-ever public screening of a motion picture, the first blue movie, *Bedtime for the Bride*, is shown in Paris. Inaugurating a tradition later upheld by *Rambone* and *E.T.: The Extra Testicle*, *Bedtime* parodies a popular play of the period.

1934
Henry Miller's sexually explicit novel *Tropic of Cancer* is published in Paris but banned in the United States, as its sequel, *Tropic of Capricorn*, will be in 1939, thereby winning the books a wide, furtive readership they otherwise might not have had.

1953
Amid the repression of the Eisenhower era, 27-year-old Hugh Hefner's new magazine, *Playboy*, makes skin-mag perusal safe for Cheeveresque Westchester commuters.

upon and mauled with the fervor of a fashion victim at a sample sale. But titillators, like clothing fads, have notoriously short life spans here in the burnt-out, "been there, done that" '90s—which accounts for the current ho-hum status of the once unsettling drag queen, the tedious popularity of prominent piercings and tattoos. Traditional turnoffs become turn-ons before turning cold almost immediately and then turning to dust. How else to explain the phenomenon of Dennis Rodman—a one-

---

There's a theory that illicit thrills work like a drug—we build up a tolerance, a familiarity such that the blood will race only with regular increases in the dosage.

---

man totem of taboos past and present—moving so quickly from intriguing outsider to overexposed joke?

Then there's the case of *Showgirls* and *Striptease*. Lousy movies, both. But the real reason they were dismissed with such noisy yawns is that today's critics and audiences desperately need to prove how impervious they are to porn content. With the onetime taboo of pornography lying in shards all around us, what a miscalculation on the filmmakers' parts to think they were fingering a cultural hot button! In the end, *Showgirls* and *Striptease* weren't lambasted for being shocking, as *Showgirls*' self-righteous screenwriter Joe Eszterhas labored so hard to suggest, but for not being shocking enough. Sillier still, once the movie tanked in theaters and Eszterhas was razzed into silence, the distributor attempted to re-

coup some p⋯
angle. The idea⋯
"brave" flick as⋯
that devotees w⋯
over at midnight⋯

Irony. It's what⋯
winds of uncertain⋯
chaos. In movie hou⋯
a couple of years ag⋯
antino. Having succes⋯
distic violence in *Reser⋯*
still ballyhooing the styl⋯
Stealers Wheel–meets–V⋯e), the director
turned his ironizer on se⋯ deviance in *Pulp Fiction*.
When portly Ving Rhames takes it up the behind from a skinny yahoo, audiences are giggling soon enough, thanks to Bruce Willis's inventive rescue (guffawing at every frame of *Pulp Fiction*, from the kid's head exploding to the "dead-nigger storage" jokes, became an insufferable mark of being in the know). Now think back twenty-five years to *Deliverance*, when portly Ned Beatty was also made to take it up the behind from a skinny yahoo. The male population was traumatized. For years guys became queasy just talking about it; the nightmarish catchphrase "Squeal like a pig!" haunted them. That there was ever a time when we were naive enough to get so flustered—it's almost too touching to be believed.

There's a theory that illicit thrills work like a drug. We build up a tolerance, a familiarity such that the blood will race only with regular increases in the dosage. The theory is largely written off as the work of moralizing alarmists. Yet why else would a movie like *Crash* even exist, a film in which the scars, gashes and metal braces of car-accident victims are the fetishes du jour? Or *Kissed*, which explores necrophilia? Why would clean-cut Ron Howard suddenly feel the need to make a movie about *Deep Throat* star Linda Lovelace, and what is classically inclined Kenneth Branagh

bout . . . *lap dancing?* Simple:
t push forth into ever seamier
hmaker or consumer—is to be left

the nation's innocence hasn't been lost in
s so much as it's been bound, gagged and set
in the culturewide crush to keep pace. Consider
granite-jawed network anchors attempting to get
their mouths around the words *penis* and *pubic hair* on
the nightly news a few years back, on the hallowed occasions of John Wayne Bobbitt's dismemberment and the
Clarence Thomas hearings. No longer is it enough to
hear of Oval Office machinations; now it's headline news
that the chief machinator has a thing for feet, while one
Paula Jones may soon reveal the particulars of the president's privates. It's hard to picture Walter Cronkite re-
laying such details. But in his day, refusing to get down
in the mud wasn't tantamount to ratings suicide.

The slow and steady sexualizing of the culture—from
the frankness of network news to the graphicness of music videos to the smuttiness of talk shows—has inevitably led to our inurement. The fact that a hooker had her
lips on Hugh Grant's nether bits becomes career-resur-
recting material for the aggressively mainstream Jay
Leno, while typical daytime talk shows carry titles like
"My Mom's Too Fat to Strip!" (So wait—the issue here
is that your mom's overweight, not the fact that *she's a
stripper?*) Coming this fall from the once genteel book
publisher Simon & Schuster is a nostalgic compendium
of Tijuana Bibles, a.k.a. "f___ books." Forbidden raunch
in their heyday in the '30s, the books feature Popeye,
Dick Tracy and other G-rated comic-strip characters re-
drawn as penis-wielding sex fiends. Even today's social-
ites seem to think that hard-core can be kind of cute,
judging from their rush a few years back to own strappy
black Barbarella togs from Gianni Versace's bondage
line—to say nothing of the enduring sheer-fabric fad,
which finds women of all shapes and ages slouching
around quasi-naked at benefits.

But nothing has numbed us quite like the new tech-

nology, which allows us to become porn aficionados
without even leaving home. There is something edifying
about having to own the choices we make—which means
hauling our asses out to the liquor store, the neighborhood drug dealer or the porn shop when we need a fix;
it provides some small opportunity to reflect on our actions. But now people of almost every socioeconomic
bent can get their cyberitic kicks in a surreal sphere of
unaccountability—downloading images of kiddie porn
and bestiality from the Internet onto their PCs, chatting
with professional sluts, commanding girls to strip with
the click of a mouse. Parked on their couches, they can
tune in T & A on cable programs such as porno gour-
mand Al Goldstein's *Midnight Blue* as well as *The Robin
Byrd Show,* a showcase for dancers accoutred in little
more than those standard dual air bags that pass for
breasts these days. Between segments, phone-sex com-

Nothing has numbed us quite like the new technology, which allows us to become porn aficionados without even leaving home.

---

mercials offer the pie-eyed viewer a gruesome smorgas-
bord of erotic options. "Meet hot bodies, leather studs
and Latin boys!" enthuses one announcer, carnival
barker-style. Then there's the "dungeon master," who in-
tones to a doomy drumbeat, "If you're serious about
leather and the fetish lifestyle, call 970- . . ."

Porn used to exist someplace else—specifically, circumscribed ghettoes called red-light districts. But now

1973	1974	1977	1981
Marlon Brando implores Maria Schneider to "get the butter" in Bernardo Bertolucci's *Last Tango in Paris,* the first A-list movie to be rated X.	Spurred by the upstart success of Larry Flynt's *Hustler,* "pubic wars" break out between the comparatively chaste *Playboy* and *Penthouse,* with the two skin-mag leaders battling to see who can show more exposed genitalia.	Hoity-toity art-world patrons and patronesses flock to galleries to see explicit homoerotic photographs taken by Robert Mapplethorpe.	Ryan O'Neal stars in *So Fine,* a light comedy in which he plays a garmento who spawns a craze when he invents a new kind of blue jeans with a see-through window that displays the buttocks.

Can a network special called *A Very Porno Christmas*, starring Larry Flynt as Santa, be far behind?

that porn has come home—now that it's a $10 billion industry deeply embedded in American life, enriching the coffers of corporate entities such as AT&T and cable giant Time Warner—red-light districts have outlived their usefulness. In New York's Times Square, until the transition from Sleazy Street to Disney theme park is complete, the Deuce's ornate triple-X theaters loom like out-of-commission rides at a dilapidated carnival, relics of a scarier day.

Indeed, a large part of porn's move to the mainstream has involved the prettying up of this historically lurid form of entertainment. To that end, porn-video companies are strategically marketing their products to better-heeled yuppie couples (an approach that seems to be working; according to *Adult Video News,* 665 million hard-core movies were rented last year—up from 75 million a decade before). Vivid Video, for instance, hired an art director and a publicist from outside the business to

give the company and its products a "classier" look. It's also signing porn actresses to exclusive contracts and hooking them up with corporate sponsors such as Fresh Jive clothing, Black Fly sunglasses and Hard Candy cosmetics, which has a new shade of lipstick called Porno. The plan is to humanize the actresses, make them seem more like happy, responsible stars, as opposed to the drug-addicted meat they were treated as back in porn's outlaw adolescence. Elsewhere, Metro Pictures is backing an arty porn film called *Zazel,* replete with an unprecedented $250,000 budget and promotional tie-ins that include a *Zazel* music CD and a CD-ROM, as well as Zazel the scent.

They may as well be marketing the latest John Tesh release, so homogenized and commercialized is the skin trade becoming. And worst of all is how sex—real sex—will suffer. Already nakedness is losing its transformative power, while coitus will soon pack all the kicks and surprises of an ATM transaction. How could it not? With porn in people's faces from the time they're old enough to punch the remote, they'll be too jaded to appreciate the exquisite poignancy of nonprofessional flesh being tendered as a precious gift. In the meantime, stay tuned for the inexorable next chapter in the Porning of America. Can a network special called A *Very Porno Christmas,* starring Larry Flynt as Santa, be far behind?

Lucy Kaylin is a GQ senior writer.

1986
Traci Lords, 18, becomes a cause célèbre (and shortly thereafter a "legitimate" actress) when the FBI arrests her for having appeared, underage, in at least one hundred porn films.

1990
The NC-17 rating is created for Philip Kauf-

man's relatively mild *Henry & June,* based on the diddlings of Henry Miller; his wife, June; and Anaïs Nin.

1991
The Clarence Thomas confirmation hearings introduce Long Dong Silver and pubic-hair jokes to evening-news broadcasts.

1992
Sharon Stone crosses and uncrosses her legs in Paul Verhoeven's *Basic Instinct.*

1992–3
Madonna unleashes her multimedia titillation trifecta: *Sex,* the book; *Erotica,* the album; and *Body of Evidence,* the movie.

1995
Sales and rentals of adult videos generate $3.1 billion in business, up from $900 million in 1985.

1996
The adult-filmmaking company Vivid Video becomes the first porn shop to cut a product-placement deal with a commercial backer.

Adult premarital sex is the 'sin' Americans wink at. But if you think casual sex is a problem only for teenagers, take a look at the numbers for grown-ups

Was it good for us?

BY DAVID WHITMAN

Teen pregnancy, Bill Clinton says, is the nation's "most serious social problem," and he has vowed to do something about it. The issue is a frequent "talking point" in his speeches, and earlier this month, in an elegant White House ceremony designed to underscore the administration's commitment, the first lady honored a dozen organizations for their work in tackling the problem.

For Clinton, as for politicians of every partisan stripe, lamenting the scourge of "babies having babies" is a no-lose proposition. Who could object? In preaching the virtues of abstinence during adolescence, however, the president and the first lady are not likely to mention one startling statistic: Many more 20-something adults than teenagers give birth to kids out of wedlock. In fact, most of the current social ills tied to sexual behavior—not only children born to unwed parents but sexually transmitted diseases, abortions, and the like—stem chiefly from adults who have sex before they marry, not from sexually active teens.

In an "enlightened" 1990s America, where a person old enough to vote and serve in the armed forces is also deemed old enough to make mature sexual decisions, the elaboration of these statistics is sobering. In 1994, just 22 percent of children born out of wedlock had mothers age 18 or under; more than half had mothers ages 20 to 29. Over half the women who obtain abortions each year, most unmarried, are in their 20s, while just a fifth are under 20. And the same age disparity is evident among those who contract sexually transmitted diseases, including AIDS. Although a disproportionate number of teens contract STDs, only 1 in 3 reported cases of gonorrhea and syphilis in 1995 involved people under 20. Teen pregnancy is an urgent problem, hard on mothers and even harder on their kids. But teenagers account for a smaller proportion of unwed births today than 20 years ago. (As late as 1975, teen girls bore the majority of all out-of-wedlock children in the United States.)

Yet when it comes to the negative social consequences of premarital sex between *adults,* there is silence in the White House—and in every other political institution. Conservatives, quick to decry sex between unwed teens and outspoken on many other sexual issues, turn suddenly shy when asked about adult premarital liaisons. Among those who declined to be interviewed for this article were William Bennett, editor of the anthology *The Book of Virtues;* Gary Bauer, head of the Family Research Council and a former aide to Ronald Reagan; John Podhoretz, a onetime speechwriter for George Bush and deputy editor of the *Weekly Standard* ("he's really not comfortable talking about the subject," said Podhoretz's assistant); and Laura Ingraham, a CBS News analyst who was featured in a 1995 *New York Times Magazine* cover story on young conservatives.

Mum's the word. The clergy, once loquacious on the topic of premarital "sin," are equally subdued. "Have you ever heard a sermon on 'living together'?" asks religious columnist Michael McManus in his 1995 book, *Marriage Savers.* Condemnation of adult premarital sex has virtually vanished from religious preaching, even in the homilies of Catholic priests. "In the pulpits there has been a backing away from moralizing about sex before marriage," says Bishop James McHugh, the bishop of Camden, N.J.

Why such reticence? The answer may seem obvious. Americans, at least tacitly, have all but given up on the notion that the appropriate premarital state is one of chastity. The Bible may have warned that like the denizens of Sodom and Gomorrah, those who give "themselves over to fornication" will suffer "the vengeance of eternal fire." Yet for most Americans, adult premarital sex has become the "sin" they not only wink at but quietly endorse. On television, adult virgins are as rare as caribou in Manhattan. Several studies have found that prime-time network shows implicitly condone premarital sex, and air as many as 8 depictions of it for every 1 of sex between married couples. And a

U.S. News poll shows that while most Americans—74 percent—have serious qualms about teens having sex before marriage, more than half believe it is not at all wrong, or wrong only sometimes, for *adults* to have premarital sex.

Yet this surface consensus reflects a rather rapid—and surprisingly complex—transformation in American attitudes. The notion that sex ought to be reserved for marriage may now seem antiquated, but it wasn't very long ago that a large majority of Americans held just that belief. As late as 1968, for example, millions of Americans found it newsworthy that two unwed 20-year-old college students would publicly admit to living together. Newspapers and newsmagazines replayed the tale of Linda LeClair, a sophomore at Barnard College, and Peter Behr, a Columbia University undergraduate, who conceded they had violated Barnard College's housing regulations by "shacking up" together in an off-campus apartment.

Love and let love. When Barnard students held protest rallies on LeClair's behalf, a beleaguered faculty-student committee relented and decided not to recommend her expulsion from the college. *Time* warned darkly of LeClair's "moment of immoral victory." And William F. Buckley likened LeClair in his syndicated column to an "unemployed concubine." Even the tabloids purported to be shocked by the couple's open cohabitation, penning stories with headlines such as "Suffragette of Love and let-love" and "Nine-to-sex coed!"

Between that dimly remembered past and today's indulgence of sexual experimentation before marriage stand the arrival of the pill and the various skirmishes of the sexual revolution. As it turns out, if converting Americans to free love and loose sexual mores was the goal, the revolution was pretty much a dud. Despite the stereotype of the promiscuous American, most men and women are still sexually conservative in belief and practice. Just over 70 percent of Americans say they have had only one sexual partner in the past year, and more than 80 percent report they have never had an extramarital affair. For the past 25 years, there has been almost no change in how Americans view adultery, homosexuality, or teenage sex— a substantial majority think all three are always, or almost always, wrong.

In the aftermath of that turbulent era, however, there was one definite casualty: Americans' long-held conviction

---

THE UNWED 30-SOMETHING

Jennifer Grossman, *30, is single and an MSNBC-TV contributor. She's a self-described libertarian but questions today's sexual freedom.*

I used to complain to my mother, who is

a liberal, about how boyfriends seemed commitment shy. And she would say, "Well, why buy the cow if the milk is free?" We're in the sexual promised land now, the milk is free, people are surfeited with sex—and yet we're starved for love. In locker rooms, in coffeehouses, women are getting together with their girlfriends the next morning after their dates and asking in hushed tones: "I hope you didn't sleep with him?"

Some of the men I've dated have been married before. The safe-sex jingle—"You're sleeping with everyone your lover has ever slept with"—has added resonance now: You're sharing emotional space with those ex-wives and girlfriends. You begin to play tricks on yourself—this one wasn't important, this one wasn't meaningful. The acceptance, even encouragement of premarital sex makes it very difficult to sustain the fantasy that we are loved alone.

I didn't kiss the man I'm dating now until the seventh date. I didn't have sex with him until the seventh month. He respects and values me a lot more than the men I dated in college, when I just was a lot more casual with my body. Women have spoiled men.

---

that virginity should be relinquished only in the marriage bed. To be sure, America has never been sexually pristine. Since the first settlers arrived, lots of unwed teens and young adults took a roll or two in the hay. And there was always a perceived double standard for men, who were expected to "sow their oats," and women, who were expected to save themselves for their husbands. Yet there are fundamental differences between the premarital sex of the 1960s and earlier eras, and that of the 1990s. In the mid-1960s, many more women were virgins at marriage than is now the case, and men and women who did engage in premarital sex often did so with their betrothed. Cohabitation was comparatively rare, and "shotgun weddings" for pregnant brides were common.

Almost certainly, television has had a central role in eroding the stigma of premarital sex. The sexual content of prime time has changed slowly, so viewers often fail to realize just how differently adult premarital sex is treated today from even a decade ago. Once, adolescents watched *Mork and Mindy,* the *Cosby Show, Little House on the Prairie,* and the like. Today, more than 6 million children under the age of 11 watch "family hour" shows that include *Beverly Hills 90210, Friends,* and *Roseanne.*

Sex, more sex. TV's characterization of out-of-wedlock sex has also done a flip-flop. Sen. Daniel Patrick Moynihan might say that television's treatment of

premarital sex is a classic example of "defining deviancy down"—what was once considered deviant or abnormal now is treated as the norm. In his book, *Prime Time,* Robert Lichter and his colleagues at the Center for Media and Public Affairs found that prime-time television now by implication endorses unmarried adults' intentions to have sex in about 3 out or 4 cases and raises concerns only about 5 percent of the time. "On shows like *Three's Company* the characters hinted around a lot about premarital sex," says Lichter. "But the shows back then did not specifically seek to justify unmarried sex."

Producers and screenwriters appear largely inured to this permissiveness, though viewers seem troubled. In a *U.S. News* poll last year, just 38 percent of the Hollywood elite were concerned about how TV depicted premarital sex, compared with 83 percent of the public. "Hollywood has glorified adult premarital sex," argues Sen. Joseph Lieberman. "And that is unhelpful if your goal is to reduce teen pregnancy and out-of-wedlock births."

In this climate, the suggestion that abstinence is preferable to sex for unwed adults seems hopelessly retrograde, about as timely as recommending that hansom cabs replace automobiles. It is virginity now that makes news. When a *TV Guide* columnist learned recently that college senior Donna Martin, the character played by Tori Spelling on

---

THE ATHLETE

A. C. Green,

a basketball star with the Dallas Mavericks, is 33 and has never married. He promotes the cause of abstinence through the Phoenix-based A. C. Green Programs for Youth.

I am still a virgin. Abstaining from extra-

marital sex is one of the most unpopular things a person can do, much less talk about. From a sheer numbers standpoint, it can be a lonely cause—but that doesn't mean it's not right.

I abstain as an adult for the same reasons I did as a teen—the principle doesn't change, or the feeling of self-respect I get. My fellow ballplayers do not tell me, "You are crazy"—it's more that they think I'm being unrealistic. It's ironic, but the guys who are parents—and especially the guys who have daughters—tend to look at sex before marriage a lot more carefully now.

Beverly Hills 90210, was scheduled to lose her virginity in the season's finale, the magazine issued a press release to detail this "scoop."

It is possible to argue that, on balance, the removal of premarital sex from the roster of moral or religious transgressions is a good thing. Certainly, most young singles believe they won't personally be hurt by premarital sex because they feel they use contraception responsibly. They minimize their own risk, on the assumption that unintended pregnancies, STDs, and abortions are problems that mostly afflict the careless.

In fact, the *U.S. News* poll shows that a majority of respondents under the age of 45 think that adult premarital sex generally benefits people quite apart from the issue of expanding their sexual pleasure. Unlike their elders, younger adults widely endorsed the sowing-one's-oats rationale for premarital sex, so long as the sowing is not done promiscuously. Less than half of those under 45 thought it was a good idea for adults to remain virgins until they marry. And a majority of respondents agreed that having had a few sexual partners makes it easier for a person to pick a compatible spouse.

America's acceptance of premarital sex also makes it easier to avoid rushing into marriage. By delaying family formation until after college, young couples escape being saddled with large loans and child-rearing duties while they are still trying to earn their degrees. And couples who wed for the first time after they turn 25 are less likely to be divorced a decade later than couples who wed while still in their teens. For all the nostalgia about the '50s, few Americans want to turn back the clock to

that era, when about half the nation's women wed before their 20th birthday. Less than 8 percent of those surveyed by *U.S. News* thought it ideal for a woman to marry before she turns 20, and fewer than 5 percent though it ideal for a man to marry before his 20s. The best age for a woman to marry, in most Americans' minds, is 24. For men, the ideal age is 25.

Yet such "benefits" may be more wishful thinking than fact. Cohabitation may seem a good "trial run" for a solid marriage. But in practice, cohabiting couples who marry—many of whom already have children—are about 33 percent more likely to divorce than couples who don't live together before their nuptials. Virgin brides, on the other hand, are *less* likely to divorce than women who lost their virginity prior to marriage.

But we didn't inhale. Cohabitation is associated with other risks for young couples. Live-in boyfriends are far more likely to beat their partners than are spouses. And young adults who move in together, without being engaged to be married, are more likely to use cocaine

and cigarettes after they start cohabiting than beforehand. All in all, muses Harvard sociologist Christopher Jencks, adult premarital sex "may ultimately prove to be a little like smoking dope in the 1960s. In retrospect, maybe it isn't so good for you after all."

In a broader sense, the public willingness to tolerate and even condone premarital sex makes it much harder for teachers, clerics, and law enforcement officials to curb other types of extramarital sex that are more controversial. Public acceptance of premarital sex has undermined the efforts of government officials to encourage abstinence among teens and to prosecute men who have out-of-wedlock sex with minors, and it has even colored the efforts of the clergy to keep gays and lesbians from being ordained. The Presbyterian Church (U.S.A.) recently enacted an amendment barring anyone currently engaged in extramarital sex—heterosexual or otherwise—from serving as an officer of the church. Put another way, sex before marriage has proved to be the runaway horse of traditional values. Once it took off, all the other old-time mores became more difficult to keep in their place.

An old joke among sex educators is that a conservative is a progressive with a teenage daughter. Few voters, with or without children, question that teens are generally less prepared to shoulder the consequences of sex than adults, or that there is an especially forceful case to be made for having teens—particularly younger adolescents—abstain from sex. Yet it is hard for parents to, say, convince a 17-year-old that she should abstain from sex now but that when she turns 18 or 21 it will be OK for her to start sleeping with her boyfriends. "I find it easy to distinguish between an adult with some emotional maturity and a 15-year-old having

---

The facts about premarital sex

■ **Sexual initiation.** In the 1960s, 25 percent of young men and 45 percent of young women were virgins at age 19; by the 1980s, fewer than 20 percent of males and females were.

■ **Sexual history.** About 30 percent of Americans say they have had one or no sex partners since turning 18; 30 percent say two to four partners; 22 percent say five to 10 partners; 20 percent say 10 partners or more.

■ **Cohabitation.** In the 1950s, roughly 9 in 10 young women got married without living with their partner, compared with 1 in 3 in the early 1990s.

■ **Virgin brides.** Percentage of white women married from 1960–65 who were virgins: 43; from 1980–85: 14.

Source: *Sex in America; The Social Organization of Sexuality; Journal of Marriage and the Family*

sex," says former Clinton White House aide William Galston, now a board member of the National Campaign to Prevent Teen Pregnancy. "Whether the 15-year-old will find it easy to make that distinction is another matter altogether. They may very well view it as hypocritical for a 45-year-old to say, 'Do as we say and not as we do.' "

Drawing a line between teen sex and adult sex is further complicated by the fact that many teenage women sleep with males age 20 and over, not with teen boys. Teen pregnancy is chiefly a result of these older men fathering out-of-wedlock babies with 18- and 19-year-old women, who are responsible for about 3 out of 5 teen births. Only a quarter of the men who impregnate women under the age of 18 are also under 18. As Mike Males put it in *The Scapegoat Generation*: "If the president really wanted to prevent junior high sex, he would lecture grown-ups."

Tough love. One renascent reform for curbing adult-teen sex is enforcement of statutory rape laws, which generally prohibit sex between girls who have not reached the age of consent (typically between ages 14 and 18) and older adult males. In the *U.S. News* poll, 64 percent of Americans said it was always wrong for a man over the age of 20 to have sex with a teenage girl. Both President Clinton and Bob Dole urged states last year to start reapplying the laws, and a handful have done so. But no state is seriously considering enforcing existing antifornication laws—which essentially prohibit consensual sex between unmarried adults.

Some of the reticence might be written off to the fear of seeming hypocritical, especially among younger conservative lawmakers: We had sex before marriage, so we can't suggest that others shouldn't—at least, not with a straight face. But the trepidation of those on the right has more complex roots, too. Conservatives with libertarian leanings believe that consensual sex between adults is a private matter, one the state shouldn't meddle in. About half those surveyed by *U.S. News* said unmarried couples who live together are "doing their own thing and not affecting anyone else." And at least some on the political right have come to accept the popular belief, echoed in the *U.S. News* poll, that premarital sex between consenting adults generally serves a positive purpose. As Richard Posner, a prominent conservative jurist and intellectual, puts it

in his book *Sex and Reason:* "There is no good reason to deter premarital sex, a generally harmless source of pleasure and for some people an important stage of marital search."

Just what, if anything, can be done about the negative consequences of premarital sex is far from clear. Twenty years ago, Jimmy Carter told employees at the Department of Housing and Urban Development: "Those of you who are living in sin—I hope you'll get married." Carter's suggestion, Galston recalls, provoked "a massive horse laugh, particularly from the press corps." More recently, state officials have begun to ponder how to reduce adult premarital

sex in a formal way, owing largely to the new welfare law. During the Reagan and Bush years, Congress authorized several small "abstinence only" programs to teach high school students the benefits of abstinence, without offering information on birth control. The new welfare law sets aside $50 million for each of the next five years for states to fund abstinence-only programs. In toto, the U.S. government will spend about nine times as much on abstinence education in 1997-98 as in previous years. The vast bulk of the spending will surely be aimed at teens. But the programs funded in the welfare law need not be limited to them.

THE CONVERT

Lisa Schiffren, *37, wrote Dan Quayle's famous 1992 Murphy Brown speech in which Quayle criticized the TV character for bearing a child out of wedlock. Schiffren married in 1993 and has a daughter.*

I did not abstain from premarital sex. I

was raised in a secular, Upper East Side Manhattan-liberal home and now I'm a quasi-religious conservative. I wish I could say that premarital sex was morally wrong. Sometimes, I think it's OK. It's very hard to send young women to college and tell them they're going to be investment bankers and lawyers, and yet they can't have sex. Plus, we don't really want people getting married too, too early. I did a lot of things in my 20s I couldn't have done if I were married, like spend a lot of time overseas.

More often than not, though, premarital sex is a bad idea. Nobody I knew at the women's college I went to would have had the guts to say that premarital sex was especially bad. Yet nobody liked a social system where sex was expected in any given relationship. The experience of my generation suggests people very rarely get what they are looking for from premarital sex, unless what they're looking for is purely sexual. When it's too available, sex itself loses its meaning.

Among the elite there is more public posturing about not smoking, or not being fat, than about not having promiscuous sexual relationships. People are afraid to sound like prigs. I myself have overcome this and am happy to be a prig. But I no longer have to date.

THE CLERGYMAN

James McHugh *is the bishop of Camden, N.J., and one of the Catholic Church's spokesmen on family issues.*

All sexual activity outside of marriage

is wrong and has no moral justification. Sex before marriage diminishes respect for sexuality itself. Many young adults who have engaged in sex before marriage aren't so sure they want their younger brothers and sisters to live through the same experience. But they feel restrained from honestly saying what they think to upcoming generations, either from guilt, ineptitude, or fear that they will be rejected or ridiculed. If everybody's doing it, and everybody accepts that everybody is doing it, then the young man or woman who has a more ennobling vision of human sexuality ends up looking like the oddball.

THE POLICY MAKER

William Galston, *a former White House aide, helped design President Clinton's teen pregnancy strategy.*

As a religious and moral matter, I per-

sonally cannot look at a long-standing relationship outside the bonds of matrimony and say, no, that's totally wrong, that's morally forbidden. I have no problems telling my 12-year-old son he should abstain from sex in high school. I would have a hard time, based on my own experience, telling my son, "Well, after you get to college, I want you to follow the same course of conduct I asked you to follow while you were in high school and lived at home." I don't know that I would want my son to wait until he was 27 or 28 to get married. I got married at 22.

There is a sense in which we believe what we believe about premarital sex because it is convenient for us to do so. It would be extremely inconvenient to conclude that all this premarital sex we tolerate isn't such a good thing, after all.

Deterrence. A second part of the new law deals more directly with the social ills that can attend premarital sex. It provides up to $100 million a year in bonuses for the five states that can show the largest reductions in out-of-wedlock births without corresponding increases in abortions. Since most out-of-wedlock births are to adults, state officials will, somehow, have to address premarital sex. Yet even conservatives aren't pretending they want the government to discourage most adult premarital sex. Their chief concern is out-of-wedlock births among welfare mothers, more than 90 percent of whom are currently 20 or older. "If the parents can support the child, fine; if they can't, then they ought to be discouraged from having it," says Posner.

THE CHRISTIAN SOLDIER

Ralph Reed *is the executive director of the Christian Coalition.* U.S. News *asked him if he was a virgin when he married.*

I wouldn't say that. I would say when

my wife and I married, we had both been faithful to each other up until that time. We did not engage in premarital sex and abstaining was important to us. . . . Yes, I think it is morally wrong to have sex before marriage. But I'm not going to condemn someone who is engaged in conduct that I don't agree with. I will encourage my children to abstain until they are married, even if they are adults.

It's hard for me to deliver lectures about finishing college before you get married, since my wife was 19 when I married her. I would prefer to have my daughter finish college before she marries, because career and livelihood issues are much more easily resolved now if you have a college degree. But I don't think you want to set up a situation where you've been so Pharisaic about not approving marriage until after college that you end up having children elope.

Even though we had to struggle financially, my wife and I were infinitely better off having gone ahead and gotten married. If we'd had to wait, it would have been harder to remain consistent with what we believed was morally right. It shouldn't be the overwhelming reason, but the truth is, the sexual drive is one of the things that brings you to your mate.

The truth, for now, is that nobody has proven ideas about how to reduce adult premarital sex, nor has anyone shown much inclination to do so. The prospects for an en masse return to premarital chastity are almost nil, though some young singles may become more sexually conservative. Earlier this month, the U.S. government announced that the proportion of teens who reported having sexual intercourse went down for the first time since similar surveys began in the 1970s.

The budding discomfort with casual sex is evident, too, in the enormous popularity of *The Rules,* the retro-guide that advises women how to coyly lure Mr. Right to the altar. Its authors don't counsel chastity. But they do advise "*Rules* girls" not to kiss a man on the first date and to put off sleeping with him for a few weeks or months. Jennifer Grossman, an MSNBC-TV contributor who is single, 30, and writes often on women's issues, argues that the appeal of *The Rules* among college-educated women reflects their search for a middle ground between casual sex and premarital chastity. "This all-you-can-eat sexual buffet is leaving a lot of men and women feeling very empty," she says. "I see a pattern among my girlfriends—when they sleep with men, they cry. Sleeping with a man you've known for a week is such an 'almost.' It's almost what you want—but a chasm away from what you really need."

In theory, more responsible use of contraception might provide another avenue for eliminating the worst complications of sex before marriage. In practice, though, the increased availability of contraception has not halted the rise in out-of-wedlock births or put an end to abortions and STDs. Adult premarital sex, the little-noticed heart of the sexual revolution, is here to stay. There may be little to do about this silent "epidemic"—except to acknowledge that sex before marriage may not always be the simple pleasure that many Americans assume it to be.

With Paul Glastris and Brendan I. Koerner

Sex in the Future:
Virtuous and Virtual?

By Kenneth Maxwell

Sex will flourish in the twenty-first century as growing openness about sexual matters and new technologies pave the way to new sexual experiences, including virtual sex.

Equated with sin since the encounter of Adam and Eve, sexuality is now emerging torturously from the dark shadows of secret shame. Ancient shibboleths and taboos are already yielding to a rapidly spreading mantle of enlightenment over a broad spectrum of humanity.

The most spectacular development in the near future will be a flourishing of openness and frankness in discussing sex and sexuality, comparable to the ease with which people have always discussed other facets of human behavior—food and drink, clothing, children, recreation, work, religion, physical ailments, appendectomies, and spats with the spouse.

Physicians, who in the past received little or no training in sexual matters except for highly specialized problems, will be carried along with the tide. Conditioned from childhood to view sex as sinful or secret, or both, old-fashioned general practitioners will be replaced by physicians who will see sexual problems and practices as major health problems important to the welfare of their patients. Conservative medical schools will reluctantly expand their curricula to include instruction in sex, sex problems, and their treatment, and this will be followed by certified board specialties.

Sex therapy will have an expanding role as part of the physician's arsenal, creating a new category of highly trained medical assistants, both male and female. It may find a place in premarital instruction in en-

suring at least an auspicious start along the rocky road of marital bliss. However, the need for premarital instruction, and in fact the need for all sex therapy, will be minimized by an enlightened view and acceptance of nudity as normal and innocuous behavior.

Modern pharmacology has already embarked on a new generation of sex drugs, but the main thrust is not for developing aphrodisiacs, but for drugs to correct sexual dysfunctions, especially to overcome impotence, problems that are more common than most people realize. So-called sex toys are of limited therapeutic value, but will have increasing use for sexual gratification. Now available in a small number of unobtrusive shops or by mail order, sex toys will come to be openly available in mall shops and will be a topic of open discussion as prudery fades.

The inevitable decline of prudery will contribute to sexual relationships that enable man and woman to see each other as equals with differences in desires and needs openly shared. Bed roles will evolve with an awakening to the fact that knowledge of intimate sexual matters is something to share and that individuals differ in their desires and needs.

Videotapes will be used increasingly for instruction as well as for erotic stimulation and entertainment. Many people view erotic movies and tapes as pornographic trash, but the fact that at least a third of erotic videos now sold are used and enjoyed by married couples suggests that an increase in demand will lead to improved quality and variety. Erotic interactive CD-ROMs are now used almost exclusively by voyeurs for entertainment, but the technology offers possibilities for educational material of a wide variety.

Gay Marriage and Legal Prostitution

The legal status of same-sex relationships is in a state of flux. The action of the state of Hawaii in authorizing same-sex marriages gave encouragement to gays and lesbians, who anticipated the protection of a federal law that recognizes marriage in any state as being valid in all states. Several states had already passed laws banning same-sex marriages, and additional states had such legislation under consideration.

It remains unpredictable to what extent several thousand years of tradition that "marriage" is solely a union of man and woman will influence justices' decisions. But even if same-sex marriages in general are denied legal standing, there will remain a strong trend toward granting specific legal rights to same-sex couples, such as hospital visitation, inheritance of assets, health insurance, and pensions. The same privileges will be granted to committed unmarried heterosexual couples.

Prostitution, a traditional human activity since at least the beginning of historical memory, will continue to flourish worldwide. In parts of the world, such as most parts of the United States, where prostitution is a criminal offense, it will be gradually decriminalized. This will come about less through a moral awakening and sense of justice and fairness than through fear of uncontrollable disease epidemics, especially if the heterosexual AIDS epidemic materializes as widely predicted. Decriminalization will open the way to licensing prostitutes, accompanied by mandatory weekly health examinations and collection of fees and taxes, which, in turn, will create funds for public prevention and treatment of venereal diseases.

Eros on the Internet

Dissemination of erotic material on the Internet is worrisome to many people, especially if they have children with access to a computer and an online service. The 1996 Communications Decency Act made it a federal crime in the United States to transmit "indecent" material over the Internet without ensuring that children cannot see it. The law also required software services to establish a rating system for use by parents who want to block objectionable programs. The American Civil Liberties Union, along with several communication businesses, immediately challenged the constitutionality of the Decency Act, and they took it to the Supreme Court. If the Act is upheld, what is "indecent" will be argued interminably.

A rating standard agreed upon by a consortium of 39 software and computer companies implemented a variety of privately developed rating systems. For example, one based on the Platform for Internet Content Selection (PICS) has a scale of nine rankings from "subtle innuendo" to "explicitly for adults," with one level reserved for technical references to sex, such as medical information. The company that offers this system ranked, at last count, 30,000 of the half million or so sites on the World Wide Web alone.

It's clear that something new and portentous has happened to eroticism, pornography, and obscenity. These time-honored forms of art and literature now wing their way on cyberspace to all parts of the world in dissemination of all levels of erotica from benign to violent, with the added feature of children being both participants and victims.

A battle of gigantic proportions is looming between the champions of free speech and the defenders of privacy. It's a battle with no end in sight. The mass of cyberporn backed up by an insatiable appetite and a free-speech commitment pitted against the anger of desperation and determination to defend the honor of home and family is a no-win crusade for either side. There will be compromises in which there will be something for everyone but not enough for anyone. Users will be permitted to use the Internet for almost anything they wish, but there will be a requirement that their identity and interests will be clearly stated and available.

Attempts to censor the Internet are futile because the information is available from so many sources. Even if a computer genius comes up with a practical way of doing it, protection of privacy and defense against objectionable intrusion will not be perfect. Hackers and clever adults will continue to find ways to gain access to and transmit unauthorized material. And children will, as always, find ways to outwit their parents.

Sex with a Computer?

A new form of erotic adventure, *virtual sex*, may soon be developed.

The technique, now called virtual reality, is envisioned as a way to enhance the pleasure of viewing a scene or action. It is not merely watching actors perform as on stage or in a movie. In virtual sex, for example, the voyeuristic pleasure of watching people engage in coital capers, or whatever, is replaced by providing the realism of the user participating in the action. The user puts on a helmet or gets into a large box, and the experience happens in the privacy of the space provided.

For a long time, we've been able to transmit sound electronically, including the intense emotions of music in its various forms. And we can supplement and intensify the feelings with visual imagery. Sensations still untapped electronically are odors, tastes, touch, pressure, and kinesthetic sensations.

In the case of odors, we can expect that research will unravel the presently unsolved mystery of human sex pheromones (body odors and flavors). Sex pheromones—mainly aphrodisiacs—are so common throughout the animal world, including the higher primates, that it is almost certain that they have a subliminal role in human sexuality, even though they escape our conscious awareness. Our clumsy effort to find the answer through a multi-billion-dollar perfume industry will be replaced by a breakthrough in biotechnology that will find one of its benefits in virtual sex. The human nose has 10 million olfactory receptors, and with training, the nose can discriminate between about 10,000 odors. There is already available an "electronic nose," called the Aroma-Scanner, that visualizes odors in 3-D, and the odors can be precisely identified with an instrument called a gas chromatograph.

Instruments of this kind will lead to the identification of human sex pheromones and their action as a prelude to how their effects can be duplicated and intensified electronically. Similar determinations will be made of the senses of touch, taste, pressure, and kinesthesia in studies of how to intensify or modify them. Virtual sex will greatly enhance normal sensations and will add some never before experienced.

Virtual-sex programs for solo use will be available, but the more popular programs will be those in which the viewer can choose one or more partners from a wide selection of choices. The choices can be, but will not have to be, those offered by a programmer. A man or woman will be able to choose his or her spouse or lover.

Sex from Afar

The most advanced techniques will make it possible for a couple to join in virtual sex even though separated. An e-mail message to set an agreed upon time will enable a traveling man or woman to enjoy the comforts of home. The availability of virtual sex will not eliminate prostitution, but for the first time, it will allow completely safe prostitution, as well as safe sex generally. People may be able to pick out a good-looking virtual partner from an electronic catalog and engage in a completely safe and fulfilling encounter.

Areas near military bases are notorious for having a plethora of cafes, bars, dance halls, dives of various kinds, B-girls, and prostitutes. Standards of health and safety will improve dramatically when virtual sex parlors are established in competition with the usual places of entertainment. Sexually transmitted diseases, including AIDS, will decline dramatically. Military commanders have the authority to declare places of entertainment off-limits if they pose a threat to the health and welfare of military personnel. Commanders will be more inclined to declare the sleazier joints off-limits if wholesome recreation becomes attractive.

Virtual sex will not necessarily be confined to establishment sex par-

Sex and Reproduction

Science and technology have drastically affected human sexuality for many years, most notably in their effect on fertility through the use of the contraceptive pill.

Infertile couples who want babies will increasingly seek and receive help from science. Artificial insemination in the future will differ greatly from the early slipshod practice of collecting sperm with minimum attention to genetic and health suitability. Much more attention will be given to sperm donors' characteristics other than health and physical appearance, especially mental achievements and other outstanding qualities.

Other methods of overcoming infertility, including *in vitro* fertilization and embryo transfer, will become increasingly available. Assisted reproductive technology, along with its variations, and surrogate motherhood are currently so expensive that availability is limited to moderately affluent couples. While improved success rates will reduce the cost, the methods will still not be cheap.

Techniques for producing and handling human embryos have suggested the possibility of using excess embryos for scientific and medical research. But ethical questions are so serious that most such research will be delayed indefinitely. Some procedures are clearly out of bounds even if possible, such as implantations of human embryos into other species and hybridizing humans with other species. Cloning human embryos for a limited purpose such as determining genetic characteristics will encounter objections.

The greatest potential for benefits from work with human embryos is the determination of genetic characteristics and correction of deficiencies. Close ethical monitoring is predictable, but gestating human embryos to term *in vitro* (outside the womb) is so far from present capability that even consideration of the ethical impact is in the distant future.

—*Kenneth Maxwell*

lors. If history is a guide, technical development will bring about miniaturization. The bulge you see in a traveler's briefcase may not be a weighty report but a two-way virtual-sex unit with a built-in modem that will make a business trip as much pleasure as staying at home.

No one has produced virtual sex, and there is no certainty that it can be done with any degree of perfection. Still, the idea will continue to challenge electronic entrepreneurs. Part of the appeal will be the privacy and safety of virtual sex in a society that is becoming increasingly aware of the threat of AIDS and other STDs. Virtual sex will be preferred by many men and women to surreptitious affairs, cocktail bar pickups, or the currently criminal patronage of prostitutes. Besides, virtual sex, as envisioned, will provide more intense sensations than actual sex, as well as sensations that are nonexistent in natural sex. Sensations will be more than addictive, they will be synergistic—a system whereby the input of one sensation enhances another, or several other sensations, rather than merely adding to them. Virtual sex will have special appeal to couples, who will be able to enhance the sensations of their own style and preferences.

Advances in Stimulation

The more advanced devices will be able to stimulate the specific pleasure centers of the brain to enhance sensations beyond anything experienced naturally. Laboratory experiments with animals have established the fact that when a sex hormone (testosterone) is injected into a cer-tain area of the hypothalamus, the animal is stimulated into female behavior regardless of its sex. And when the hormone is injected into another nearby area of the hypothalamus, the animal is stimulated into behaving as a male.

The animals were unable to communicate what their sensations were like, but it is well known that the hypothalamus, which is both part of the brain and an organ of internal secretion, is the emotional switchboard of the brain, standing in command of sexual development, performance, and emotions. The hypothalamus has connections to the eye nerves (hence its ability to reset the circadian rhythm) and to the amygdala, where at least some of the emotion signals originate. Imaging machines, more sensitive than those now used for medical diagnosis, will make it possible to map the brain in detail and to pinpoint areas of emotions and sensations.

People would not want needles, even as small as hypodermics, stuck into their brains to get their kicks. Although chemicals taken by mouth are capable of reaching the brain, the most effective way to activate the pleasure centers without side effects will be a noninvasive probe, possibly with a low-energy colored laser. People will choose between enhanced male sensations or enhanced female sensations, or both at the same time. Because of the intensity of the sensations, the sessions might have to be limited in duration, say no more than a few minutes at a time, to avoid overloading the brain circuits. But they could be repeated as frequently as the nerve cells regenerate their functional capacity.

Conclusion: The Future of Sex

The modern world's view of sex ranges from restraint to tolerance to "the more the better," especially if the result is more children. Still, the sex scene is on the verge of new developments in the Western world. In some places and in some societies there will be little observable change in the immediate future, but a strong undercurrent of change will have global effects.

Change will be brought about by the control or manipulation of sex-related developments and activities, especially population control and care of pregnant women and children. Some things may get worse before they get better, and changes will be accompanied by acrimonious debate and prolonged disputes. But the long-term trend will be a vast improvement in the quality of life.

The world of sex is at the threshold of trends amounting to a twenty-first-century revolution, bringing about the most dramatic changes in sexual relationships, habits, health, pleasures, pains, and living standards the world has ever seen.

About the Author
Kenneth Maxwell is the author of *A Sexual Odyssey: From Forbidden Fruit to Cybersex*, from which this article is adapted with permission of Plenum Press. The book is available from the Futurist Bookstore for $25.95 ($23.95 for Society members), cat. no. B-2025.

He is an emeritus professor of biology at California State University–Long Beach. His address is P.O. Box 3217, Idyllwild, California 92549

Abnormal: Anything considered not to be normal, i.e., not conforming to the subjective standards a social group has established as the norm.

Abortifacients: Substances that cause termination of pregnancy.

Abortion: The termination of a pregnancy.

Acquaintance (date) rape: A sexual encounter forced by someone who is known to the victim.

Acquired immunodeficiency syndrome (AIDS): Fatal disease caused by a virus that is transmitted through the exchange of bodily fluids, primarily in sexual activity and intravenous drug use.

Activating effect: The direct influence some hormones can have on activating or deactivating sexual behavior.

Actual use failure rate: A measure of how often a birth control method can be expected to fail when human error and technical failure are considered.

Adolescence: Period of emotional, social, and physical transition from childhood to adulthood.

Adultery: Extramarital sex.

Adultery toleration: Marriage partners extending the freedom to each other to have sex with others.

Affectional: Relating to feelings or emotions, such as romantic attachments.

Agenesis (absence) of the penis (ae-JEN-a-ses): A congenital condition in which the penis is undersized and nonfunctional.

AIDS: Acquired immunodeficiency syndrome.

Ambisexual: Alternate term for bisexual.

Amniocentesis: A process whereby medical problems with a fetus can be determined while it is still in the womb; a needle is inserted into the amniotic sac, amniotic fluid is withdrawn, and fetal cells are examined.

Anal intercourse: Insertion of the penis into the rectum of a partner.

Androgen: A male hormone, such as testosterone, that affects physical development, sexual desire, and behavior.

Androgynous: Possessing high frequencies of both masculine and feminine behaviors and traits.

Anejaculation: Lack of ejaculation at the time of orgasm.

Apgar test: An exam that determines the overall health of a newborn by testing his or her color, appearance, heart rate, reflex ability, and respiration.

Aphrodisiacs (af-ro-DEE-si-aks): Foods or chemicals purported to foster sexual arousal; they are believed to be more myth than fact.

Apoptosis: Programmed cell death that occurs naturally in living tissues. HIV may induce abnormal apoptosis in immune cells.

Apotemnophilia: A rare condition characterized by the desire to function sexually after having a leg amputated.

Areola (a-REE-a-la): Darkened, circular area of skin surrounding the nipple of the breast.

Artificial insemination: Injection of the sperm cells of a male into a woman's vagina, with the intention of conceiving a child.

Asceticism (a-SET-a-siz-um): Usually characterized by celibacy, this philosophy emphasizes spiritual purity through self-denial and self-discipline.

Asexuality: A condition characterized by a low interest in sex.

Autoerotic asphyxiation: Accidental death from pressure placed around the neck during masturbatory behavior.

Autofellatio (fe-LAY-she-o): A male providing oral stimulation to his own penis, an act most males do not have the physical agility to perform.

Autogynephilia: The tendency of some males to become sexually aroused by the thought or image of themselves with female attributes.

Bartholin's glands (BAR-tha-lenz): Small glands located in the minor lips that produce some secretion during sexual arousal.

Behavior therapy: Therapy that uses techniques to change patterns of behavior; often employed in sex therapy.

Berdache (bare-DAHSH): Anthropological term for cross-dressing in other cultures.

Bestiality (beest-ee-AL-i-tee): A human being having sexual contact with an animal.

Biological essentialists: Those who believe that sexual orientation is an inborn trait, resulting from biological factors during development.

Biphobia: Prejudice, negative attitudes, and misconceptions relating to bisexual people and their lifestyles.

Bisexual: Refers to some degree of sexual activity with or attraction to members of both sexes.

Bond: The emotional link between parent and child created by cuddling, cooing, and physical and eye contact early in a newborn's life.

Bondage: Tying, restraining, or applying pressure to body parts as part of sexual arousal.

Brachioproctic activity (brake-ee-o-PRAHK-tik): Known in slang as "fisting"; a hand is inserted into the rectum of a partner.

Brothel: House of prostitution.

Bulbourethral glands: Also called Cowper's glands.

Call boys: Highly paid male prostitutes.

Call girls: Highly paid female prostitutes.

Case study: An in-depth analysis of a particular individual and how he or she might have been helped to solve a sexual or other problem.

Catharsis theory: A suggestion that viewing pornography will provide a release for sexual tension, thus preventing antisocial behavior.

Celibacy (SELL-a-ba-see): Choosing not to share sexual activity with others.

Cervical cap: A contraceptive device that is shaped like a large thimble and fits over the cervix and blocks sperm from entering the uterus.

Cervical intraepithelial neoplasia (CIN): Abnormal, precancerous cells sometimes identified in a Pap smear.

Cervix (SERV-ix): Lower "neck" of the uterus that extends into the back part of the vagina.

Cesarean section: A surgical method of childbirth in which delivery occurs through an incision in the abdominal wall and uterus.

Chancroid (SHAN-kroyd): An STD caused by the bacterium *Hemophilus ducreyi* and characterized by sores on the genitals, which, if left untreated, could result in pain and rupture of the sores.

Child molesting: Sexual abuse of a child by an adult.

Chlamydia (klu-MID-ee-uh): Now known to be a common STD, this organism is a major cause of urethritis in males; in females it often presents no symptoms.

Circumcision: Of the clitoris—surgical procedure that cuts the prepuce, exposing the clitoral shaft; in the male, surgical removal of the foreskin from the penis.

Climacteric: Mid-life period experienced by both men and women when there is greater emotional stress than usual and sometimes physical symptoms.

Climax: Another term for orgasm.

Clinical research: The study of the cause, treatment, or prevention of a disease or condition by testing large numbers of people.

Clitoridectomy: Surgical removal of the clitoris; practiced routinely in some cultures.

Clitoris (KLIT-a-rus): Sexually sensitive organ found in the female vulva; it becomes engorged with blood during arousal.

Clone: The genetic-duplicate organism produced by the cloning process.

Cloning: A process involving the transfer of a full complement of chromosomes from a body cell of an organism into an ovum from which the chromosomal material has been removed; if allowed to develop into a new organism, it is an exact genetic duplicate of the one from which the original body cell was taken; the process is not yet used for humans, but it has been performed in lower animal species.

Cohabitation: Living together and sharing sex without marrying.

Coitus (ko-EET-us *or* KO-ut-us): Heterosexual, penis-in-vagina intercourse.

Coitus interruptus: A method of birth control in which the penis is withdrawn from the vagina prior to ejaculation.

Comarital sex: One couple swapping sexual partners with another couple; also called mate swapping.

Combining of chromosomes: The process by which a sperm unites with an egg, normally joining 23 pairs of chromosomes to establish the genetic "blueprint" for a new individual. The sex chromosomes establish its sex: XX for female and XY for male.

Coming out: To acknowledge to oneself and others that one is a lesbian, a gay male, or bisexual.

Condom: A sheath worn over the penis during intercourse to collect semen and prevent conception or venereal disease.

Consensual adultery: Permission given to at least one partner within the marital relationship to participate in extramarital sexual activity.

Controlled experiment: Research in which the investigator examines what is happening to one variable while all other variables are kept constant.

Coprophilia: Sexual arousal connected with feces.

Core gender identity: A child's early inner sense of its maleness, femaleness, or ambivalence, established prior to puberty.

Corona: The ridge around the penile glans.

Corpus luteum: Cell cluster of the follicle that remains after the ovum is released, secreting hormones that help regulate the menstrual cycle.

Cowper's glands: Two small glands in the male that secrete an alkaline fluid into the urethra during sexual arousal.

Cross-genderists: Transgenderists.

Cryptorchidism (krip-TOR-ka-diz-um): Condition in which the testes have not descended into the scrotum prior to birth.

Cunnilingus (kun-a-LEAN-gus): Oral stimulation of the clitoris, vaginal opening, or other parts of the vulva.

Cystitis (sis-TITE-us): A nonsexually transmitted infection of the urinary bladder.

Deoxyribonucleic acid (DNA): The chemical in each cell that carries the genetic code.

Depo-Provera: An injectable form of progestin that can prevent pregnancy for 3 months; it was approved for use in the United States in 1992.

Deprivation homosexuality: Can occur when members of the opposite sex are unavailable.

Desire phase: Sex researcher and therapist Helen Singer Kaplan's term for the psychological interest in sex that precedes a physiological, sexual arousal.

Deviation: Term applied to behaviors or orientations that do not conform to a society's accepted norms; it often has negative connotations.

Diaphragm (DY-a-fram): A latex rubber cup, filled with spermicide, that is fitted to the cervix by a clinician; the woman must learn to insert it properly for full contraceptive effectiveness.

Diethylstilbestrol (DES): Synthetic estrogen compound once given to mothers whose pregnancies were at high risk of miscarrying.

Dilation: The gradual opening of the cervical opening of the uterus prior to and during labor.

Direct sperm injection: A technique involving the injection of a single sperm cell directly into an ovum. It is useful in cases where the male has a low sperm count.

Discrimination: The process by which an individual extinguishes a response to one stimulus while preserving it for other stimuli.

Dysfunction: Condition in which the body does not function as expected or desired during sex.

Dysmenorrhea (dis-men-a-REE-a): Painful menstruation.

Dyspareunia: Recurrent or persistent genital pain related to sexual activity.

E. coli (*Escherichia coli*): Bacteria naturally living in the human colon, which often cause urinary tract infection.

Ectopic pregnancy (ek-TOP-ik): The implantation of a blastocyst somewhere other than in the uterus (usually in the fallopian tube).

Ejaculation: Muscular expulsion of semen from the penis.

Ejaculatory inevitability: The sensation in the male that ejaculation is imminent.

ELISA (enzyme-linked immunosorbent assay): The primary test used to determine the presence of HIV in humans.

Embryo (EM-bree-o): The term applied to the developing cells when, about a week after fertilization, the blastocyst implants itself in the uterine wall.

Endometrial hyperplasia (hy-per-PLAY-zhee-a): Excessive growth of the inner lining of the uterus (endometrium).

Endometriosis (en-doe-mee-tree-O-sus): Growth of the endometrium out of the uterus into surrounding organs.

Endometrium: Interior lining of the uterus, innermost of three layers.

Endorphins: A chemical produced by the brain in response to physical intimacy and sexual satisfaction.

Epidemiology (e-pe-dee-mee-A-la-jee): The branch of medical science that deals with the incidence, distribution, and control of disease in a population.

Epididymis (ep-a-DID-a-mus): Tubular structure on each testis in which sperm cells mature.

Epididymitis (ep-a-did-a-MITE-us): Inflammation of the epididymis of the testis.

Episiotomy (ee-piz-ee-OTT-a-mee): A surgical incision in the vaginal opening made by the clinician or obstetrician to prevent the baby from tearing the opening in the process of being born.

Epispadias (ep-a-SPADE-ee-as): Birth defect in which the urinary bladder empties through an abdominal opening and the urethra is malformed.

Erectile dysfunction: Difficulty achieving or maintaining penile erection (impotence).

Erection: Enlargement and stiffening of the penis as internal muscles relax and blood engorges the columns of spongy tissue.

Erogenous zone (a-RAJ-a-nus): Any area of the body that is sensitive to sexual arousal.

Erotica: Artistic representations of nudity or sexual activity.

Erotomania: A very rare form of mental illness characterized by a highly compulsive need for sex.

Erotophilia: Consistent positive responding to sexual cues.

Erotophobia: Consistent negative responding to sexual cues.

Estrogen (ES-tro-jen): Hormone produced abundantly by the ovaries; it plays an important role in the menstrual cycle.

Estrogen replacement therapy (ERT): Controversial treatment of the physical changes of menopause by administering dosages of the hormone estrogen.

Ethnocentricity: The tendency of the members of one culture to assume that their values and norms of behavior are the "right" ones in comparison to other cultures.

Ethnography: The anthropological study of other cultures.

Ethnosexual: Referring to data concerning the sexual beliefs and customs of other cultures.

Excitement: The arousal phase of sex researchers William Masters and Virginia Johnson's four-phase model of the sexual response cycle.

Exhibitionism: Exposing the genitals to others for sexual pleasure.

External values: The belief systems available from one's society and culture.

Extramarital sex: Married person having sexual intercourse with someone other than her or his spouse; adultery.

Fallopian tubes: Structures that are connected to the uterus and lead the ovum from an ovary to the inner cavity of the uterus.

Fellatio: Oral stimulation of the penis.

Female condom: A lubricated polyurethane pouch that is inserted into the vagina for intercourse to collect semen and help prevent disease transmission and pregnancy.

Female sexual arousal disorder: Difficulty for a woman in achieving sexual arousal.

Fetal alcohol syndrome (FAS): A condition in a fetus characterized by abnormal growth, neurological damage, and facial distortion caused by the mother's heavy alcohol consumption.

Fetishism (FET-a-shizm): Sexual arousal triggered by objects or materials not usually considered to be sexual.

Fetus: The term given to the embryo after 2 months of development in the womb.

Fibrous hymen: Condition in which the hymen is composed of unnaturally thick, tough tissue.

Follicles: Capsules of cells in which an ovum matures.

Follicle-stimulating hormone (FSH): Pituitary hormone that stimulates the ovaries or testes.

Foreplay: Sexual activities shared in early stages of sexual arousal, with the term implying that they are leading to a more intense, orgasm-oriented form of activity such as intercourse.

Foreskin: Fold of skin covering the penile glans; also called prepuce.

Frenulum (FREN-yu-lum): Thin, tightly-drawn fold of skin on the underside of the penile glans; it is highly sensitive.

Frotteurism: Gaining sexual gratification from anonymously pressing or rubbing one's genitals against others, usually in crowded settings.

G Spot: A vaginal area that some researchers feel is particularly sensitive to sexual stimulation.

Gamete intra-fallopian transfer (GIFT): Direct placement of ovum and concentrated sperm cells into the woman's fallopian tube to increase the chances of fertilization.

Gay: Refers to persons who have a predominantly same-gender sexual orientation and identity. More often applied to males.

Gender dysphoria (dis-FOR-ee-a): Some degree of discomfort with one's identity as male or female, and/or nonconformity to the norms considered appropriate for one's physical sex.

Gender identity: A person's inner experience of gender feelings of maleness, femaleness, or some ambivalent position between the two.

Gender identity disorder: The expression of gender identity in a way that is socially inconsistent with one's anatomical gender; may also be described as gender dysphoria.

Gender transportation: Gender dysphoria.

Gene therapy: Treatment of genetically caused disorders by substitution of healthy genes.

General sexual dysfunction: Difficulty for a woman in achieving sexual arousal.

Generalization: Application of specific learned responses to other, similar situations or experiences.

Genetic engineering: The modification of the gene structure of cells to change cellular functioning.

Genital herpes (HER-peez): Viral STD characterized by painful sores on the sex organs.

Genital warts: Small lesions on genital skin caused by papilloma virus; this STD increases later risks of certain malignancies.

Glans: Sensitive head of the female clitoris, visible between the upper folds of the minor lips; in the male, the sensitive head of the penis.

Gonadotropin releasing hormone (GnRH) (go-nad-a-TRO-pen): Hormone from the hypothalamus that stimulates the release of FSH and LH by the pituitary.

Gonads: Sex and reproductive glands, either testes or ovaries, that produce hormones and, eventually, reproductive cells (sperm or eggs).

Gonorrhea (gon-uh-REE-uh): Bacterial STD causing urethral pain and discharge in males; often no initial symptoms in females.

Granuloma inguinale (gran-ya-LOW-ma in-gwa-NAL-ee or -NALE): STD characterized by ulcerations and granulations beginning in the groin and spreading to the buttocks and genitals.

Group marriage: Three or more people in a committed relationship who share sex with one another.

Hard-core pornography: Pornography that makes use of highly explicit depictions of sexual activity or shows lengthy scenes of genitals.

Hedonists: People who believe that pleasure is the highest good.

Hemophiliac (hee-mo-FIL-ee-ak): Someone with the hereditary blood defect hemophilia, primarily affecting males and characterized by difficulty in clotting.

Hepatitis B: Liver infection caused by a sexually transmitted virus (HBV).

Heterosexism: The assumption that people are, or should be, attracted to members of the other gender.

Heterosexual: Attractions or activities between males and females.

HIV: Human immunodeficiency virus.

Homophobia (ho-mo-PHO-bee-a): Strongly held negative attitudes and irrational fears relating to gay men and/or lesbians and their lifestyles.

Homosexual: The term that is traditionally applied to romantic and sexual attractions and activities between members of the same gender.

Hookers: Street name for female prostitutes.

Hormone implants: Contraceptive method in which hormone-releasing plastic containers are surgically inserted under the skin.

Hormone pumping: A fertility-enhancing technique involving the injection of progesterone into a woman's system.

Hormone replacement therapy (HRT): Treatment of the physical changes of menopause by administering dosages of the hormones estrogen and progesterone.

Hot flash: A flushed, sweaty feeling in the skin caused by dilated blood vessels, often associated with menopause.

Human chorionic gonadotropin (HCG): A hormone detectable in the urine of a pregnant woman. Most home pregnancy tests work by detecting its presence in woman's urine.

Human immunodeficiency virus: The virus that initially attacks the human immune system, eventually causing AIDS.

Hustlers: Male street prostitutes.

H-Y antigen: A biochemical produced in an embryo when the Y chromosome is present; it causes fetal gonads to develop into testes.

Hymen: Membranous tissue that can cover part of the vaginal opening.

Hyperfemininity: A tendency to exaggerate characteristics typically associated with femininity.

Hypermasculinity: A tendency on the part of someone to exaggerate manly behaviors, sometimes called machismo.

Hypersexuality: Unusually high level of interest in and drive for sex.

Hypoactive sexual desire (HSD) disorder: Loss of interest and pleasure in what were formerly arousing sexual stimuli.

Hyposexuality: An especially low level of sexual interest and drive.

Hypospadias (hye-pa-SPADE-ee-as): Birth defect caused by incomplete closure of the urethra during fetal development.

Imperforate hymen: Lack of any openings in the hymen.

Impotence (IM-pa-tens): Difficulty achieving or maintaining erection of the penis.

In vitro fertilization (IVF): A process whereby the union of the sperm and egg occurs outside the mother's body.

Incest (IN-sest): Sexual activity between closely related family members.

Incest taboo: Cultural prohibitions against incest, typical of most societies.

Infertility: The inability to produce offspring.

Infibulation: Surgical procedure, performed in some cultures, that nearly seals the opening of the genitals.

Informed consent: The consent given by research subjects, indicating their willingness to participate in a study, after they are informed about the purpose of the study and how they will be asked to participate.

Inhibited sexual desire (ISD): Loss of interest and pleasure in formerly arousing sexual stimuli.

Internal values: Intrinsic values.

Intersexuality: A combination of female and male anatomical structures, so that the individual cannot be clearly defined as male or female.

Interstitial-cell-stimulating hormone (ICSH): Pituitary hormone that stimulates the testes to secrete testosterone; known as luteinizing hormone (LH) in females.

Intrauterine devices (IUDs): Birth control method involving the insertion of a small plastic device into the uterus.

Intrinsic values: The individualized beliefs and attitudes that a person develops by sorting through external values and personal needs.

Introitus (in-TROID-us): The outer opening of the vagina.

Kiddie porn: Term used to describe the distribution and sale of photographs and films of children or young teenagers engaging in some form of sexual activity.

Kleptomania: Extreme form of fetishism in which sexual arousal is generated by stealing.

Labor: Uterine contractions in a pregnant woman; an indication that the birth process is beginning.

Lactation: Production of milk by the milk glands of the breasts.

Lamaze method (la-MAHZ): A birthing process based on relaxation techniques practiced by the expectant mother; her partner coaches her throughout the birth.

Laparoscopy: Simpler procedure for tubal ligation, involving the insertion of a small fiber optic scope into the abdomen, through which the surgeon can see the fallopian tubes and close them off.

Laparotomy: Operation to perform a tubal ligation, or female sterilization, involving an abdominal incision.

Latency period: A stage in human development characterized, in Freud's theory, by little interest in or awareness of sexual feelings; recent research tends to suggest that latency does not exist.

Lesbian (LEZ-bee-un): Refers to females who have a predominantly same-gender sexual orientation and identity.

Libido (la-BEED-o or LIB-a-do): A term first used by Freud to define human sexual longing or sex drive.

Lumpectomy: Surgical removal of a breast lump, along with a small amount of surrounding tissue.

Luteinizing hormone (LH): Pituitary hormone that triggers ovulation in the ovaries and stimulates sperm production in the testes.

Lymphogranuloma venereum (LGV) (lim-foe-gran-yu-LOW-ma-va-NEAR-ee-um): Contagious STD caused by several strains of Chlamydia and marked by swelling and ulceration of lymph nodes in the groin.

Major lips: Two outer folds of skin covering the minor lips, clitoris, urethral opening, and vaginal opening.

Male condom: A sheath worn over the penis during intercourse that collects semen and helps prevent disease transmission and conception.

Male erectile disorder: Difficulty achieving or maintaining penile erection (impotence).

Mammography: Sensitive X-ray technique used to discover small breast tumors.

Marital rape: A woman being forced by her husband to have sex.

Masochist: The individual in a sadomasochistic sexual relationship who takes the submissive role.

Massage parlors: A business that provides massage treatment; places where women can be hired to perform sexual acts in addition to or in lieu of a massage.

Mastectomy: Surgical removal of all or part of a breast.

Ménage à trois (may-NAZH-ah-TRWAH): *See* Troilism.

Menarche (MEN-are-kee): Onset of menstruation at puberty.

Menopause (MEN-a-poz): Time in mid-life when menstruation ceases.

Menstrual cycle: The hormonal interactions that prepare a woman's body for possible pregnancy at roughly monthly intervals.

Menstruation (men-stru-AY-shun): Phase of menstrual cycle in which the inner uterine lining breaks down and sloughs off; the tissue, along with some blood, flows out through the vagina; also called the period.

Midwives: Medical professionals, both women and men, trained to assist with the birthing process.

Minor lips: Two inner folds of skin that join above the clitoris and extend along the sides of the vaginal and urethral openings.

Miscarriage: A natural termination of pregnancy.

Modeling theory: Suggests that people will copy behavior they view in pornography.

Molluscum contagiosum (ma-LUS-kum kan-taje-ee-O-sum): A skin disease transmitted by direct bodily contact, not necessarily sexual, that is characterized by eruptions on the skin that appear similar to whiteheads, with a hard seed-like core.

Monogamous: Sharing sexual relations with only one person.

Monorchidism (ma-NOR-ka-dizm): Presence of only one testis in the scrotum.

Mons: Cushion of fatty tissue located over the female's pubic bone.

Moral values: Beliefs associated with ethical issues, or rights and wrongs; they are often a part of sexual decision making.

Müllerian ducts (myul-EAR-ee-an): Embryonic structures that develop into female sexual and reproductive organs unless inhibited by male hormones.

Müllerian inhibiting substance: Hormone produced by fetal testes that prevents further development of female structures from the Müllerian ducts.

Multiplier effect: When biological and socioenvironmental factors build on one another more and more in the process of human development.

National Birth Control League: An organization founded in 1914 by Margaret Sanger to promote use of contraceptives.

Natural childbirth: A birthing process that encourages the mother to take control, thus minimizing medical intervention.

Necrophilia (nek-ro-FILL-ee-a): Having sexual activity with a dead body.

Nongonococcal urethritis (NGU) (non-gon-uh-KOK-ul yur-i-THRYT-us): Urethral infection or irritation in the male urethra caused by bacteria or local irritants.

Nonspecific uethritis (NSU) (yur-i-THRYT-us): Infection or irritation in the male urethra caused by bacteria or local irritants.

Normal: A subjective term used to describe sexual behaviors and orientations. Standards of normalcy are determined by social, cultural, and historical standards.

Normal asexuality: An absence or low level of sexual desire, considered normal for a particular person.

Normalization: Integration of mentally retarded persons into the social mainstream as much as possible.

Norplant implants: Contraceptive method in which hormone-releasing rubber cylinders are surgically inserted under the skin.

Nymphomania (nim-fa-MANE-ee-a): A term sometimes used to describe erotomania in women.

Obscenity: Depiction of sexual activity in a repulsive or disgusting manner.

Onanism (O-na-niz-um): A term sometimes used to describe masturbation, it comes from the biblical story of Onan, who practiced coitus interruptus and "spilled his seed on the ground."

Open-ended marriage: Marriage in which each partner in the primary relationship grants the other freedom to have emotional and sexual relationships with others.

Opportunistic infection: A disease resulting from lowered resistance of a weakened immune system.

Organizing effect: Manner in which hormones control patterns of early development in the body.

Orgasm (OR-gaz-em): A rush of pleasurable physical sensations and series of contractions associated with the release of sexual tension; usually accompanied by ejaculation in men.

Orgasmic release: Reversal of the vasocongestion and muscular tension of sexual arousal, triggered by orgasm.

Orgy (OR-jee): Group sex.

Osteoporosis(ah-stee-o-po-ROW-sus): Disease caused by loss of calcium from the bones in postmenopausal women, leading to brittle bones and stooped posture.

Ova: Egg cells produced in the ovary. One cell is an ovum; in reproduction, it is fertilized by a sperm cell.

Ovaries: Pair of female gonads, located in the abdominal cavity, that produce ova and female hormones.

Ovulation: Release of a mature ovum through the wall of an ovary.

Ovum donation: Use of an egg from another woman for conception, with the fertilized ovum then being implanted in the uterus of the woman wanting to become pregnant.

Oxytocin: Pituitary hormone that plays a role in lactation and in uterine contractions; brain secretions that act as natural tranquilizers and pain relievers.

Pansexual: Lacking highly specific sexual orientations or preferences; open to a range of sexual activities.

Pap smear: Medical test that examines a smear of cervical cells to detect any cellular abnormalities.

Paraphilia (pair-a-FIL-ee-a): A newer term used to describe sexual orientations and behaviors that vary from the norm; it means "a love beside."

Paraphiliac: A person who is drawn to one or more of the paraphilias.

Partial zona dissection (PZD): A technique used to increase the chances of fertilization by making a microscopic incision in the zona pellucida of an ovum. This creates a passageway through which sperm may enter the egg more easily.

Pedophilia (peed-a-FIL-ee-a): Another term for child sexual abuse.

Pelvic inflammatory disease (PID): A chronic internal infection associated with certain types of IUDs.

Penile strain gauge: A device placed on the penis to measure even subtle changes in its size due to sexual arousal.

Penis: Male sexual organ that can become erect when stimulated; it leads urine and sperm to the outside of the body.

Perimetrium: Outer covering of the uterus.

Perinatal: A term used to describe things related to pregnancy, birth, or the period immediately following the birth.

Perineal area (pair-a-NEE-al): The sensitive skin between the genitals and the anus.

Peyronie's disease (pay-ra-NEEZ): Development of fibrous tissue in spongy erectile columns within the penis.

Phimosis (fye-MOE-sus): A condition in which an abnormally long, tight foreskin on the penis does not retract easily.

Pimps: Men who have female prostitutes working for them.

Placenta (pla-SENT-a): The organ that unites the fetus to the mother by bringing their blood vessels closer together; it provides nourishment for and removes waste from the developing baby.

Plateau phase: The stable, leveled-off phase of sex researchers William Masters and Virginia Johnson's four-phase model of the sexual response cycle.

Plethysmograph: A laboratory measuring device that charts physiological changes over time. Attached to a penile strain gauge, it can chart changes in penis size. This is called penile plethysmography.

Polygamy: The practice, in some cultures, of being married to more than one spouse.

Pornography: Photographs, films, or literature intended to be sexually arousing through explicit depictions of sexual activity.

Potentiation: Establishment of stimuli early in life that form ranges of response for later in life.

Premature birth: A birth that takes place prior to the 36th week of pregnancy.

Premature ejaculation: Difficulty that some men experience in controlling the ejaculatory reflex, which results in rapid ejaculation.

Premenstrual syndrome (PMS): Symptoms of physical discomfort, moodiness, and emotional tensions that occur in some women for a few days prior to menstruation.

Preorgasmic: A term often applied to women who have not yet been able to reach orgasm during sexual response.

Prepuce (PREE-peus): In the female, tissue of the upper vulva that covers the clitoral shaft.

Priapism (pry-AE-pizm): Continual, undesired, and painful erection of the penis.

Primary dysfunction: A difficulty with sexual functioning that has always existed for a particular person.

Progesterone (pro-JES-ter-one): Ovarian hormone that causes the uterine lining to thicken.

Prolapse of the uterus: Weakening of the supportive ligaments of the uterus, causing it to protrude into the vagina.

Promiscuity (prah-mis-KIU-i-tee): Sharing casual sexual activity with many different partners.

Prostaglandin: Hormone-like chemical whose concentrations increase in a woman's body just prior to menstruation.

Prostaglandin- or saline-induced abortion: Used in the 16th–24th weeks of pregnancy, prostaglandins, salt solutions, or urea are injected into the amniotic sac, administered intravenously, or inserted into the vagina in suppository form to induce contractions and fetal delivery.

Prostate: Gland located beneath the urinary bladder in the male; it produces some of the secretions in semen.

Prostatitis (pras-tuh-TITE-us): Inflammation of the prostate gland.

Pseudohermaphrodite: A person who possesses either testes or ovaries in combination with some external genitals of the other sex.

Pseudonecrophilia: A fantasy about having sex with the dead.

Psychosexual development: Complex interaction of factors that form a person's sexual feelings, orientations, and patterns of behavior.

Psychosocial development: The cultural and social influences that help shape human sexual identity.

Puberty: Time of life when reproductive capacity develops and secondary sex characteristics appear.

Pubic lice: Small insects that can infect skin in the pubic area, causing a rash and severe itching.

Pubococcygeus (PC) muscle (pyub-o-kox-a-JEE-us): Part of the supporting musculature of the vagina that is involved in orgasmic response and over which a woman can exert some control.

Pyromania: Sexual arousal generated by setting fires.

Random sample: A representative group of the larger population that is the focus of a scientific poll or study in which care is taken to select participants without a pattern that might sway research results.

Rape trauma syndrome: The predictable sequence of reactions that a victim experiences following a rape.

Recreational adultery: Extramarital sex with a low level of emotional commitment and performed for fun and variety.

Recreational marriage: Recreational adultery.

Refractory period: Time following orgasm during which a man cannot be restimulated to orgasm.

Reinforcement: In conditioning theory, any influence that helps shape future behavior as a punishment or reward stimulus.

Resolution phase: The term for the return of a body to its unexcited state following orgasm.

Retarded ejaculation: A male who has never been able to reach an orgasm.

Retrograde ejaculation: Abnormal passage of semen into the urinary bladder at the time of ejaculation.

Retrovirus (RE-tro-vi-rus): A class of viruses that reproduces with the aid of the enzyme reverse transcriptase, which allows the virus to integrate its genetic code into that of the host cell, thus establishing permanent infection.

Rh factor: A blood-clotting protein agent whose presence or absence in the blood signals an Rh+ or Rh- person.

Rh incompatibility: Condition in which a blood protein of the infant is not the same as the mother's; antibodies formed in the mother can destroy red blood cells in the fetus.

Rho GAM: Medication administered to a mother to prevent formation of antibodies when the baby is Rh positive and its mother Rh negative.

Rhythm method: A natural method of birth control that depends on an awareness of the woman's menstrual/fertility cycle.

RU 486: A French abortion drug; a progesterone antagonist used as a postcoital contraceptive.

Rubber dam: Small square sheet of latex, such as that used in dental work, placed over the vulva, vagina, or anus to help prevent transmission of HIV during sexual activity.

Sadist: The individual in a sadomasochistic sexual relationship who takes the dominant role.

Sadomasochism (sade-o-MASS-o-kiz-um): Refers to sexual themes or activities involving bondage, pain, domination, or humiliation of one partner by the other.

Sample: A representative group of a population that is the focus of a scientific poll or study.

Satyriasis (sate-a-RYE-a-sus): A term sometimes used to describe erotomania in men.

Scabies (SKAY-beez): A skin disease caused by a mite that burrows under the skin to lay its eggs, causing redness and itching; transmitted by bodily contact that may or may not be sexual.

Scrotum (SKROTE-um): Pouch of skin in which the testes are contained.

Secondary dysfunction: A difficulty with sexual functioning that develops after some period of normal sexual functioning.

Selective reduction: The use of abortion techniques to reduce the number of fetuses when there are more than three in a pregnancy, thus increasing the chances of survival for the remaining fetuses.

Self-gratification: Giving oneself pleasure, as in masturbation; a term typically used today instead of more negative descriptors.

Self-pleasuring: Self-gratification; masturbation.

Semen (SEE-men): Mixture of fluids and sperm cells that is ejaculated through the penis.

Seminal vesicle (SEM-un-al): Gland at the end of each vas deferens that secretes a chemical that helps sperm to become mobile.

Seminiferous tubules (sem-a-NIF-a-rus): Tightly coiled tubules in the testes in which sperm cells are formed.

Sensate focus: Early phase of sex therapy treatment, in which the partners pleasure each other without employing direct stimulation of sex organs.

Sex addiction: Inability to regulate sexual behavior.

Sex therapist: Professional trained in the treatment of sexual dysfunctions.

Sexual aversion disorder: Avoidance of or exaggerated fears toward forms of sexual expression (sexual phobia).

Sexual differentiation: The developmental processes—biological, social, and psychological—that lead to different sexes or genders.

Sexual dysfunctions: Difficulties people have in achieving sexual arousal and in other stages of sexual response.

Sexual harassment: Unwanted sexual advances or coercion that can occur in the workplace or academic settings.

Sexual individuality: The unique set of sexual needs, orientations, fantasies, feelings, and activities that develops in each human being.

Sexual orientation: A person's erotic and emotional attraction toward and interest in members of one or both genders.

Sexual revolution: The changes in thinking about sexuality and sexual behavior in society that occurred in the 1960s and 1970s.

Sexual surrogates: Paid partners used during sex therapy with clients lacking their own partners; only rarely used today.

Sexually transmitted diseases (STDs): Various diseases transmitted by direct sexual contact.

Shaft: In the female, the longer body of the clitoris, containing erectile tissue; in the male, cylindrical base of penis that contains three columns of spongy tissue: two corpora cavernosa and a corpus spongiosum.

Shunga: Ancient scrolls used in Japan to instruct couples in sexual practices through the use of paintings.

Situational homosexuality: Deprivation homosexuality.

Skene's glands: Secretory cells located inside the female urethra.

Smegma: Thick, oily substance that may accumulate under the prepuce of the clitoris or penis.

Social constructionists: Those who believe that same-gender sexual orientation is at least partly the result of social and environmental factors.

Social learning theory: Suggests that human learning is influenced by observation of and identification with other people.

Social scripts: A complex set of learned responses to a particular situation that is formed by social influences.

Sodomy laws: Laws that, in some states, prohibit a variety of sexual behaviors, often described as deviate sexual intercourse. These laws are often enforced discriminatorily against particular groups, such as gay males.

Sonograms: Ultrasonic rays used to project a picture of internal structures such as the fetus; often used in conjunction with amniocentesis or fetal surgery.

Spectatoring: Term used by sex researchers William Masters and Virginia Johnson to describe self-consciousness and self-observation during sex.

Sperm: Reproductive cells produced in the testes; in fertilization, one sperm unites with an ovum.

Sperm banks: Centers that store frozen sperm for the purpose of artificial insemination.

Spermatocytes (sper-MAT-o-sites): Cells lining the seminiferous tubules from which sperm cells are produced.

Spermicidal jelly (cream): Sperm-killing chemical in a gel base or cream, used with other contraceptives such as diaphragms.

Spermicides: Chemicals that kill sperm; available as foams, creams, jellies, or implants in sponges or suppositories.

Sponge: A thick polyurethane disk that holds a spermicide and fits over the cervix to prevent conception.

Spontaneous abortion: Another term for miscarriage.

Staphylococcus aureus (staf-a-low-KAK-us): The bacteria that can cause toxic shock syndrome.

Statutory rape: A legal term used to indicate sexual activity when one partner is under the age of consent; in most states that age is 18.

STDs: Sexually transmitted diseases.

Sterilization: Rendering a person permanently incapable of conceiving, usually by interrupting passage of the egg or sperm.

Straight: Slang term for heterosexual.

Streetwalkers: Female prostitutes who work on the streets.

Suppositories: Contraceptive devices designed to distribute their spermicide by melting or foaming in the vagina.

Syndrome (SIN-drome): A group of signs or symptoms that occur together and characterize a given condition.

Syphilis (SIF-uh-lus): Sexually transmitted disease (STD) characterized by four stages, beginning with the appearance of a chancre.

Systematic desensitization: Step-by-step approaches to unlearning tension-producing behaviors and developing new behavior patterns.

Testes (TEST-ees): Pair of male gonads that produce sperm and male hormones.

Testicular cancer: Malignancy on the testis that may be detected by testicular self-examination.

Testicular failure: Lack of sperm and/or hormone production by the testes.

Testosterone (tes-TAS-ter-one): Major male hormone produced by the testes; it helps to produce male secondary sex characteristics.

Testosterone replacement therapy: Administering testosterone injections to increase sexual interest or potency in older men; not considered safe for routine use.

Theoretical failure rate: A measure of how often a birth control method can be expected to fail when used without error or technical problems.

Thrush: A disease caused by a fungus and characterized by white patches in the oral cavity.

Toucherism: Gaining sexual gratification from the touching of an unknown person's body, such as on the buttocks or breasts.

Toxic shock syndrome (TSS): An acute disease characterized by fever and sore throat, and caused by normal bacteria in the vagina that are activated if tampons or contraceptive devices such as diaphragms or sponges are left in for long periods of time.

Transgenderists: People who live in clothing and roles considered appropriate for the opposite sex for sustained periods of time.

Transsexuals: People who feel as though they should have the body of the opposite sex.

Transvestism: Dressing in clothes considered appropriate for the other gender.

Transvestite: An individual who dresses in clothing and adopts mannerisms considered appropriate for the opposite sex.

Trichomoniasis (trik-uh-ma-NEE-uh-sis): A vaginal infection caused by the *Trichomonas* organism.

Troilism (TROY-i-lizm): Sexual activity shared by three people.

True hermaphrodite: A person who has one testis and one ovary. External appearance may vary.

Tubal ligation: A surgical cutting and tying of the fallopian tubes to induce permanent female sterilization.

Umbilical cord: The tubelike tissues and blood vessels originating at the embryo's navel that connect it to the placenta.

Urethra (yu-REE-thrah): Tube that passes from the urinary bladder to the outside of the body.

Urethral opening: Opening through which urine passes to the outside of the body.

Urophilia: Sexual arousal connected with urine or urination.

Uterus (YUTE-a-rus): Muscular organ of the female reproductive system; a fertilized egg implants itself within the uterus.

Vacuum curettage (kyur-a-TAZH): A method of induced abortion performed with a suction pump.

Vagina (vu-JI-na): Muscular canal in the female that is responsive to sexual arousal; it receives semen during heterosexual intercourse for reproduction.

Vaginal atresia (a-TREE-zha): Birth defect in which the vagina is absent or closed.

Vaginal atrophy: Shrinking and deterioration of vaginal lining, usually the result of low estrogen levels during aging.

Vaginal fistulae (FISH-cha-lee *or* -lie): Abnormal channels that can develop between the vagina and other internal organs.

Vaginismus (vaj-uh-NIZ-mus): Involuntary spasm of the outer vaginal musculature, making penetration of the vagina difficult or impossible.

Vaginitis (vaj-uh-NITE-us): General term for inflammation of the vagina.

Values: System of beliefs with which people view life and make decisions, including their sexual decisions.

Variation: A less pejorative term to describe nonconformity to accepted norms.

Varicose veins: Overexpanded blood vessels; can occur in veins surrounding the vagina.

Vas deferens: Tube that leads sperm upward from each testis to the seminal vesicles.

Vasa efferentia: Larger tubes within the testes, into which sperm move after being produced in the seminiferous tubules.

Vasectomy (va-SEK-ta-mee *or* vay-ZEK-ta-mee): A surgical cutting and tying of the vas deferens to induce permanent male sterilization.

Villi: Fingerlike projections of the chorion; they form a major part of the placenta.

Viral hepatitis: Inflammation of the liver caused by a virus.

Voyeurism (VOYE-yu-rizm): Sexual gratification from viewing others who are nude or who are engaging in sexual activities.

Vulva: External sex organs of the female, including the mons, major and minor lips, clitoris, and opening of the vagina.

Vulvovaginitis: General term for inflammation of the vulva and/or vagina.

Western blot: The test used to verify the presence of HIV antibodies already detected by the ELISA.

Wolffian ducts (WOOL-fee-an): Embryonic structures that develop into male sexual and reproductive organs if male hormones are present.

Yeast infection: A type of vaginitis caused by an overgrowth of a fungus normally found in an inactive state in the vagina.

Zero population growth: The point at which the world's population would stabilize, and there would be no further increase in the number of people on Earth. Birthrate and death rate become essentially equal.

Zona pellucida (ZO-nah pe-LOO-sa-da): The transparent, outer membrane of an ovum.

Zoophilia (zoo-a-FILL-ee-a): Bestiality.

Zygote: An ovum that has been fertilized by a sperm.

SOURCES

Sexuality Today: The Human Perspective, Kelly, Gary F., Fifth Edition, 1995. Dushkin/McGraw-Hill, Guilford, CT 06437.

Pregnancy, Childbirth, and Parenting (Wellness), 1992. Dushkin/McGraw-Hill, Guilford, CT 06437.

Credits/Acknowledgments

Cover design by Charles Vitelli

1. Sexuality and Society
Facing overview—Photo by Sandy Nicholas.

2. Sexual Biology, Behavior, and Orientation
Facing overview—AP/Wide World photo. 64—Illustration by Edward Briant. 84 & 85—Reprinted from Body Alchemy: Transsexual Portraits by Loren Cameron. © 1996 by Loren Cameron. Published by Cleis Press, P.O. Box 8933, Pittsburgh, PA 15221.

3. Interpersonal Relationships
Facing overview—Photo by Pamela Carley.

4. Reproduction
Facing overview—Dushkin Publishing Group illustration by Mike Eagle.

5. Sexuality through the Life Cycle
Facing overview—Photo by Marcuss Oslander.

6. Old/New Sexual Concerns
Facing overview—Photo by Pamela Carley.

ANNUAL EDITIONS ARTICLE REVIEW FORM

NAME: _____ DATE: _____

TITLE AND NUMBER OF ARTICLE: _____

BRIEFLY STATE THE MAIN IDEA OF THIS ARTICLE: _____

_____

LIST THREE IMPORTANT FACTS THAT THE AUTHOR USES TO SUPPORT THE MAIN IDEA:

_____

_____

_____

_____

WHAT INFORMATION OR IDEAS DISCUSSED IN THIS ARTICLE ARE ALSO DISCUSSED IN YOUR TEXTBOOK OR OTHER READINGS THAT YOU HAVE DONE? LIST THE TEXTBOOK CHAPTERS AND PAGE NUMBERS:

_____

_____

_____

_____

_____

LIST ANY EXAMPLES OF BIAS OR FAULTY REASONING THAT YOU FOUND IN THE ARTICLE:

_____

_____

_____

_____

LIST ANY NEW TERMS/CONCEPTS THAT WERE DISCUSSED IN THE ARTICLE, AND WRITE A SHORT DEFINITION:

_____

_____

_____

_____

*Your instructor may require you to use this ANNUAL EDITIONS Article Review Form in any number of ways: for articles that are assigned, for extra credit, as a tool to assist in developing assigned papers, or simply for your own reference. Even if it is not required, we encourage you to photocopy and use this page; you will find that reflecting on the articles will greatly enhance the information from your text.

We Want Your Advice

ANNUAL EDITIONS revisions depend on two major opinion sources: one is our Advisory Board, listed in the front of this volume, which works with us in scanning the thousands of articles published in the public press each year; the other is you—the person actually using the book. Please help us and the users of the next edition by completing the prepaid article rating form on this page and returning it to us. Thank you for your help!

ANNUAL EDITIONS: HUMAN SEXUALITY 98/99
Article Rating Form

Here is an opportunity for you to have direct input into the next revision of this volume. We would like you to rate each of the 49 articles listed below, using the following scale:

1. **Excellent: should definitely be retained**
2. **Above average: should probably be retained**
3. **Below average: should probably be deleted**
4. **Poor: should definitely be deleted**

Your ratings will play a vital part in the next revision. So please mail this prepaid form to us just as soon as you complete it.
Thanks for your help!

Rating	Article	Rating	Article
	1. Sweden Looks Anew at Ways to Reach and Teach Its Young People about Sexuality		25. Celibate Passion: The Hidden Rewards of Quitting Sex
	2. Tradition or Outrage?		26. The Healing Power of Intimacy
	3. Adventures in the Skin Trade		27. Protecting against Unintended Pregnancy: A Guide to Contraceptive Choices
	4. A Shot in the Dark		28. Rethinking Birth Control
	5. Sexual Pleasure Unscripted		29. How Reliable Are Condoms?
	6. Storm Troopers in the Culture War		30. The Drug-Induced Abortion
	7. A Time for Partnership		31. Infertility, Inc
	8. We Are Men. Hear Us Roar		32. Making Love Again
	9. Recipes for Lust		33. Age-by-Age Guide to Nudity
	10. Your Sexual Landscape		34. Raising Sexually Healthy Kids
	11. The Orgasm Wars		35. Could Your Precious Child Be Gay?
	12. Testosterone Rules		36. Breaking through the Wall of Silence: Gay, Lesbian, and Bisexual Issues for Middle Level Educators
	13. Risky Sex: The New Bedroom Mistakes Women Are Making		37. Men and Sex at 20, 30, 40
	14. AIDS: Crushing HIV/the Second Key		38. The Joy of Midlife Sex
	15. Are Women the Weaker Sex?		39. Everything You Always Wanted to Know about Sex after 50 (But Were Afraid to Ask)
	16. Horizontal Fitness: How to Keep Your Sex Drive Humming		40. The Town That Closed Its Eyes
	17. Roll Over, Ward Cleaver		41. Healing the Scars
	18. Bisexuality		42. Lock Up Your Sons! This Is the Sexual Revolution
	19. Portrait of a New Man		43. Cyndi Potete's Fire and Rain
	20. The 1997 Body Image Survey Results		44. Wings of Desire
	21. A Woman's Guide to Flirting		45. The AIDS Exception: Privacy vs. Public Health
	22. Men for Sale		46. Do Ask, Do Tell
	23. 'It' Doesn't Just Happen: A Lifetime Prescription for Sizzling Sex		47. The Porning of America
	24. Better Sex in Three Days		48. Was It Good for Us?
			49. Sex in the Future: Virtuous and Virtual?

(Continued on next page)

ABOUT YOU

Name _____ Date _____

Are you a teacher? ❏ Or a student? ❏

Your school name _____

Department _____

Address _____

City _____ State _____ Zip _____

School telephone # _____

YOUR COMMENTS ARE IMPORTANT TO US!

Please fill in the following information:

For which course did you use this book? _____

Did you use a text with this *ANNUAL EDITION*? ❏ yes ❏ no

What was the title of the text? _____

What are your general reactions to the *Annual Editions* concept?

Have you read any particular articles recently that you think should be included in the next edition?

Are there any articles you feel should be replaced in the next edition? Why?

Are there any World Wide Web sites you feel should be included in the next edition? Please annotate.

May we contact you for editorial input?

May we quote your comments?